Practical Math

A Reference Guide and Problem Sets

Book Staff and Contributors

Paul Thomas   *Director, Mathematics*
Harold Lawrance, Jr.   *Content Specialist*
Kay McCarthy   *Senior Text Editor*
Suzanne Montazer   *Creative Director, Print and ePublishing*
Stephanie Shaw Williams   *Print Visual Designer, Cover Designer*
Lee Horton   *Picture Editor*
Jean Stringer   *Rights Manager*
Michael Melnyk   *Mathematical Accuracy Editor*
Martin Donnelly, Harold Lawrance, Jr., Michele Patrick   *Writers*
Amy Eward   *Senior Manager, Writers*
Susan Raley   *Senior Manager, Editors*
Dan Smith   *Senior Project Manager*

Maria Szalay   *Executive Vice President, Product Development*
John Holdren   *Senior Vice President, Content and Curriculum*
David Pelizzari   *Vice President, K^{12} Content*
Kim Barcas   *Vice President, Creative*
Laura Seuschek   *Vice President, Assessment and Research*
Christopher Frescholtz   *Senior Director, Program Management*

Lisa Dimaio Iekel   *Director, Print Production and Manufacturing*
Ray Traugott   *Production Manager*

At Stride, Inc. (NYSE: LRN)—formerly K12 Inc.—we are reimagining lifelong learning as a rich, deeply personal experience that prepares learners for tomorrow. Since its inception, Stride has been committed to removing barriers that impact academic equity and to providing high-quality education for anyone— particularly those in underserved communities. The company has transformed the teaching and learning experience for millions of people by providing innovative, high-quality, tech-enabled education solutions, curriculum, and programs directly to students, schools, the military, and enterprises in primary, secondary, and post-secondary settings. Stride is a premier provider of K-12 education for students, schools, and districts, including career learning services through middle and high school curriculum. Providing a solution to the widening skills gap in the workplace and student loan crisis, Stride equips students with real world skills for in-demand jobs with career learning. For adult learners, Stride delivers professional skills training in healthcare and technology, as well as staffing and talent development for Fortune 500 companies. Stride has delivered millions of courses over the past decade and serves learners in all 50 states and more than 100 countries. The company is a proud sponsor of the Future of School, a nonprofit organization dedicated to closing the gap between the pace of technology and the pace of change in education. More information can be found at stridelearning.com, K12.com, destinationsacademy.com, galvanize.com, techelevator.com, and medcerts.com.

978-1-60153-411-8

Printed by Walsworth, Marceline, MO, USA, May 2023.

Practical Math

A Reference Guide and Problem Sets

Contents

How to Use This Book

This book contains eight chapters. Each chapter begins with an opener, an introduction, and a review of particular math skills. The chapter then presents a series of explanatory topics and problem sets. Finally, a chapter review problem set concludes the chapter.

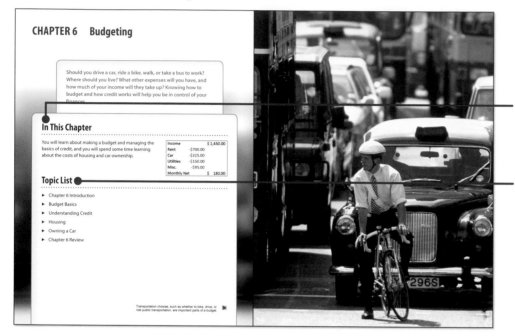

The **Chapter Opener** introduces the subject that will be covered.

In This Chapter describes the concepts and skills covered in the chapter.

Topic List is a list of specific topic titles.

The **Chapter Introduction** topic describes what's coming up in the chapter and gives a real-world example of what you will learn. It concludes with a problem set for you to do to get ready for the math in the chapter.

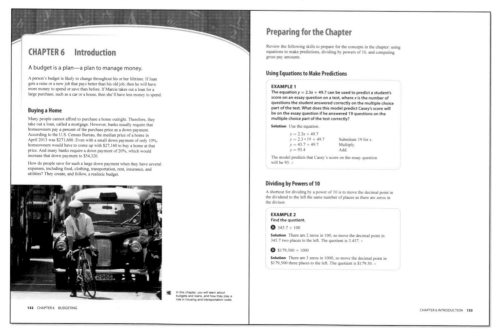

Preparing for the Chapter presents several examples with their solutions. The problem set at the end of each Chapter Introduction topic gives you a chance to use what you saw in the examples and to make sure you are ready for the chapter.

Each topic has explanations and examples.

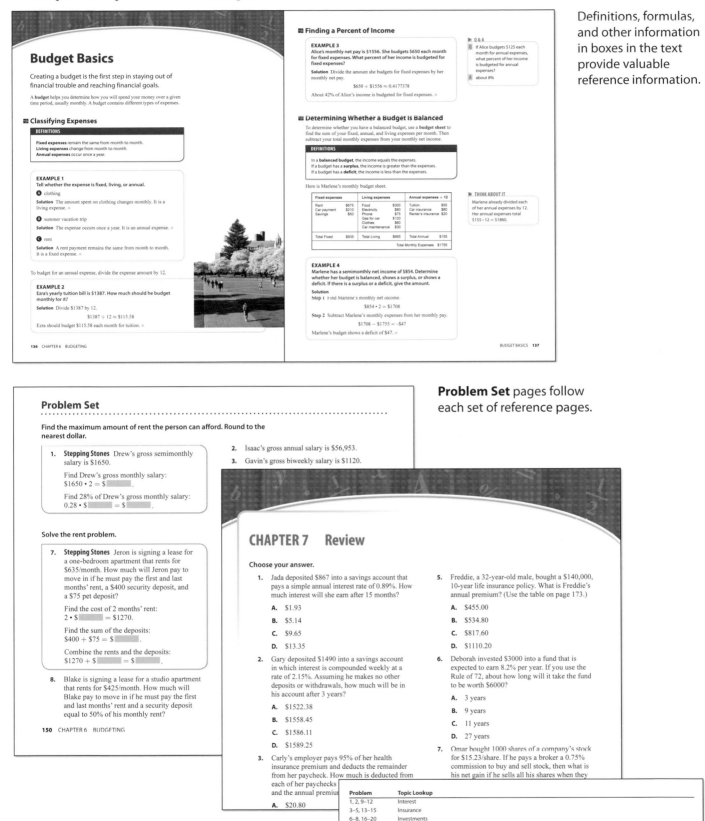

Definitions, formulas, and other information in boxes in the text provide valuable reference information.

Problem Set pages follow each set of reference pages.

The **Chapter Review** problem set covers the most important skills and concepts of the chapter. A topic lookup at the end of each Chapter Review tells you the topics you can review for each problem.

Appendices

The appendices include quantitative and general reference information.

Quantitative Reference Information

- Financial Reference Tables

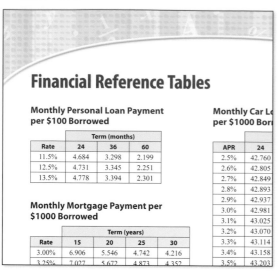

- 2012 Federal Tax Table

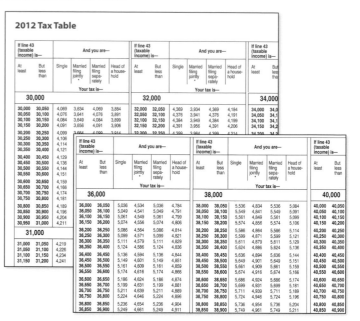

General Reference Information

- Pronunciation Guide
- Glossary
- Symbols
- Formulary
- Selected Answers
- Illustrations Credits
- Data Sources
- Index

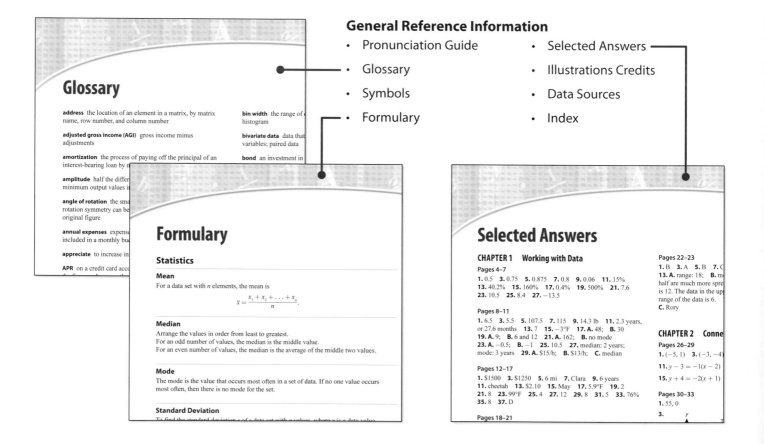

Introduction

Welcome to *Practical Math*

This reference guide accompanies the online portion of K12 Inc.'s Practical Math program. The topics and problem sets in this reference guide explain and illustrate how to solve problems. They make sense on their own, but they are not the entire story. The online component of the course is critical. Online, you will see text, interactive pieces, and multimedia tools that provide the rest of the story.

Math is all around us in many practical ways. The first part of this book shows you how to make sense of data and uncertainty. The study of statistics gives you important tools that can help you understand the loads of data all around you. Life is full of uncertainty, and your knowledge of probability can provide tools for making good decisions in situations with uncertainty.

Most of the second half of the book is about financial literacy. Money is pretty handy to have around. Everyone should know how to manage finances, including how to deal with personal budgets, credit, and savings.

You can use math to model and solve some real-world situations involving growth, art, and music. Two chapters in this book show you some of those ways.

Get to Work

Math is learned at the tip of a pencil. As you work through the topics in this book, you will see worked examples that show you how to solve some problems. The most important part of each topic, however, is the problem set at the end. Reading problem solutions can help you find good strategies and best practices for solving problems, but only when you solve problems yourself will you really learn math.

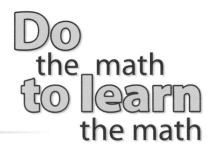

Do the math to learn the math

CHAPTER 1   Working with Data

How much debt does the country have? How is the budget spent on various programs? How many people don't have health insurance? Data are all around us, and politicians use statistics to communicate about lots of data. In this chapter, you will learn how to work with statistical measures and graphs that will help you understand data.

In This Chapter

You will learn about statistical measures and statistical graphs and how people use them to communicate facts, estimations, and predictions.

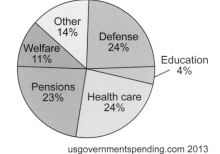

usgovernmentspending.com 2013

Topic List

- ► Chapter 1 Introduction
- ► Measures of Center
- ► Statistical Graphs
- ► Measures of Spread
- ► Chapter 1 Review

Politicians use statistics to present their view of data and to make arguments. ▶

CHAPTER 1   Introduction

Scientists use data. Their reports typically contain statistical measures and graphs.

Whether scientists are working indoors or out, they are likely working with numbers. Inside the lab, they may be determining bacteria counts or densities of fibers. Outside the lab, it may be water temperatures or pH levels. Whatever their field, scientists deal with data. They must be able to collect, make sense of, and describe data to others.

Earthquakes

Only big earthquakes that do major damage typically make headlines. But earthquakes occur every day, all over the world. Scientists collect and keep track of earthquake data. The data include a quake's latitude, longitude, depth, and magnitude, resulting in a large table of numbers. What good are all those numbers?

Scientists use the numbers to determine which regions have the greatest chance of an earthquake in the future. This information helps people and businesses in those regions prepare. For example, construction workers in high-quake regions will follow different codes to build safer structures. And homeowners in high-quake regions may have the option to buy earthquake insurance.

◀ In this chapter, you will learn ways to make sense of and to describe data.

Preparing for the Chapter

Review the following skills to prepare for the concepts in the chapter: converting fractions to decimals, converting decimals to percents, and identifying coordinates on a number line.

Converting Fractions to Decimals

To convert a fraction to a decimal, divide the numerator by the denominator.

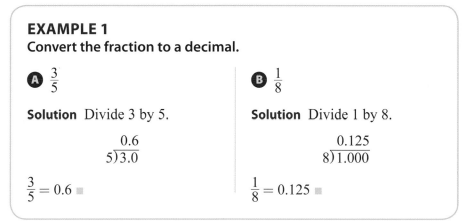

EXAMPLE 1
Convert the fraction to a decimal.

A $\frac{3}{5}$

Solution Divide 3 by 5.

$$5\overline{)3.0} = 0.6$$

$\frac{3}{5} = 0.6$ ∎

B $\frac{1}{8}$

Solution Divide 1 by 8.

$$8\overline{)1.000} = 0.125$$

$\frac{1}{8} = 0.125$ ∎

Converting Decimals to Percents

To convert a decimal to a percent, multiply the decimal by 100 and add the percent sign. A shortcut for multiplying by 100 is moving the decimal point two places to the right, adding zeros if necessary.

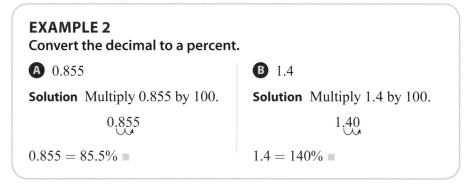

EXAMPLE 2
Convert the decimal to a percent.

A 0.855

Solution Multiply 0.855 by 100.

0.855

$0.855 = 85.5\%$ ∎

B 1.4

Solution Multiply 1.4 by 100.

1.40

$1.4 = 140\%$ ∎

Identifying Coordinates on a Number Line

DEFINITIONS

A **coordinate** is a number that locates a point on a number line.

To identify a coordinate, use the tick marks.

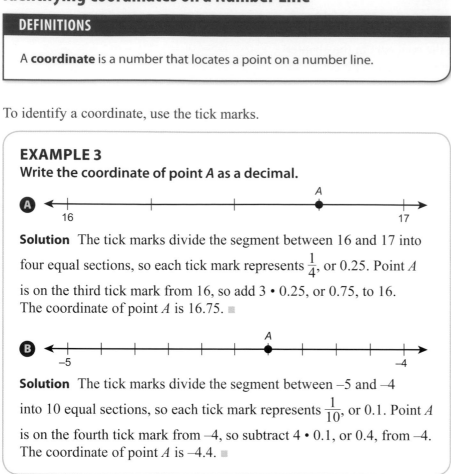

EXAMPLE 3
Write the coordinate of point A as a decimal.

A

Solution The tick marks divide the segment between 16 and 17 into four equal sections, so each tick mark represents $\frac{1}{4}$, or 0.25. Point A is on the third tick mark from 16, so add 3 • 0.25, or 0.75, to 16. The coordinate of point A is 16.75. ∎

B

Solution The tick marks divide the segment between –5 and –4 into 10 equal sections, so each tick mark represents $\frac{1}{10}$, or 0.1. Point A is on the fourth tick mark from –4, so subtract 4 • 0.1, or 0.4, from –4. The coordinate of point A is –4.4. ∎

Problem Set

Convert the fraction to a decimal.

1. $\frac{1}{2}$

2. $\frac{2}{5}$

3. $\frac{3}{4}$

4. $\frac{7}{10}$

5. $\frac{7}{8}$

6. $\frac{1}{4}$

7. $\frac{4}{5}$

8. $\frac{3}{100}$

9. $\frac{3}{50}$

10. $\frac{9}{20}$

Convert the decimal to a percent.

11. 0.15

12. 0.38

13. 0.402

14. 0.232

15. 1.6

16. 3.09

17. 0.004

18. 2.5

19. 5

20. 0.0106

Write the coordinate of point *A* as a decimal.

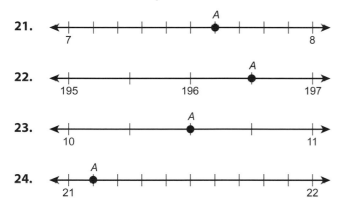

21.
22.
23.
24.

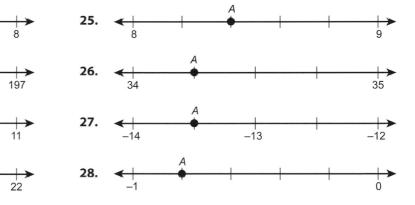

25.
26.
27.
28.

Measures of Center

When you describe a data set, it is important to find a number that the data tend to center around.

⬗ Finding a Mean

DEFINITIONS

The **mean** is the sum of the data values divided by the number of data values. It is also called the *average*.

A **frequency distribution** is a table or graph that describes the number of times a value or an interval of values occurs in a data set.

▶ **NOTATION**

The symbol $\bar{x}$ (read as "*x*-bar") can be used to represent the mean.

EXAMPLE 1

Here are the high temperatures (in degrees Fahrenheit) in Dallas for the week of July 15, 2012. Find the mean high temperature.

$$91, 96, 98, 99, 101, 105, 107$$

Solution $\dfrac{91 + 96 + 98 + 99 + 101 + 105 + 107}{7} = \dfrac{697}{7} \approx 99.6$

The mean high temperature is about 99.6°F. ∎

A data set with many of the same values may be shown in a frequency table.

▶ **THINK ABOUT IT**

The sum of the data values is the sum of the products of each frequency and value. The number of data values is the sum of the frequencies.

EXAMPLE 2

Here are the low temperatures (in degrees Fahrenheit) in Dallas from July 1 to July 15, 2012. Find the mean low temperature.

Temperature	73	74	75	77	78
Number of days	2	3	4	5	1

NOAA NCDC 2012a

Solution $\dfrac{2 \cdot 73 + 3 \cdot 74 + 4 \cdot 75 + 5 \cdot 77 + 1 \cdot 78}{15} = \dfrac{1131}{15} = 75.4$

The mean low temperature is 75.4°F. ∎

⬛ Achieving a Certain Mean

EXAMPLE 3

A meteorologist predicts the average daily rainfall for 4 days to be 0.5 in. The rainfall amounts on the first 3 days are 0.4 in., 0.25 in., and 0.75 in. What must the rainfall amount be on the fourth day for the prediction to be correct?

Solution Translate "the average daily rainfall for 4 days to be 0.5" into an equation. Use the known rainfall amounts for the first 3 days. Use x for the rainfall amount on the fourth day.

$$\frac{0.4 + 0.25 + 0.75 + x}{4} = 0.5$$

$$\frac{1.4 + x}{4} = 0.5$$

$$1.4 + x = 2$$

$$x = 0.6$$

The rainfall amount on the fourth day must be 0.6 in. ▪

> ▶ **THINK ABOUT IT**
>
> You can solve this problem without using x. If the average after 4 days must be 0.5, then the total must be $4(0.5) = 2$. So the amount on the fourth day must be 2 minus the amounts already fallen.

⬛ Finding a Median

DEFINITION

The **median** is the middle value when the data are ordered. If the number of data values is even, the median is the average of the two middle values.

EXAMPLE 4

Here are the low temperatures (in degrees Fahrenheit) in Chicago from February 1 to February 8, 2013. Find the median low temperature for this time period.

$$0, 8, 9, 13, 6, 11, 31, 23$$

Solution Order the data and identify the two middle values.

$$0, 6, 8, 9, 11, 13, 23, 31$$

Find the average of the two middle values.

$$\frac{9 + 11}{2} = \frac{20}{2} = 10$$

The median low temperature is 10°F. ▪

Finding a Mode

EXAMPLE 5

Here are the daily snowfall amounts (in inches) in Chicago from February 1 to February 7, 2013. Find the mode of the snowfall amounts.

$$0.5, 1.8, 0.5, 2.4, 0.5, 0.0, 1.4$$

Solution Find the value that occurs most often. The value 0.5 occurs three times. The mode is 0.5 in. ▪

Problem Set

Find the mean. Round to the nearest tenth if needed.

1. **Stepping Stones**

Value	3	5	6	10
Frequency	4	6	3	7

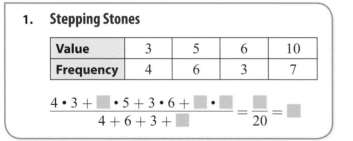

$$\frac{4 \cdot 3 + \blacksquare \cdot 5 + 3 \cdot 6 + \blacksquare \cdot \blacksquare}{4 + 6 + 3 + \blacksquare} = \frac{\blacksquare}{20} = \blacksquare$$

2. 15, 10, 3, 17, 9

3. 5.5, 7.2, 10.9, 3.5, 3.5, 7.2, 0.8

4. 25, 14, 17, 0, 13, 0, 21, 30

5. 125, 100, 104, 90, 111, 115

6.

Value	1	2	3	4	5
Frequency	7	1	3	2	2

7.

Value	50	100	150	200
Frequency	3	3	2	2

8.

Value	45	52	53	55	59
Frequency	3	2	2	4	1

Solve. Round to the nearest tenth if needed.

9. Marcus bought pumpkins that weigh 8 lb, 11 lb, 23 lb, and 15 lb. What is the mean weight of his pumpkins?

10. Fiona kept track of how many text messages she sent each day one week. The numbers were 21, 57, 32, 25, 33, 42, and 46. On average, how many text messages did she send each day?

11. A reporter asked employees how long they have been at their current job. The responses were 2 years, 18 months, 6 months, $3\frac{1}{2}$ years, and 4 years. What is the mean length of time the employees have been at their current job?

12. Greg earned scores of 88, 91, 75, and 72 on four science tests. Determine his score on the fifth test if his average for the five tests was 81.

13. Leah predicts that an average of 5 passengers will board the bus at each of the 6 stops along her route. The numbers of passengers who board at the first 5 stops are 3, 7, 5, 6, and 2. How many passengers need to board at the sixth stop for her prediction to be true?

14. The table shows the weights of the bowling balls on a rack.

Weight (lb)	9	10	12	13	16
Number of balls	2	2	4	5	3

Find the mean weight of the bowling balls.

15. The temperature rating of a sleeping bag is the lowest temperature the manufacturer expects a person would be comfortable in the sleeping bag. The table shows the ratings of the bags that a trekking group took on a trip.

Rating (°F)	−20	−10	0	5	10
Number of bags	2	4	4	3	2

Find the mean temperature rating of the bags.

16. Find the missing frequency given that the mean age is 6.4.

Age	2	4	▪	10
Number of children	8	3	8	6

For each data set, find the following:
A. median
B. mode

17. **Stepping Stones** 48, 30, 62, 25, 66, 30, 50

    Order the data: 25, 30, ▪, ▪, ▪, 62, 66.

    A. ▪ is the median because it is the middle number.

    B. ▪ is the mode because it occurs most often.

18. 15, 17, 8, 23, 14

19. 6, 11, 12, 12, 7, 6

20. 4, 3, 8, 0, 6, 4, 9, 2

21. 173, 162, 190, 128, 145

22. 33, 25, 22, 22, 28, 41, 33, 41, 41, 22

23. −1, 0, 3, 4, −3, −1

24. 3.8, 4.5, 5.1, 2.4, 3.9, 5.8

Solve.

25. The number of cars Gary sold each month was 12, 5, 9, 11, 14, and 10. What was Gary's median number of sales per month?

26. Five homes in a town are listed for sale. Their sale prices are $128,000, $242,000, $195,000, $880,000, and $189,000. What is the median sale price?

27. Children of the following ages are enrolled at a day-care center: four 1-year-olds, three 2-year-olds, and five 3-year-olds. What are the median and mode of the ages of the children at the center?

28. A coach is ordering T-shirts for his team. He orders a half dozen of size 40, a dozen of size 42, a dozen of size 44, and a half dozen of size 46. Find the median and mode of the sizes of all the shirts ordered.

29. The pay rates (in dollars per hour) that employees at a factory earn are 13, 14.5, 15, 16, 18, 21, 16, 13, 12.5, 18, and 13.

    A. Find the median pay rate.

    B. Find the mode of the pay rates.

    C. Which measure better represents the center of this data set?

30. The yearly salaries, in thousands of dollars, of employees in a small company are 33, 42, 29, 47, 110, and 43.

    A. Find the median salary.

    B. Find the mean salary.

    C. Which measure better represents the center of this data set?

Statistical Graphs

Graphs help us draw conclusions about data.

▶ **BY THE WAY**

Cat 1 means "category 1." Each category matches with a range of wind speeds.

➡ Interpreting Everyday Graphs

Glance at any news media, and you'll likely find graphs. Common graphs include **circle graphs**, **bar graphs**, and **line graphs**.

EXAMPLE 1

There were 20 cyclones in the Atlantic basin in 2011. Use the circle graph to find how many of the cyclones were tropical storms or depressions.

Solution The circle graph shows that 60% + 5%, or 65%, of all the cyclones were tropical storms or depressions. Find 65% of 20.

$$0.65 \cdot 20 = 13$$

Thirteen of the cyclones were tropical storms or depressions. ▪

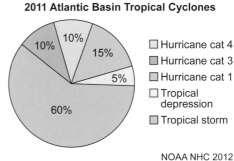

2011 Atlantic Basin Tropical Cyclones

□ Hurricane cat 4
■ Hurricane cat 3
■ Hurricane cat 1
□ Tropical depression
■ Tropical storm

NOAA NHC 2012

EXAMPLE 2

The double bar graph shows the number of each type of cyclone in the Atlantic basin in 2011 and 2012.

Ⓐ How many cyclones were in the Atlantic basin in 2012?

Solution Look at the heights of the red bars: $9 + 5 + 3 + 2 = 19$. There were 19 cyclones in the Atlantic basin in 2012. ▪

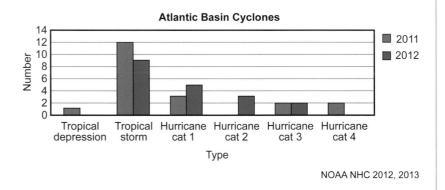

Atlantic Basin Cyclones

■ 2011
■ 2012

NOAA NHC 2012, 2013

Ⓑ What types of cyclones were there more of in 2012 than 2011?

Solution Find the types of cyclones for which the red bars are taller than the blue bars. There were more category 1 and category 2 hurricanes in 2012 than in 2011. ▪

EXAMPLE 3

The line graph shows the number of hurricanes in the Atlantic basin from 2003 through 2012.

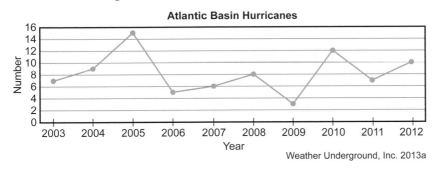

Atlantic Basin Hurricanes

Weather Underground, Inc. 2013a

Ⓐ Which year had the most hurricanes?

Solution Look for the highest point on the graph. It occurs at 2005, when there were 15 hurricanes. ■

Ⓑ Between which two consecutive years did the greatest increase in hurricanes occur?

Solution Find the steepest line that rises from left to right. The greatest increase occurred between 2009 and 2010. ■

⤷ Interpreting a Stem-and-Leaf Plot

DEFINITIONS

A **stem-and-leaf plot** shows the shape of the distribution of a data set. For each data value, the rightmost digit is the **leaf** and the digit or digits to the left of the leaf is the **stem**.

Each row in a stem-and-leaf plot contains one stem, which is to the left of the vertical line. The leaves for that stem are to the right of the vertical line.

▶ **BY THE WAY**

In the western Pacific, strong cyclones are called typhoons instead of hurricanes.

EXAMPLE 4

The stem-and-leaf plot shows the number of cyclones in the western Pacific from 1994 to 2010. Find the mode of the data set.

Solution Look for the leaf that repeats most often in the same row. The leaf of 7 occurs five times in the row for the stem of 2. Combine the stem, 2, with the leaf, 7, to find the value of the mode: 27. ■

1	9
2	6 7 7 7 7 7 9
3	1 1 4 4 5 5 6
4	1 9

Key: 1|9 = 19

Weather Underground, Inc. 2013b

Interpreting Frequency Distributions

DEFINITIONS

A **line plot** displays individual data values as dots on a number line. A **histogram** uses rectangles to display the frequency of data values that occur within intervals. Each interval in a histogram is a **bin**.

▶ BY THE WAY

In Examples 5 and 6, strong earthquakes are considered to be those with magnitudes 6.0 or greater.

EXAMPLE 5

The line plot shows the number of strong earthquakes that occurred in the United States each year from 1993 to 2012. In how many of those years were there six or more strong earthquakes?

Solution Each dot represents a year. Count the number of dots above 6, 7, 8, 9, and 10. There were 12 years with six or more strong earthquakes. ■

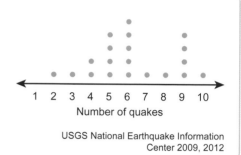

Number of quakes

USGS National Earthquake Information Center 2009, 2012

EXAMPLE 6

The histogram shows the number of strong earthquakes that occurred in the world each year from 1993 to 2012. In how many of those years were there fewer than 150 strong earthquakes?

Solution Find the sum of the frequencies of the first two bins: $3 + 4 = 7$. There were 7 years with fewer than 150 strong earthquakes. ■

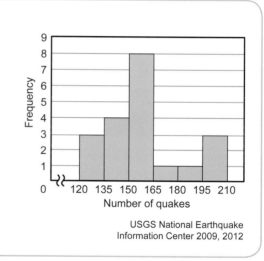

Number of quakes

USGS National Earthquake Information Center 2009, 2012

This histogram shows the same data from Example 6. Notice that decimals replace the frequencies along the vertical axis, which allows you to make comparisons relative to the total. The third bin shows, for example, that there were between 150 and 164 strong quakes in 40% of the given years.

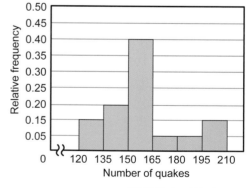

Number of quakes

USGS National Earthquake Information Center 2009, 2012

Problem Set

A restaurant owner spent $25,000 running his restaurant one month. The circle graph shows how he spent the money.

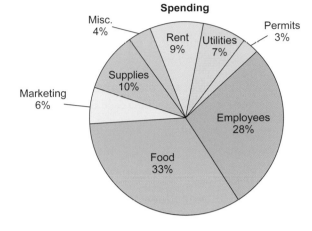

Spending

1. **Stepping Stones** How much money was spent on marketing?

    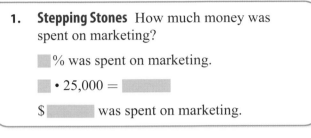

    ■% was spent on marketing.

    ■ • 25,000 = ■

    $ ■ was spent on marketing.

2. How much money was spent on rent and utilities?

3. How much more money was spent buying food than paying employees?

4. How much money was spent on items that were not food?

A salesperson let five customers test-drive vehicles as far as they wished. The bar graph shows how far each customer drove.

5. **Stepping Stones** How much farther did Maggie drive than Kyle?

    Maggie drove ■ mi and Kyle drove ■ mi.

    ■ − ■ = ■

    Maggie drove ■ more miles than Kyle.

6. Which customers drove the same number of miles?

7. Who drove the shortest distance?

8. What percent of Leyla's distance did Clara drive?

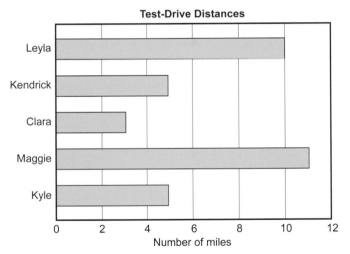

The double bar graph shows how long, on average, different animals live both in the wild and in captivity.

9. How much longer does a tiger live in captivity than in the wild?

10. Which animals have the same average life span in the wild?

11. Which animal's life span in captivity is closest to its life span in the wild?

12. Which animal's life span increases by the greatest percent when in captivity?

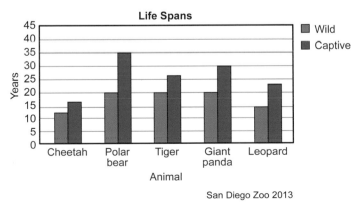

San Diego Zoo 2013

The line graph shows the average daily cost, rounded to the nearest 10¢, that a homeowner paid for electricity each month of a year.

13. What was the average daily cost in February?

14. For which months was the average daily cost $2.00?

15. In which month(s) was the average daily cost less than $2.00?

16. Between which two consecutive months did the average daily cost decrease the most?

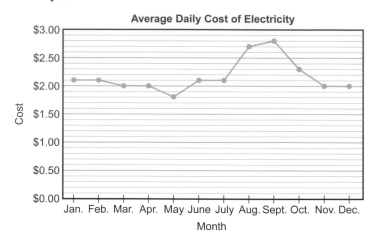

The stem-and-leaf plot shows the temperatures of patients who registered at a clinic one day.

17. **Stepping Stones** What is the difference between the greatest and least temperatures?

    The greatest temperature is ▨ and the least temperature is ▨.

    ▨ − ▨ = ▨

```
 97 | 2  8
 98 | 1  3  3  5  6  7  7  7
 99 | 0  0  0  4
100 | 0  2  4  4  6
101 | 5  9
102 | 3  3
103 | 1
```

Key: 98 | 3 = 98.3°F

18. How many patients registered at the clinic that day?

19. How many patients had a temperature of 100.4°F?

20. How many patients had a temperature less than 100°F?

21. How many more patients had a temperature of at least 100°F than those with a temperature of less than 98°F?

22. What is the mode of the temperatures?

23. What is the median of the temperatures?

At a fund-raising event, participants got to throw one bowling ball down a lane. For every pin that a participant knocked down, the manager donated $2 to that participant's charity of choice. The line plot shows the number of pins each participant knocked down.

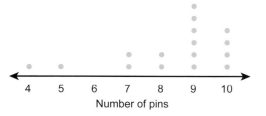

24. How many participants were there?

25. What was the fewest number of pins any participant knocked down?

26. How many participants knocked down 7 pins?

27. How many participants each raised at least $16 with their throw?

28. **Challenge** How much money was raised during the event?

On a team's opening day, fans in a baseball stadium were asked how many home games they plan to attend this season. The histogram shows the results.

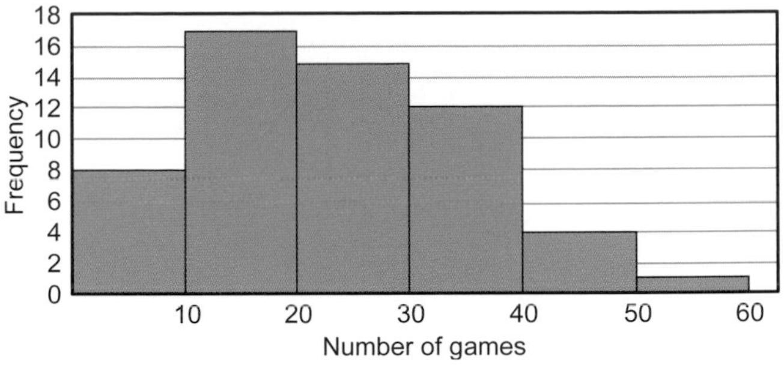

29. How many fans plan on attending fewer than 10 games?

30. How many fans plan on attending fewer than 20 games?

31. How many fans plan on attending more than 40 games?

32. How many fans were surveyed?

The histogram shows the average number of tornadoes per year for each of the 50 U.S. states from 1991 to 2010.

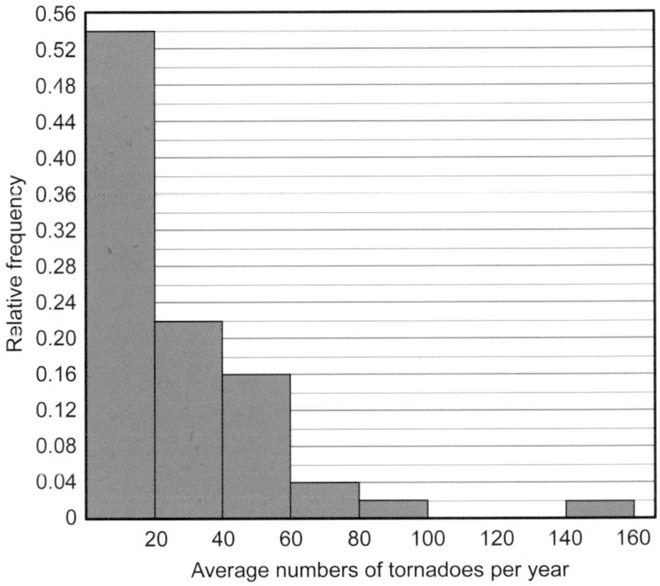

NOAA NCDC 2012b

33. Stepping Stones What percent of the states have, on average, fewer than 40 tornadoes per year?

The height of the first bin is ___.

The height of the second bin is ___.

The sum of the heights is ___.

Convert the decimal to a percent: ___.

34. What percent of the states have, on average, more than 80 tornadoes per year?

35. How many states have, on average, more than 40 but fewer than 60 tornadoes per year?

36. How many states have, on average, more than 140 but fewer than 160 tornadoes per year?

Choose the answer.

37. Which data set matches the histogram?

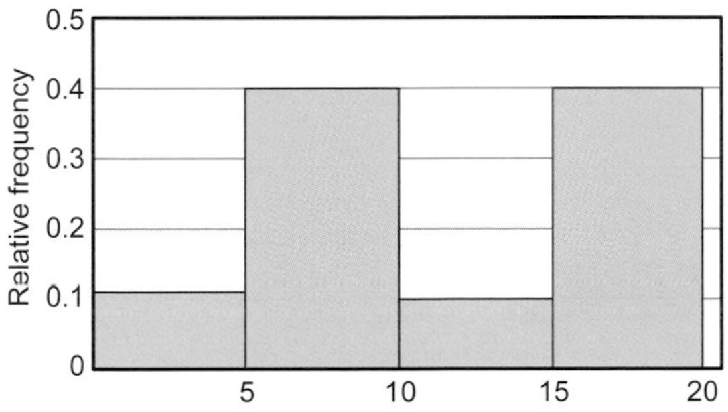

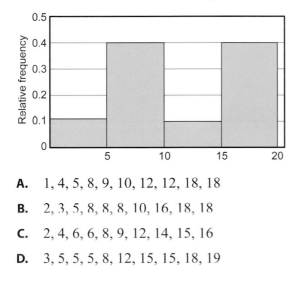

A. 1, 4, 5, 8, 9, 10, 12, 12, 18, 18

B. 2, 3, 5, 8, 8, 8, 10, 16, 18, 18

C. 2, 4, 6, 6, 8, 9, 12, 14, 15, 16

D. 3, 5, 5, 5, 8, 12, 15, 15, 18, 19

38. Which data set matches the circle graph?

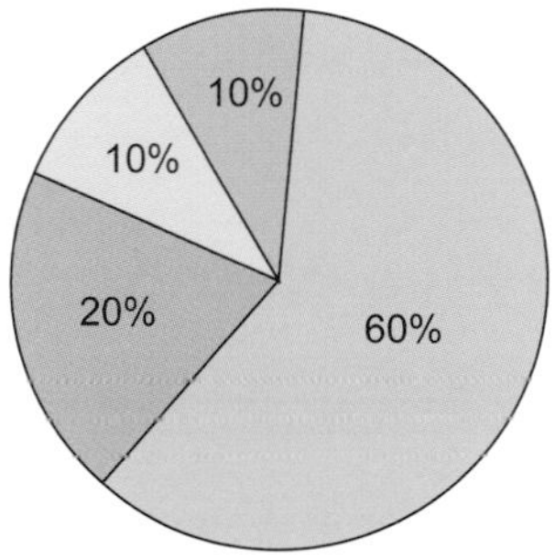

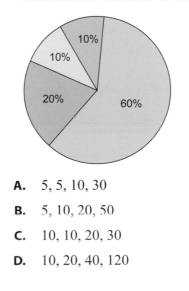

A. 5, 5, 10, 30

B. 5, 10, 20, 50

C. 10, 10, 20, 30

D. 10, 20, 40, 120

Measures of Spread

Data values can be clustered together or spread out far from each other.

Finding a Five-Number Summary

DEFINITION

The **five-number summary** of a data set consists of the following:
- Minimum, or least value
- First quartile (Q_1), or median of the lower half of the data
- Second quartile (Q_2), or median of all the data
- Third quartile (Q_3), or median of the upper half of the data
- Maximum, or greatest value

> ▶ **THINK ABOUT IT**
>
> The three **quartiles** divide the data set into four equal parts.

EXAMPLE 1

In the continental United States, there are 10 states with volcanoes. The number of volcanoes in each of those states is shown. Find the five-number summary of the data set.

$$1, 1, 2, 2, 3, 4, 4, 7, 17, 19$$

Solution Find the median of all the values. Then find the median of each half of data.

$$1, \ 1, \textcircled{2}, 2, \ 3, \Big| 4, \ 4, \textcircled{7}, \ 17, \ 19$$
$$Q_1 \quad \text{med: } 3.5 \quad Q_3$$

Smithsonian Institution, Global Volcanism Program 2002a

The five-number summary is min: 1, Q_1: 2, med: 3.5, Q_3: 7, max: 19. ▪

Interpreting a Five-Number Summary

DEFINITIONS

The **range** of a data set is the difference between the maximum and minimum values.

$$\text{Range} = \text{Max} - \text{Min}$$

The **interquartile range (IQR)** is the difference between the first and third quartiles.

$$\text{IQR} = Q_3 - Q_1$$

EXAMPLE 2

Volcanologists divide Australia and its outer islands into 10 regions. The five-number summary for the number of volcanoes in each of those regions is shown.

$$\text{min: 1, } Q_1\text{: 3, med: 8, } Q_3\text{: 14, max: 19}$$

Compare this data set to the data set for volcanoes in the continental United States.

Solution Both data sets have a range of $19 - 1$, or 18. However, the IQR of the U.S. set is $7 - 2$, or 5, and the IQR of the Australian set is $14 - 3$, or 11. The IQRs show that the data in the Australian set are more spread out than the data in the U.S. set. Also, the median of the Australian set is closer to the midpoint between its minimum and maximum, indicating a more balanced spread. ■

Interpreting a Box Plot

DEFINITIONS

A **box plot** is a display of a five-number summary. The **box** shows the interquartile range with a vertical line through the median. The **whiskers** extend to the minimum and maximum values.

EXAMPLE 3

Volcanologists divide Mexico, Central America, and South America into 14 regions. The box plot shows the number of volcanoes in each of these regions.

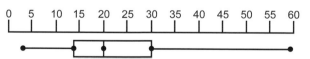

Smithsonian Institution, Global Volcanism Program 2002b, 2002c

What can you say about the spread of the data?

Solution The third and fourth sections are longer than the first and second sections. This means the values in the upper half of the data set are more spread out than those in the lower half of the data set. ■

> **THINK ABOUT IT**
>
> The five-number summary of the data set is min: 3, Q_1: 14, med: 20, Q_3: 30, max: 59.

> **REMEMBER**
>
> Each of the four sections in a box plot has about the same number of values.

Computing Standard Deviation

FORMULA FOR FINDING STANDARD DEVIATION

To find the standard deviation s of a data set with n values, where x is a data value and $\bar{x}$ is the mean, use the formula.

$$s = \sqrt{\frac{\sum(x - \bar{x})^2}{n - 1}}$$

> **NOTATION**
>
> Read $\sum$ as "the sum of." The numerator in the formula is the sum of the squares of the differences between each data value and the mean.

EXAMPLE 4

Find the standard deviation of the data set.

$$1, 1, 2, 2, 3, 4, 4, 7, 17, 19$$

Solution

Step 1 Find the mean of the data set.

$$\bar{x} = \frac{1 + 1 + 2 + 2 + 3 + 4 + 4 + 7 + 17 + 19}{10} = \frac{60}{10} = 6$$

Step 2 Find the sum of the squares of the differences between each data value and the mean. Use a table to organize your work.

Step 3 Divide the sum by $n - 1$.

$$\frac{390}{10 - 1} = \frac{390}{9} = 43.\overline{3}$$

Step 4 Take the square root of the result.

$$s = \sqrt{43.\overline{3}} \approx 6.6 \ \blacksquare$$

x	$(x - \bar{x})^2$
1	$(1 - 6)^2 = 25$
1	$(1 - 6)^2 = 25$
2	$(2 - 6)^2 = 16$
2	$(2 - 6)^2 = 16$
3	$(3 - 6)^2 = 9$
4	$(4 - 6)^2 = 4$
4	$(4 - 6)^2 = 4$
7	$(7 - 6)^2 = 1$
17	$(17 - 6)^2 = 121$
19	$(19 - 6)^2 = 169$
Sum	390

Problem Set

For each data set, find the following:
A. five-number summary
B. range
C. IQR

1. **Stepping Stones** 2, 3, 4, 5, 7, 9, 9, 11, 12

   A. min: ▨, Q_1: 3.5, median: ▨, Q_3: ▨, max: 12

   B. range: 12 − ▨ = ▨

   C. IQR: ▨ − 3.5 = ▨

2. 23, 27, 42, 45, 49, 53, 62, 71, 76, 80

3. 7, 13, 13, 15, 21, 25, 36, 38

4. 2, 9, 4, 7, 3, 1, 4, 5

5. 200, 84, 115, 190, 203, 75, 150, 99, 176

6. 8, 0, 3, −5, 7, −1, 4, 11, −2, 3, 2, 4, 8

Solve.

7. Thirty singers entered a singing competition. Here is the five-number summary of the entrants' ages.

   min: 19, Q1: 27, med: 31, Q3: 33, max: 36

   A. Find the IQR of the data set.

   B. Tell what the IQR means in this situation.

   C. Is the data set more spread out in the ages below 31 or above 31? Explain.

8. These five-number summaries show scores from two judges.

   Judge A: min: 8, Q_1: 10, med: 17, Q_3: 19, max: 20
   Judge B: min: 12, Q_1: 14, med: 15, Q_3: 17, max: 18

   Compare the data sets.

9. The box plot shows the heights, in inches, of the plants in a greenhouse.

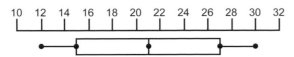

   10 12 14 16 18 20 22 24 26 28 30 32

   A. What is the median height?

   B. What is the range of the heights?

   C. The box is longer than the whiskers. What does that indicate?

10. The box plots show students' scores on a pre-test and post-test.

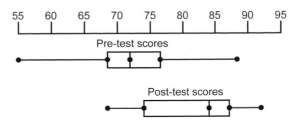

   55   60   65   70   75   80   85   90   95

   Pre-test scores

   Post-test scores

   A. Describe the spread of the pre-test scores.

   B. Estimate the difference between the post-test and pre-test median scores.

   C. Compare the spread of the pre-test and post-test scores.

Find the standard deviation of the data set. Round to the nearest tenth if needed.

11. **Stepping Stones** 5, 7, 8, 10, 20

   Step 1 $\bar{x} = 10$

   Step 2 Complete the table.

   Step 3 $\dfrac{\blacksquare}{5 - 1} \approx \blacksquare$

   Step 4 $s = \sqrt{\blacksquare} \approx \blacksquare$

x	$(x - \bar{x})^2$
5	25
7	9
8	▨
10	▨
20	▨
	Sum: ▨

12. 2, 4, 7, 8, 9

13. 70, 71, 71, 73, 76, 77

14. 18, 38, 46, 90

15. 2, 2, 6, 6, 9, 10, 14, 15

Solve.

16. Data Set A has a mean of 215 and a standard deviation of 35. Data Set B has a mean of 400 and a standard deviation of 12. Which data set is more spread out?

17. The number of text messages a teenager sent each day for six days is 21, 21, 6, 22, 23, and 24. Suppose the value 6 were removed from the data. How would the mean and standard deviation change?

18. Without calculating, explain which data set would have the **greater** standard deviation.

   Set A: 35, 38, 41, 43, 53
   Set B: 4, 19, 30, 35, 51

19. Without calculating, explain which data set would have the **least** standard deviation.

   Set A: 46, 55, 72, 103, 103
   Set B: 33, 99, 100, 100, 100
   Set C: 54, 59, 61, 63, 66

20. What is the standard deviation of a data set whose values are all the same?

CHAPTER 1   Review

Choose the answer.

1. What is the mean of the data set?

16, 32, 41, 54, 32

- **A.** 32
- **B.** 35
- **C.** 38
- **D.** 41

2. What is the median of the data set?

4, 5, 9, 11, 9, 2, 4, 9

- **A.** 4
- **B.** 7
- **C.** 9
- **D.** 10

3. Dawson has 14 baseball cards worth $5 each, 8 baseball cards worth $3 each, and 20 baseball cards worth $2 each. What is the mean value of his baseball cards?

- **A.** $3.19
- **B.** $4.20
- **C.** $4.47
- **D.** $5.20

4. What is the interquartile range of the data set?

35, 36, 38, 41, 47, 49, 63, 67, 71, 75

- **A.** 29
- **B.** 32
- **C.** 40
- **D.** 48

5. Estimate which data set has the greatest standard deviation.

- **A.** 50, 70, 90, 110
- **B.** 50, 50, 200, 200
- **C.** 150, 150, 150, 150, 150
- **D.** 100, 110, 120, 130, 140, 150

6. If Barry's total budget is $500, then how much did he budget for books and clothes?

Barry's Budget

- **A.** $200
- **B.** $275
- **C.** $325
- **D.** $465

7. The histogram shows the number of pieces of mail Jamel received each day for 15 days.

On how many days did he receive more than 4 pieces of mail?

- **A.** 5
- **B.** 6
- **C.** 7
- **D.** 8

8. Which data set has two modes?

- **A.** −4, 3, 1, 4, 5, 2, 3
- **B.** −1, 0, 3, 3, 3, 4, 6
- **C.** 0, 5, 3, −4, 1, −3, −1
- **D.** 1, 6, −3, 6, 5, 2, −3

Solve.

9. A science teacher needs to use a substance to make four samples that have a mean mass of 500 g. She has three samples with masses of 450, 475, and 600 g. What must the mass of the fourth sample be?

10. The line plot shows the ages of puppies that are up for adoption.

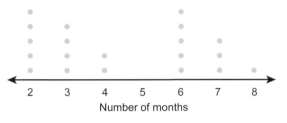

Number of months

A. How many puppies are either 6 or 7 months old?

B. What percent of the puppies are less than 4 months old?

11. The stem-and-leaf plot shows the typing speeds, in words per minute (wpm), of several job applicants.

```
2 | 3  9  9
3 | 0  4  7  8
4 | 5  5  8
5 | 3  6  2
6 | 2
```

Key: 2|3 = 23

A. What is the median typing speed?

B. How many applicants typed more than 30 wpm but less than 50 wpm?

12. The numbers of flowers on four different plants are 7, 2, 3, and 8. Find the standard deviation of these numbers to the nearest tenth.

13. The box plot shows the lengths of video clips, in minutes.

A. What is the range of the times?

B. What is the median time?

C. Compare the spread of the data in the lower and upper halves.

14. The ages of the guests on a museum tour are 32, 14, 18, 29, 65, 50, 48, 44, and 28. Find the five-number summary of the ages.

15. The bar graph shows the scores of players in two games.

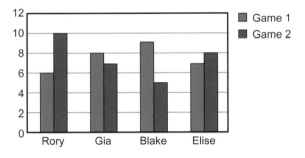

A. Who won Game 1?

B. Who did better in Game 2 than in Game 1?

C. Who had the greatest combined score from the two games?

CHAPTER 2   Connections Between Data

How is a person's heart rate tied to his age? Is blood pressure connected with heart problems? How much oxygen should someone have in her blood when recovering from surgery? In this chapter, you will learn how to identify and use connections between data.

In This Chapter

You will learn how to describe and use the connections between sets of data. You'll see how to interpret scatter plots and how to use linear and other mathematical models to describe patterns and make predictions.

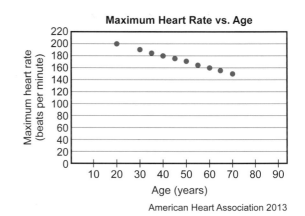

Maximum Heart Rate vs. Age

American Heart Association 2013

Topic List

- ▶ Chapter 2 Introduction
- ▶ Scatter Plots
- ▶ Correlation
- ▶ Linear Regression
- ▶ More Regression
- ▶ Chapter 2 Review

Doctors and nurses use data to help patients. ▶

CHAPTER 2 Introduction

Engineers gather and study data about our driving habits to help make roads safer.

Think of a road near your home. What should the speed limit for a given stretch of the road be? Should a stop sign be placed at a given intersection? Do weather conditions affect the number of car accidents and the severity of those accidents? Engineers answer those and many other questions by gathering and analyzing data.

Speed vs. Stopping Distances

The table shows the approximate stopping distances for a vehicle traveling at various speeds on a dry road.

Speed (mph)	15	25	35	45	55	65	75
Stopping distance (ft)	44	85	136	196	265	345	433

From the table it appears that as the speed increases, the distance required to stop increases. But before engineers make that claim, they must be certain that driving speed and stopping distance are truly related—and not the result of chance. Engineers, and you, can use mathematical methods to determine the connections among data values or sets of data.

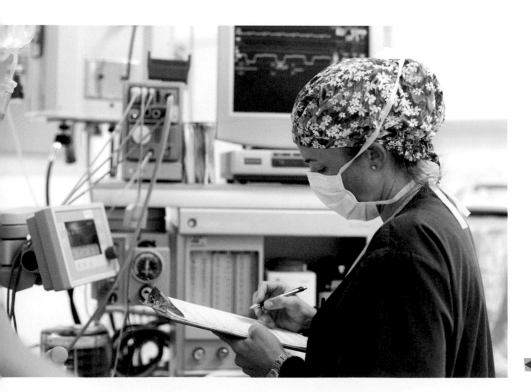

In this chapter, you will learn how to use data to create a model and solve problems.

Preparing for the Chapter

Review the following skills to prepare for the concepts in the chapter: identifying a point in the coordinate plane, finding the slope of a line, and writing the equation of a line in point-slope form.

Identifying a Point in the Coordinate Plane

Identify a point in the **coordinate plane** by writing its coordinates in the form of an **ordered pair**. Write the **x-coordinate** first and the **y-coordinate** second.

To identify the x-coordinate, count the number of units the point is located to the left or right of the **origin**. If the point is

- Left of the origin, the x-coordinate is negative.

- Right of the origin, the x-coordinate is positive.

- On the y-axis, the x-coordinate is zero.

To identify the y-coordinate, count the number of units the point is located above or below the origin. If the point is

- Above the origin, the y-coordinate is positive.

- Below the origin, the y-coordinate is negative.

- On the x-axis, the y-coordinate is zero.

EXAMPLE 1
Identify the coordinates of the point.

A P

Solution Point P is 2 units to the right and 3 units below the origin. The coordinates are $(2, -3)$. ▪

B Q

Solution Point Q is 4 units to the left of the origin and located on the x-axis. The coordinates are $(-4, 0)$. ▪

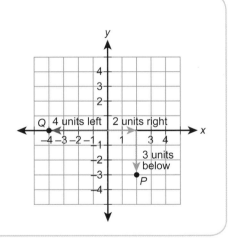

Finding the Slope of a Line

To find the **slope** of a line, identify two points on the line and use the slope formula.

SLOPE FORMULA

The slope m of a line containing the two points (x_1, y_1) and (x_2, y_2) can be found using the formula $m = \dfrac{y_2 - y_1}{x_2 - x_1}$.

EXAMPLE 2
Find the slope of the line.

Solution Identify two points on the line: $(2, 3)$ and $(5, 9)$. Substitute 2 for x_1, 3 for y_1, 5 for x_2, and 9 for y_2.

$$m = \frac{y_2 - y_1}{x_2 - x_1}$$
$$= \frac{9 - 3}{5 - 2}$$
$$= \frac{6}{3}$$
$$= 2$$

The slope of the line is 2. ▪

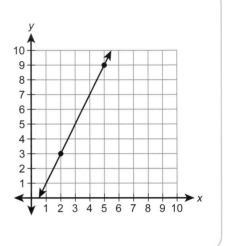

Writing the Equation of a Line

DEFINITION

The **point-slope form** of a linear equation that includes point (x_1, y_1) and has slope m is $y - y_1 = m(x - x_1)$.

EXAMPLE 3
Use point-slope form to write an equation of the line that has a slope of 4 and contains the point (−2, 3).

Solution Substitute 3 for y_1, 4 for m, and −2 for x_1.

$$y - y_1 = m(x - x_1)$$
$$y - 3 = 4(x - (-2))$$
$$y - 3 = 4(x + 2) \ \blacksquare$$

Problem Set

Identify the coordinates of the point.

1. A
2. B
3. C
4. D
5. E
6. F

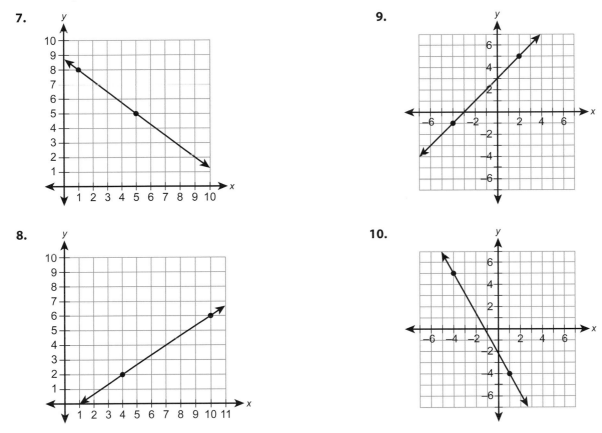

Find the slope of the line.

7.

9.

8.

10.

Use point-slope form to write an equation of the line that has the indicated slope and contains the given point.

11. $m = -1; (2, 3)$

12. $m = 3; (5, -2)$

13. $m = \frac{1}{2}; (4, 0)$

14. $m = \frac{2}{5}; (-3, 7)$

15. $m = -2; (-1, -4)$

16. $m = 1.3; (-6.1, 5.3)$

Scatter Plots

Graphing a paired data set can show trends and enable you to make predictions.

➤ Creating a Scatter Plot

> **DEFINITION**
>
> A **scatter plot** shows two sets of data plotted as ordered pairs in a coordinate plane.

Creating a scatter plot is really just a matter of plotting the ordered pairs on the coordinate plane. However, it is important to consider appropriate scales for the horizontal and vertical axes.

▶ **THINK ABOUT IT**

Paired data are sometimes called *bivariate data*.

EXAMPLE 1

The table shows the standings, as of April 4, 2013, of the top eight teams in the Eastern Conference of the National Basketball Association (NBA). Create a scatter plot for the data.

Solution The number of wins ranges from 36 to 58, so it makes sense to go from 0 to 60, by fives, on the horizontal axis. The number of losses ranges from 16 to 38, so it makes sense to go from 0 to 50, also by fives, on the vertical axis.

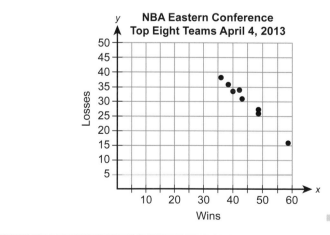

NBA Eastern Conference		
Team	**Wins**	**Losses**
Miami	58	16
New York	48	26
Indiana	48	27
Brooklyn	43	31
Atlanta	42	34
Chicago	40	33
Boston	39	36
Milwaukee	36	38

ShrpSports 2013

Identifying Clusters and Outliers

DEFINITIONS

A **cluster** is a group of points that are close together in comparison with the other points.

An **outlier** is a point that is far from the rest of the values or does not follow the general trend of the other values.

EXAMPLE 2

Identify any clusters or outliers in the scatter plot.

Solution Look for points that are closer together than the rest of the points. The five points with distances between 3 km and 5 km, and costs between $6.50 and $8.00, form a cluster.

The point representing 19 km and $6 is an outlier. ▪

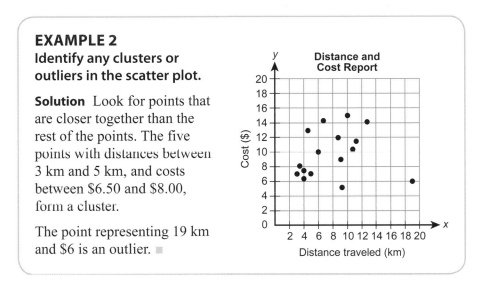

Interpreting a Scatter Plot

EXAMPLE 3

The scatter plot shows the grades earned for 10 students enrolled in both a math class and a history class.

Ⓐ One student earned a grade of 3 in history. What is that student's math grade?

Solution Find 3 on the horizontal axis. Then look up to find a point. From that point, look left to the vertical axis. The student's math grade is a 5. ▪

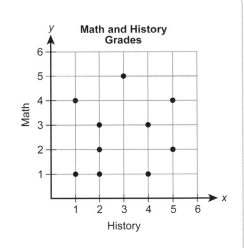

Ⓑ What is the most common history grade? How many students earned that grade in history?

Solution Count the number of points on each vertical line. The most common history grade is 2. Three students earned that grade. ▪

Ⓒ What is the mean math grade of the students?

Solution Look to the vertical axis to find the math grades. Three students earned a grade of 1, two students earned a grade of 2, two students earned a grade of 3, two students earned a grade of 4, and one student earned a grade of 5.

$$\bar{x} = \frac{(3 \cdot 1) + (2 \cdot 2) + (2 \cdot 3) + (2 \cdot 4) + (1 \cdot 5)}{10} = \frac{3 + 4 + 6 + 8 + 5}{10} = \frac{26}{10} = 2.6$$

The mean math grade is 2.6. ▪

Problem Set

Make a scatter plot for the data set.

1. Stepping Stones

Study time (min)	Test score
10	55
20	65
30	60
40	74
50	80
60	85

Label the horizontal axis **Study time (min)** and the vertical axis ▨ .

The number of minutes range from 10 to ▨ . Go from 0 to ▨ , by tens, on the horizontal axis.

The test scores range from ▨ to 85. Go from ▨ to 100, by tens, on the vertical axis.

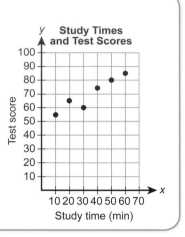

2.

Age	Text messages
16	21
23	18
15	25
33	11
29	9
16	28
40	4

3.

Time	Temperature (°F)
3:00 p.m.	63
5:00 p.m.	65
7:00 p.m.	60
9:00 p.m.	53
11:00 p.m.	49
1:00 a.m.	44

4.

Year of car	Advertised price of car ($)
2010	17,000
2007	19,000
2011	21,000
2009	45,000
2010	32,000
2007	39,000
2012	11,000

Identify any clusters or outliers in the scatter plot.

5. Stepping Stones

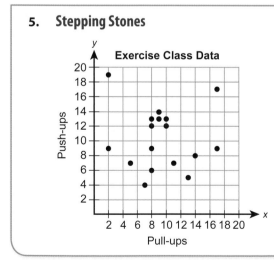

Because they are bunched closer together than the other points, the six points with numbers of pull-ups between ▨ and 10, and numbers of push-ups between 12 and ▨ , form a cluster. The points with coordinates (2, ▨) and (▨ , ▨) are outliers because they are far from the other points.

6.

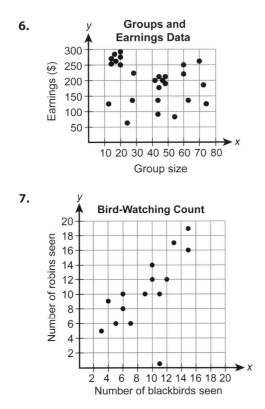

Groups and Earnings Data

7.

Bird-Watching Count

8.

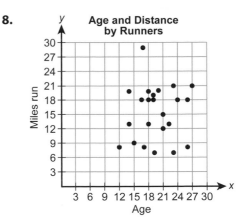

Age and Distance by Runners

The scatter plot shows the winning time in the men's 200 m dash event in six consecutive Olympics.

9. **Stepping Stones** What was the approximate winning time in 2008?

   Look for 2008 on the horizontal axis and look up. The winning time was about ▆ s.

10. What was the approximate winning time in 1992?

11. In what year was the approximate winning time 19.8 s?

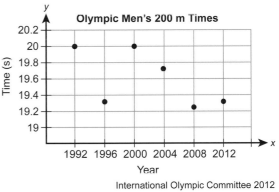

Olympic Men's 200 m Times

International Olympic Committee 2012

The scatter plot shows the number of minutes Guya practiced the flute each day in a given week.

12. How many minutes did Guya practice on Tuesday?

13. On which day did Guya practice 50 min?

14. On which day(s) did Guya practice less than 30 min?

15. What is Guya's median practice time per day during the given week? Round to the nearest tenth, if necessary.

16. What is Guya's mean practice time per day during the given week?

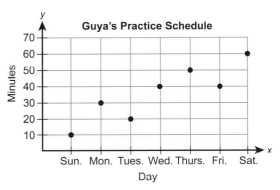

Guya's Practice Schedule

Correlation

You can use a single number to describe the relationship between the variables in a scatter plot.

⊗ Describing an Association

To completely describe the **association**, or relationship, between two variables, give both the direction of the association and its strength.

DEFINITION

If two variables have a **positive association**, then the data values from one set increase as the data values from the other set increase.

If two variables have a **negative association**, then the data values from one set decrease as the data values from the other set increase.

If two variables have **no association**, then the points appear randomly scattered when the data sets are graphed on a scatter plot.

▶ **TIP**

In a positive association, points tend to move up from left to right. In a negative association, points tend to move down from left to right.

Generally speaking, the stronger an association, the more closely the points fit a pattern. The strength of an association can be described as **strong**, **moderate**, or **weak**.

EXAMPLE 1
Determine the direction and strength of the association between the variables. If there is no association, write *no association*.

A

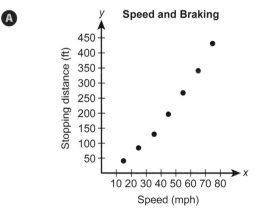

B

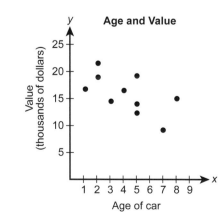

Solution As the speeds increase, the stopping distances increase, so the direction is positive. The points are very close to forming a straight line, which is a strong positive association. ■

Solution As the ages increase, the values generally decrease, so the direction is negative. The points loosely follow along a line, which is a moderate negative association. ■

C

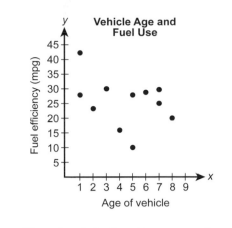

Vehicle Age and Fuel Use

Solution There is a lot of scatter among the points. But the younger vehicles tend to have higher fuel efficiencies, which is a weak negative association. ▪

D

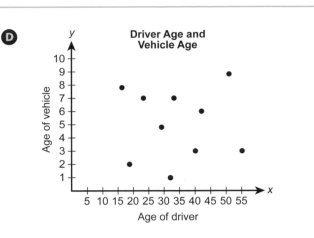

Driver Age and Vehicle Age

Solution There is no pattern at all among the points. So there is no association between the age of the driver and the age of the vehicle. ▪

⬧ Estimating the Correlation Coefficient

Correlation is another word for *association*.

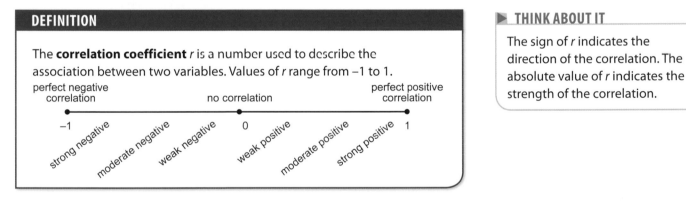

DEFINITION

The **correlation coefficient** r is a number used to describe the association between two variables. Values of r range from -1 to 1.

▶ **THINK ABOUT IT**

The sign of r indicates the direction of the correlation. The absolute value of r indicates the strength of the correlation.

EXAMPLE 2

Estimate the correlation coefficient between the variables.

A

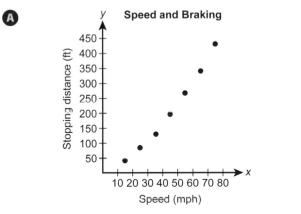

Speed and Braking

B

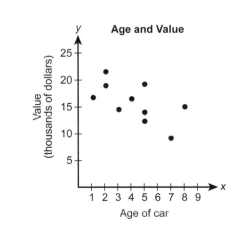

Age and Value

Solution This is a very strong positive correlation, so a good estimate for r is about 0.98. ▪

Solution This is a moderate negative correlation, so a good estimate for r is about -0.65. ▪

▶ Finding *r*

You can find a correlation coefficient by using a graphing calculator. On a TI-83/84 graphing calculator, first make sure your diagnostics are on by pressing 2nd CATALOG, scrolling to DiagnosticOn, and pressing ENTER.

HOW TO FIND *r* ON A TI-83/84 CALCULATOR

To find *r*:

Step 1 Press **STAT**, and then select **1: Edit**.

Step 2 Enter the *x*-coordinates in L1 and the corresponding *y*-coordinates in L2.

Step 3 Press **STAT**, arrow over to **CALC**, select **4: LinReg(ax+b)**, and press **ENTER**. The value of *r* is on the last line.

▶ **TIP**

For other types of calculators, consult the user's manual.

EXAMPLE 3

The table shows fuel efficiency ratings for the top 10 most fuel-efficient vehicles (excluding electric and plug-in hybrid electric vehicles) in 2013. Find and interpret *r*.

City mpg	51	53	47	47	45	42	41	43	44	40
Highway mpg	48	46	47	47	45	48	44	40	40	39

www.fueleconomy.gov 2013

Solution

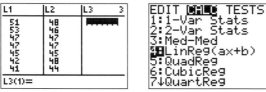

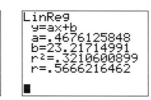

The value of *r* is about 0.57. There is a moderate positive correlation between the city miles per gallon and the highway miles per gallon of the 10 vehicles. ■

You can also use a spreadsheet to find *r*. In most spreadsheet programs, enter "=" and then type CORREL. Then enter the arrays, or lists of data (A2:A11 and B2:B11 in this example), and press OK. Other spreadsheet programs will have similar commands.

	A	B	C
1	City mpg	Highway mpg	
2	51	48	
3	53	46	
4	47	47	
5	47	47	
6	45	45	
7	42	48	
8	41	44	
9	43	40	
10	44	40	
11	40	39	
12			
13	0.56662		
14			

A13 ▾ *fx* =CORREL(A2:A11,B2:B11)

A strong correlation between two variables may or may not indicate a cause–effect relationship between the variables. For example, there may be a strong correlation between the number of umbrellas sold in a town and the water levels in nearby rivers. But umbrella sales do not make water levels rise. The strong correlation is most likely due to a third variable—amount of rainfall.

▶ **BY THE WAY**

If there is a cause–effect relationship, then either *x* may cause *y*, or *y* may cause *x*.

Problem Set

Determine the direction and strength of the association between the variables. If there is no association, write *no association*.

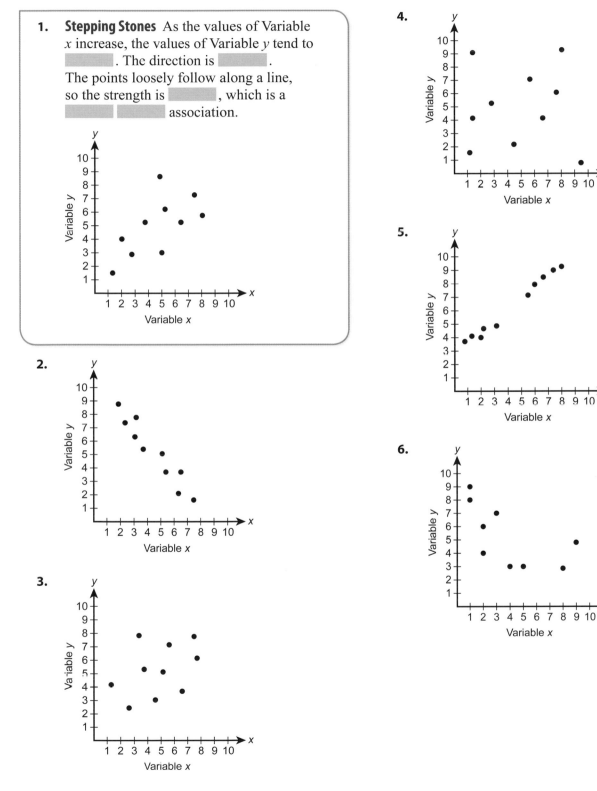

1. **Stepping Stones** As the values of Variable *x* increase, the values of Variable *y* tend to ▨▨▨▨. The direction is ▨▨▨▨. The points loosely follow along a line, so the strength is ▨▨▨▨, which is a ▨▨▨▨ ▨▨▨▨ association.

2.

3.

4.

5.

6.

Create a scatter plot for the data set. Determine the direction and strength of the association between the variables. If there is no association, write *no association*.

7. Stepping Stones

Laps	14	8	20	16	12	10	15	10
Minutes	9	3	12	9	5	4	8	5

Create a scatter plot of the data by graphing ordered pairs in the form (laps, minutes). The points tend to ▭ from left to right, and they closely follow a line, which is a ▭ ▭ association.

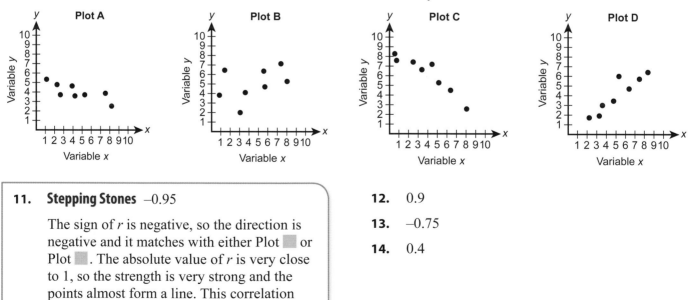

8.

Training hours	0	12	2	10	9	5	6	4
Accidents	8	0	5	1	3	2	2	0

9.

History score	30	19	40	20	40	24	35	18	15	44
Math score	45	28	19	21	28	16	16	48	15	33

10.

Days	2	6	1	8	2	5	7	4	5	10
Cost ($)	145	125	40	175	75	100	230	115	150	180

Use estimation to match the correlation coefficient with the scatter plot.

11. Stepping Stones −0.95

The sign of *r* is negative, so the direction is negative and it matches with either Plot ▭ or Plot ▭ . The absolute value of *r* is very close to 1, so the strength is very strong and the points almost form a line. This correlation coefficient matches with Plot ▭ .

12. 0.9

13. −0.75

14. 0.4

Find the value of *r*.

15.

State	FL	NY	VA	TX	OK	PA	HI	CO
Land area (1000 mi²)	54	47	40	262	69	45	6	104
Water area (mi²)	4672	1895	1006	5056	1231	490	38	376

USGS Water Science School 2013a

16.

Country	Ukraine	Ethiopia	Guam	South Africa	Yemen	Mexico	Nigeria	Macau
Male life expectancy	63.07	53.99	75.46	50.34	62.05	73.84	48.95	81.47
Female life expectancy	74.77	59.21	81.73	48.45	66.27	79.63	55.33	87.54

CIA 2013

17.

City	Chicago	Atlanta	Miami	Seattle	Boise	New Orleans	Helena	Los Angeles
Average minimum temp. (°F) in Jan.	19	37	58	33	22	45	8	47
Latitude (°)	42.3	33.9	26.3	48.1	43.7	30.8	47.1	34.3

MSTE, University of Illinois 2013

18.

Vegetable	Carrot	Kale	Onion	Peas	Celery	Potato	Spinach	Broccoli
Calcium (mg)	19	94	22	67	16	20	10	42
Iron (mg)	0.4	1.2	0.2	3.2	0.2	2.7	0.3	0.8

USDA ARS 2002

Solve.

19. The correlation coefficient for the costs and screen sizes of the televisions in an electronics store is 0.82. Explain how the costs and screen sizes are related.

20. The correlation coefficient for the ages of drivers in a driver safety class and the number of traffic violations they have received is –0.61. Explain how the ages and numbers of violations are related.

21. For Data Set A, the value of *r* is 0.6. For Data Set B, the value of *r* is –0.6.

   A. In what way are the correlations between the variables in each data set the same?

   B. In what way are the correlations between the variables in each data set different?

22. An outdoor reporter finds a positive correlation between the number of granola bars a hiker eats on a trip and the number of bug bites the hiker receives. Name a third variable that could explain the correlation.

23. A researcher notices a positive correlation between the amount of bottled water and the amount of sunscreen sold in a city. Name a third variable that could explain the correlation.

Linear Regression

For strongly correlated data, it is useful to find the equation of a line that fits the data.

In some paired data sets, one variable depends on, or can be explained by, the other. The **input variable** is the independent variable, x. The **output variable** is the dependent variable, y.

Identifying Input and Output Variables

EXAMPLE 1
Identify the input variable and the output variable.

A cost of a collision repair and the speed traveling before the collision

Solution The speed affects the amount of damage and, therefore, the cost of repairs. The input variable is the speed and the output variable is the cost. ■

B time parked in a parking garage and cost of parking

Solution The cost is determined by the length of time parked. The input variable is the time and the output variable is the cost. ■

▶ **BY THE WAY**

The input variable can be called the *explanatory variable*, and the output variable can be called the *response variable*.

Finding the Equation of a Linear Model

A line drawn to fit the points in a scatter plot is a **linear model** of the data.

AN EASY WAY TO FIND A LINEAR MODEL

To find an equation of a linear model:
Step 1 Choose two points that are on, or close to, the line.
Step 2 Substitute the coordinates of the points into the slope formula.
Step 3 Substitute the slope and the coordinates of either point into the point-slope form of a line.

EXAMPLE 2
Write an equation of a linear model for the data.

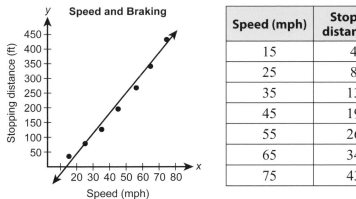

Speed (mph)	Stopping distance (ft)
15	44
25	85
35	136
45	196
55	265
65	345
75	433

► **THINK ABOUT IT**

The stopping distance is dependent on the speed, so the stopping distance is the output variable and is graphed on the vertical axis.

Solution

Step 1 The points (25, 85) and (65, 345) are closest to the line.

Step 2 Substitute the coordinates into the slope formula.

$$m = \frac{y_2 - y_1}{x_2 - x_1} = \frac{345 - 85}{65 - 25} = \frac{260}{40} = 6.5$$

Step 3 Substitute 6.5 for m, 25 for x_1, and 85 for y_1. Rearrange into slope-intercept form.

$$y - y_1 = m(x - x_1)$$
$$y - 85 = 6.5(x - 25)$$
$$y - 85 = 6.5x - 162.5$$
$$y = 6.5x - 77.5$$

The equation of the linear model is $y = 6.5x - 77.5$. ▪

► **REMEMBER**

In the form $y = mx + b$, m is the slope and b is the y-intercept.

➲ Using the Linear Model

EXAMPLE 3
Use the equation of the linear model in Example 2 to answer the questions.

Ⓐ What is the meaning of the slope in the context of the situation?

Solution The slope is 6.5, or $\frac{6.5}{1}$. For every increase of 1 mph in speed, the stopping distance increases by 6.5 ft. ▪

Ⓑ What would be the stopping distance of a car traveling 90 mph?

Solution Substitute 90 for x and solve for y.

$$y = 6.5x - 77.5$$
$$y = 6.5 \cdot 90 - 77.5$$
$$y = 585 - 77.5$$
$$y = 507.5$$

The stopping distance would be 507.5 ft. ▪

► **THINK ABOUT IT**

The accuracy of predictions in scatter plots increases as |r| gets closer to 1.

C How fast was a car traveling if it took 300 ft to stop?

Solution Substitute 300 for y and solve for x.

$$y = 6.5x - 77.5$$
$$300 = 6.5x - 77.5$$
$$377.5 = 6.5x$$
$$58.1 \approx x$$

The car was traveling at about 58 mph. ∎

Different people may draw different linear models for a scatter plot. The **least squares regression line** (often simply referred to as the **regression line**) is the one line that fits the data best. You can use technology to find the least squares regression equation.

▶ **TIP**

The least squares regression line is sometimes called the *line of best fit*.

⮞ Finding the Regression Equation

On a TI-83/84 graphing calculator, the equation appears on the same screen as r. Here are the screens used in finding the least squares regression equation for the speeds and stopping distances in Example 2.

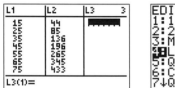  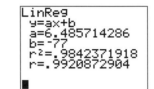

▶ **TIP**

See the Correlation topic in this chapter for more detailed steps for finding r.

Substitute the values for a and b into the equation $y = ax + b$. Rounding the value of a to three decimal places, the least squares regression equation is $y = 6.486x - 77$. Notice that this is close to, but not exactly, the equation found in Example 2.

You can also use a spreadsheet to determine the equation. You may need to first graph the data. In one program, you select the data and choose Scatter from the Insert > Charts menu. Then you add a trend line, selecting the option to display the equation in the chart.

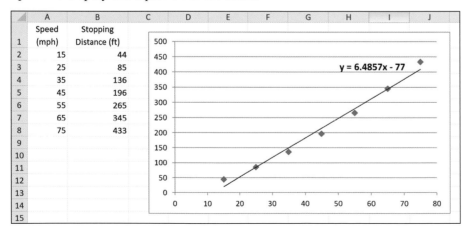

Interpreting the Coefficient of Determination

The **coefficient of determination**, written r^2, is the square of the correlation coefficient r. It tells what percent of the variation, or differences, in y can be explained by the regression line.

On a calculator, r^2 appears on the same screen as r. The third calculator screen shows that $r^2 \approx 0.984$, so 98.4% of the variation in the stopping distances is explained by the variation in the speed of the vehicle. Only 1.6% of the variation is unexplained by the linear model. You can be more confident in predictions made by using a model with a greater r^2-value than from a model with a lower r^2-value.

> ▶ **TIP**
>
> You can find the value of r^2 in a spreadsheet. You may have the option to display it while adding a trend line.

Problem Set

Identify the input variable and the output variable.

1. cost of electric bill and amount of electricity used

2. number of rowers in a rowboat and the speed of the rowboat

3. number of runners in a race and number of injuries treated during the race

4. value of a car and age of the car

Write the equation of the linear model.

5. **Stepping Stones** The points (49, 55) and (■, 25) are closest to the line.

$$m = \frac{25 - 55}{\boxed{} - 49} = \frac{-30}{\boxed{}} = \boxed{}$$

$$y - y_1 = m(x - x_1)$$

$$y - 55 = \boxed{}(x - 49)$$

$$y - 55 = \boxed{}\,x + \boxed{}$$

$$y = \boxed{}\,x + \boxed{}$$

x	y
17	69
31	69
34	58
49	55
54	45
62	47
71	30
83	37
89	25

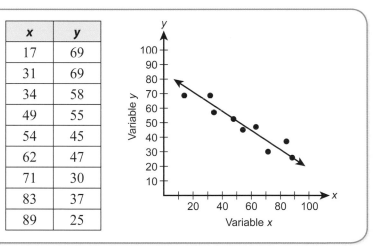

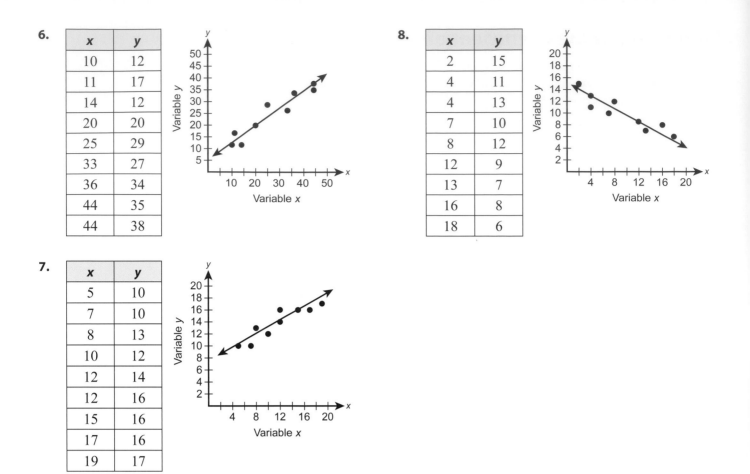

6.

x	y
10	12
11	17
14	12
20	20
25	29
33	27
36	34
44	35
44	38

8.

x	y
2	15
4	11
4	13
7	10
8	12
12	9
13	7
16	8
18	6

7.

x	y
5	10
7	10
8	13
10	12
12	14
12	16
15	16
17	16
19	17

The equation $y = 6.3x + 67.4$ is a linear model for data comparing the ages of boys between 2 and 10 years old (x) and their average heights in centimeters (y).

9. **Stepping Stones** What is the meaning of the slope in the context of this situation?

The slope is ▢. For every increase of 1 year, the average height increases by ▢ cm.

10. What is the average height of a 5-year-old boy?

11. What is the average height of an 8-year-old boy?

12. How old would you expect a boy who is 85 cm tall to be?

13. Use the equation to predict the average height of an 11-year-old boy.

14. The r-value of the data pairs is about 0.993. However, the output for an input of 30 is beyond a reasonable height. Explain.

The equation $y = 1.2x + 8.9$ is a linear model for data comparing the ages of babies between 1 and 11 months old (x) and their average weights in pounds (y).

15. What is the meaning of the slope in the context of this situation?

16. What is the average weight of a 2-month-old baby?

17. What is the average weight of a 10-month-old baby?

18. A baby weighs 17.5 lb. What is the best estimate for the age of the baby?

Use technology to find the least squares regression equation.

19.

Variable x	5	7	15	13	8	15	9	9	12	4
Variable y	18	16	3	7	12	5	10	15	9	19

20.

Variable x	2	7	25	13	4	15	33	10	19	27
Variable y	16	19	22	21	19	19	26	21	22	25

21.

Variable x	2006	2007	2008	2009	2010	2011	2012
Variable y	98	104	105	106	109	112	116

The table shows the average annual cost of tuition at 4-year institutions from 2003 to 2010.

School year starting . . .	2003	2004	2005	2006	2007	2008	2009	2010
Average cost of tuition at 4-year institutions ($)	15,505	16,510	17,451	18,471	19,363	20,409	21,093	22,092

U.S. Department of Education NCES 2012

22. Find the least squares regression equation using the school year (in number of years after 2000) for the input variable and the average cost (in thousands of dollars) for the output variable.

23. What is the best estimate for the average cost of tuition at a 4-year institution in the school year starting in 2002?

24. What is the best estimate for the average cost of tuition at a 4-year institution in the school year starting in 2020?

25. What is the meaning of the slope in the context of this situation?

Solve.

26. Shelly found that the coefficient of determination between the age of a runner x and the runner's finishing position y was about 0.728. What can she conclude?

27. Rob investigated the length of essays submitted to a teacher x and the score the teacher gave the essay y. He found that $r \approx 0.813$. Find and interpret the coefficient of determination.

The table shows the federal minimum wage for the years 1980 through 2012.

Years after 2000	−20	−12	−9	−4	0	6	8	9	12
Federal minimum wage ($)	3.10	3.35	3.80	4.25	5.15	5.15	5.85	6.55	7.25

DOL 2012

28. Find the least squares regression equation using the number of years after 2000 for the input variable and the federal minimum wage for the output variable.

29. Estimate the federal minimum wage in 1970.

30. What is the meaning of the slope in the context of this situation?

31. Predict the federal minimum wage in 2030.

32. Find the coefficient of determination.

33. Explain the meaning of the coefficient of determination in the context of the situation.

More Regression

Not all patterns are straight-line patterns.

The points in the scatter plot of the number of registered buses in the United States from 1950 to 2010 tend to fall along a line. But the points in the scatter plot of the average number of registered automobiles per licensed driver in the United States from 1950 to 2010 tend to fall along a parabola.

> ▶ **REMEMBER**
> A parabola is the graph of a quadratic function.

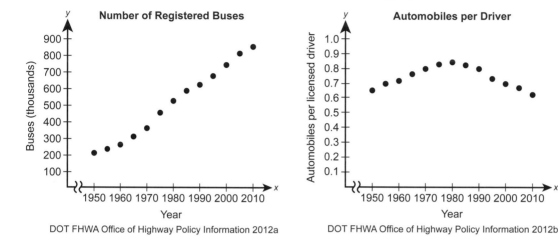

DOT FHWA Office of Highway Policy Information 2012a   DOT FHWA Office of Highway Policy Information 2012b

⬛ Finding a Quadratic Regression Equation

You can use a calculator to find a quadratic regression equation. On a TI-83/84 calculator, choose **5: QuadReg** from the CALC menu. Notice that the input values are entered as the number of years since 1900.

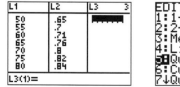

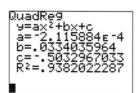

Substitute the values for a, b, and c into the equation $y = ax^2 + bx + c$, which is the standard form of a quadratic equation. When rounded to four significant digits, the quadratic regression equation is approximately $y = 0.0002x^2 + 0.0334x - 0.5033$.

To find the quadratic regression equation in a certain spreadsheet program, create a scatter plot, select a polynomial regression type after choosing to add a trend line, and pick 2 for the order because x is raised to a power of 2 in a quadratic equation.

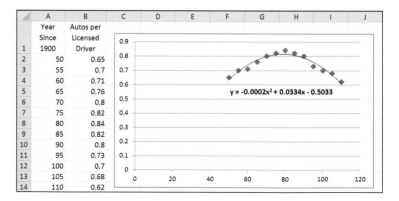

▶ Using a Quadratic Regression Equation

EXAMPLE 1
Use the equation of the quadratic regression curve to estimate the number of automobiles per licensed driver in 1987.

Solution Because the input variable is the number of years since 1900, substitute 87 for x and solve for y.

$$y = -0.0002x^2 + 0.0334x - 0.5033$$
$$y = -0.0002 \cdot 87^2 + 0.0334 \cdot 87 - 0.5033$$
$$y = -1.514 + 2.906 - 0.5033 = 0.8889$$

In 1987, there was an average of about 0.9 automobiles per licensed driver. ■

▶ REMEMBER

The order of operations tells you to evaluate exponents before multiplying.

▶ Finding an Exponential Regression Equation

Some data pairs fit well to an exponential model. In an exponential function, the outputs increase or decrease at an increasingly greater rate.

This graph shows the number of registered trucks in the United States from 1930 to 2010. Notice how the increases between decades tend to get larger over time.

To find an exponential regression equation on a TI-83/84 calculator, scroll down to choose **0: ExpReg** from the CALC menu. Again, the input values have been entered as the number of years since 1900.

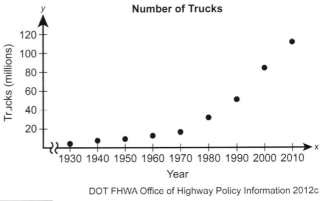

Number of Trucks

DOT FHWA Office of Highway Policy Information 2012c

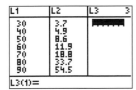  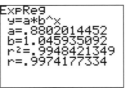

Substitute the values for a and b into the equation $y = a \cdot b^x$, which is one form of an exponential equation. When the values are rounded, the exponential regression equation is approximately $y = 0.8802 \cdot 1.0459^x$.

The exponential regression equation for these same data on a certain spreadsheet is $y = 0.8802 \cdot e^{0.0449x}$. The letter e represents a special number whose value is approximately 2.71828. You can use this value to make the equation from the spreadsheet look like the equation from the calculator: $e^{0.0449x} \approx 2.71828^{0.0449x} \approx 1.0459^x$.

▶ TIP

Some calculators have a key labeled e^x.

Using an Exponential Regression Equation

EXAMPLE 2
Use the equation of the exponential regression curve to predict the number of registered trucks that will be in the United States in 2020.

Solution Because the input variable is the number of years since 1900, substitute 120 for x and solve for y.

$$y = 0.8802 \cdot 1.0459^x$$
$$y = 0.8802 \cdot 1.0459^{120}$$
$$y \approx 0.8802 \cdot 218.1823221 \approx 192.04408$$

In 2020, there will be about 192 million registered trucks in the United States. ■

▶ **THINK ABOUT IT**

The prediction is based on the assumption that current trends will continue, which they may not.

Determining the Best Regression Model

The points in the scatter plot of the number of registered trucks in the United States tend to fall along the right side of a parabola that opens upward. Therefore, you may wonder if a quadratic model would fit the data better than the exponential model.

To determine which type of regression best fits a data set, use the coefficient of determination, which may appear as either r^2 or R^2. The closer the coefficient is to 1, the better the fit.

▶ **BY THE WAY**

In some data sets, the differences between the coefficients of determination vary widely.

Here are the approximate coefficients of determination for the data about the number of registered trucks in the United States.

> linear regression: 0.852
> quadratic regression: 0.993
> exponential regression: 0.995

Both a quadratic model and an exponential model fit the data set very well. However, the exponential model has a slightly better fit because $0.995 > 0.993$.

The graph of the quadratic regression is shown in solid red, while the graph of the exponential regression is shown in dashed green.

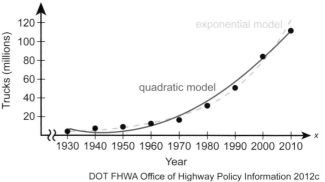

DOT FHWA Office of Highway Policy Information 2012c

Problem Set

Determine whether a linear model or a quadratic model appears to be a better fit.

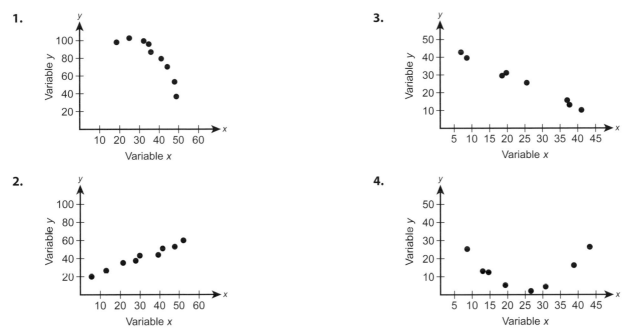

1.

2.

3.

4.

The display gives the result of performing a quadratic regression on a data set where the inputs are speeds in miles per hour and the outputs are the corresponding braking distances in feet.

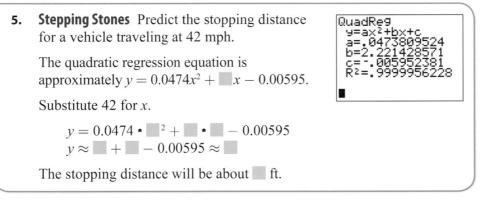

5. **Stepping Stones** Predict the stopping distance for a vehicle traveling at 42 mph.

The quadratic regression equation is approximately $y = 0.0474x^2 + \boxed{}x - 0.00595$.

```
QuadReg
y=ax²+bx+c
a=.0473809524
b=2.221428571
c=-.005952381
R²=.9999956228
■
```

Substitute 42 for x.

$$y = 0.0474 \cdot \boxed{}^2 + \boxed{} \cdot \boxed{} - 0.00595$$
$$y \approx \boxed{} + \boxed{} - 0.00595 \approx \boxed{}$$

The stopping distance will be about $\boxed{}$ ft.

6. Predict the stopping distance for a vehicle traveling at 20 mph.

7. Predict the stopping distance for a vehicle traveling at 78 mph.

Use technology to find the quadratic regression equation.

8.

x	3	6	5	10	5	4	7	2	9
y	7	2	4	5	3	5	1	12	2

9.

x	54	81	15	26	30	41	70	92	61
y	143	80	19	64	83	137	99	25	126

The table shows the average number of miles traveled per person in the United States for different years.

Year	1915	1925	1935	1945	1955	1965	1975	1985	1995	2005
Average mi traveled/ person	194	1056	1796	1788	3650	4569	6147	7460	9099	10,181

DOT FHWA Office of Highway Policy Information 2012d

10. Find the quadratic regression equation using the years since 1900 for the input variable and the average number of miles for the output variable.

11. Estimate the average number of miles traveled per person in 1961.

12. Estimate the average number of miles traveled per person in 2008.

The table shows the number of mobile cellular subscriptions per 100 people in Australia for different years.

Year	1993	1995	1997	1999	2001	2003	2005	2007	2009	2011
Cellular subscriptions/ 100 people	4	12	25	33	57	72	90	101	101	108

World Bank 2013

13. Find the quadratic regression equation using the years since 1990 for the input variable and the number of cellular subscriptions for the output variable.

14. Predict the number of cellular subscriptions per 100 people in Australia in 2030.

The display gives the result of performing an exponential regression on a data set where the inputs are years since 2000 and the outputs are the corresponding mobile cellular subscriptions per 100 people in Zimbabwe.

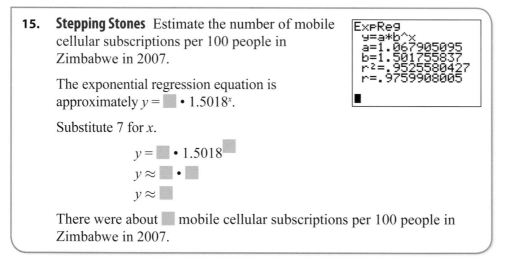

15. **Stepping Stones** Estimate the number of mobile cellular subscriptions per 100 people in Zimbabwe in 2007.

The exponential regression equation is approximately $y = \boxed{} \cdot 1.5018^x$.

Substitute 7 for x.

$$y = \boxed{} \cdot 1.5018^{\boxed{}}$$
$$y \approx \boxed{} \cdot \boxed{}$$
$$y \approx \boxed{}$$

There were about $\boxed{}$ mobile cellular subscriptions per 100 people in Zimbabwe in 2007.

```
ExpReg
 y=a*b^x
 a=1.067905095
 b=1.501755837
 r²=.9525580427
 r=.9759908005
■
```

16. Estimate the number of mobile cellular subscriptions per 100 people in Zimbabwe in 2003.

17. Estimate the number of mobile cellular subscriptions per 100 people in Zimbabwe in 2009.

Use technology to find the exponential regression equation.

18.

x	52	79	8	26	30	41	70	85	61
y	41	80	4	15	11	23	68	117	46

19.

x	13	6	17	5	18	20	8	9	14
y	109	568	38	849	40	3	340	257	92

The table shows the value of a baseball card for different years.

Age (years)	1	2	3	4	5	6	7	8	9	10
Value ($)	0.05	0.05	0.10	0.25	0.25	1	2.50	5.25	10	16

20. Find the exponential regression equation using the age for the input variable and the value for the output variable.

21. Predict the value of the card when the card is 12 years old.

22. Predict the value of the card when the card is 15 years old.

The table shows the cost of gasoline per gallon in the United States in certain years.

Year	1992	1994	1996	1997	2000	2004	2006	2007	2008
Cost/gallon ($)	1.19	1.17	1.29	1.29	1.56	1.92	2.64	2.85	3.32

DOT FHWA Office of Highway Policy Information 2012e

23. Find the exponential regression equation using the years since 1990 for the input variable and the cost for the output variable.

24. Estimate the cost of gasoline in the United States in 1998.

25. Estimate the cost of gasoline in the United States in 2011.

Determine whether a linear, a quadratic, or an exponential model best fits the data.

26.

Year	1975	1980	1985	1990	1995	2000	2005	2010
Worldwide PC sales (millions)	0.05	1.1	11	24	58	132	207	325

eTForecasts 2013

27.

Reaction distance (m)	5.5	9.2	11	14.7	18.3	22
Braking distance (m)	5.3	14.8	21.4	38	59.4	85.5

Road Safety Authority 2007

28.

Age (years)	1	3	4	6	7	8	10
Value of vehicle ($)	23,830	17,895	15,585	12,625	11,000	9790	7685

CHAPTER 2   Review

Choose the answer.

1. The scatter plot shows the ages and number of laps that each of 8 track team members ran.

    How old is the member who ran the greatest number of laps?

    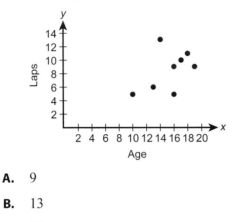

    A. 9

    B. 13

    C. 14

    D. 19

2. Look at the scatter plot in Problem 1. What is the median number of laps that the track team members ran?

    A. 16

    B. 15.375

    C. 9

    D. 8.5

3. Look at the scatter plot in Problem 1. Which is the best description of the association between the ages and the number of laps that each member ran?

    A. strong positive

    B. weak positive

    C. strong negative

    D. weak negative

4. Which is the most likely value for the correlation coefficient r between the variables?

    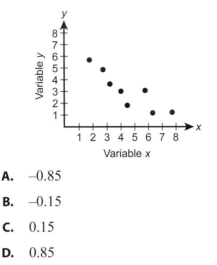

    A. −0.85

    B. −0.15

    C. 0.15

    D. 0.85

5. The correlation coefficient r between the distances that people live from a museum and the numbers of times they have visited the museum is 0.6. What percent of the variance in the number of museum visits is *unexplained*?

    A. 36%

    B. 40%

    C. 60%

    D. 64%

6. The tables give the height of a plant at different ages. Which statement is true?

Age (years)	0.5	1	2	3.5
Height (cm)	6	13	14.5	19

Age (years)	4	5	6.5	8
Height (cm)	22	28	32	39

    A. Either a linear model or a quadratic model would best fit the data.

    B. Either a linear model or an exponential model would best fit the data.

    C. Either a quadratic model or an exponential model would best fit the data.

The table shows the number of medical clinics and the number of bowling alleys in several cities.

Clinics	14	1	6	5	10	6	11	8	6	16
Bowling alleys	12	3	6	7	7	8	9	15	7	12

7. Create a scatter plot for the data.

8. Which ordered pairs form a cluster?

9. Which point is an outlier?

10. Find the value of r.

11. A cause–effect relationship between medical clinics and bowling alleys is unlikely. What could explain the positive association between the variables?

The table shows the number of registered automobiles in Delaware between 1950 and 2010.

Year	1950	1960	1970	1980	1990	2000	2010
Automobiles (thousands)	92.1	163.2	263.1	321.6	379.4	400.3	434.0

DOT FHWA Office of Highway Policy Information 2012f

12. Find the linear regression equation using the years since 1900 for the input variable and the number of automobiles for the output variable.

13. What is the meaning of the slope in the context of this situation?

14. Find and interpret the coefficient of determination.

15. Predict the number of registered automobiles in Delaware in 2025.

The table shows the areas of poster boards in an art store and how many of each size were sold in one month.

Area (in²)	600	154	616	462	308	1260	864	1728
Number sold	56	25	52	49	39	45	60	14

16. Find the quadratic regression equation using the area for the input variable and the number sold for the output variable.

17. The store begins stocking 30 in. by 50 in. poster boards. What is the best prediction for the number it will sell per month?

The table shows the nominal gross domestic product (GDP) for the United States in different years.

Year	1915	1930	1945	1960	1975	1990	2005
GDP (millions of dollars)	38,675	91,200	223,000	526,400	1,637,700	5,800,500	12,623,000

MeasuringWorth 2013

18. Find the exponential regression equation using the years since 1900 for the input variable and the GDP for the output variable.

19. Predict the GDP of the United States in 2045.

20. Does a quadratic regression equation model the data better than the exponential equation? Explain why or why not.

Problem	Topic Lookup		Problem	Topic Lookup
1, 2, 7–9	Scatter Plots		5, 12–15	Linear Regression
3, 4, 10, 11	Correlation		6, 16–20	More Regression

CHAPTER 3   Uncertainty

What are my chances of winning that big, stuffed teddy bear? Should I play the lottery? This chapter focuses on how you can use mathematics to help make sound estimations about uncertain events.

In This Chapter

You will learn about counting methods and how to use mathematics to measure uncertainty and make estimations and predictions.

X	P(X)	Value	EV
None	0.5	−2.0	−1.0
Blue	0.15	1.0	0.15
Purple	0.05	10.0	0.5
Other	0.3	0.25	0.075
		Sum	−0.275

Topic List

The tools of probability can help you analyze games. ▶

CHAPTER 3   Introduction

Mathematics can bring order to what once seemed unpredictable.

The United States consists of a large, diverse group of people. Determining what the U.S. public is thinking can be daunting. To understand public opinion, researchers can use mathematics.

Politics

Did you ever wonder how television networks predict the winner of an election even before all the votes are counted? Candidates themselves often know whether they have won or lost even before the last vote has been cast.

To predict election results, researchers find a representative sample of the voting population. Then they ask those voters questions from which the researchers can draw meaningful inferences. Researchers then use math to analyze the information they gathered. Mathematics provides a way for people to make accurate predictions based on a limited amount of information.

In this chapter, you will learn how mathematics can be used to understand uncertain events.

Preparing for the Chapter

Review the following skills to prepare for the concepts in the chapter: applying the fundamental counting principles, converting a decimal to a fraction, and simplifying a basic factorial expression.

Applying the Fundamental Counting Principles

An **outcome** is the result in a probability experiment, while an **event** is a set of one or more outcomes.

DEFINITION

According to the **Fundamental Counting Principle for Addition**, if event A can be completed in m ways and event B can be completed in n ways and there is no way of completing both events at the same time, then the number of ways of completing event A or event B is $m + n$. If there are k ways to complete both events at once, then the number of ways of completing event A or event B is $m + n - k$.

To apply the Fundamental Counting Principle for Addition, determine whether event A and event B can or can't be completed at the same time.

EXAMPLE 1
There were 4 women, 6 men, 5 girls, and 3 boys at the holiday dinner.

Ⓐ In how many ways can 1 woman or 1 man be chosen to set the table?

Solution There are 4 ways of choosing a woman and 6 ways of choosing a man. Since both events can't happen simultaneously, the solution is $4 + 6 = 10$. ■

Ⓑ In how many ways can 1 female or 1 child be chosen to set the table?

Solution There are 9 ways of choosing a female and 8 ways of choosing a child. Five of the children, however, are also females. Therefore, the solution is $9 + 8 - 5 = 12$. ■

DEFINITION

According to the **Fundamental Counting Principle for Multiplication**, if event A has m outcomes and event B has n outcomes, then event A followed by event B has $m \cdot n$ outcomes.

To apply the Fundamental Counting Principle for Multiplication, identify the number of outcomes for each event.

EXAMPLE 2
How many different outfits can Arnold wear if he has 4 pairs of pants and 3 shirts?

Solution Multiply the number of pants by the number of shirts: $4 \cdot 3 = 12$. Arnold can make 12 different outfits. ■

Converting a Decimal to a Fraction

You can convert a decimal to a fraction in lowest terms. First write a fraction with a denominator that is a power of 10. Then simplify if possible.

EXAMPLE 3
Write the decimal as a fraction in lowest terms.

A 0.8

Solution Write the decimal as a fraction with a denominator of 10, and then simplify.

$$0.8 = \frac{8}{10} = \frac{4}{5}$$ ■

B 0.32

Solution Write as a fraction with a denominator of 100, and then simplify.

$$0.32 = \frac{32}{100} = \frac{8}{25}$$ ■

Simplifying a Basic Factorial Expression

DEFINITION

The expression **n!**, spoken as *n* factorial, where *n* is greater than zero, is the product of all positive integers beginning with *n* and counting backward to 1. Zero factorial is a special case, defined as $0! = 1$.

EXAMPLE 4
Find 7!.

Solution
$7! = 7 \cdot 6 \cdot 5 \cdot 4 \cdot 3 \cdot 2 \cdot 1$ Express as a product of all positive integers less than or equal to 7.

$\quad = 5040$ Simplify. ■

Problem Set

Use the Fundamental Counting Principle for Addition to solve.

1. In how many ways can Pedro draw a red or a green marble from a jar containing 11 red marbles and 6 green marbles?

2. Ellen has 3 science fiction books and 5 adventure books. In how many ways can she choose an adventure book or a science fiction book?

3. A tennis team has six 10-year-old girls, four 11-year-old girls, five 10-year-old boys, and eight 11-year-old boys. In how many ways can the team's coach choose an 11-year-old or a girl to play number one singles for the team?

4. The science club has 4 junior girls, 9 senior girls, 2 junior boys, and 3 senior boys. In how many ways can one member of the club be chosen if the member must either be a junior or a boy?

Use the Fundamental Counting Principle for Multiplication to solve.

5. In a local election, there are 5 candidates for the office of mayor and 4 candidates for the office of vice mayor. In how many ways can the offices be filled?

6. At a local pizza parlor, patrons have 3 choices of cheese and 5 choices of meat. In how many different ways can a patron choose 1 type of cheese and 1 type of meat?

7. Rachel is planning her courses for next year. She can choose from 2 science classes and 4 math classes. In how many ways can she choose 1 science class and 1 math class?

8. Carrie has 3 sweaters and 2 pairs of jeans. In how many possible ways can Carrie choose 1 sweater and 1 pair of jeans?

9. Tito is traveling from Miami to San Francisco by way of Denver. If there are 5 flights from Miami to Denver and 6 flights from Denver to San Francisco, in how many ways can he make the trip?

10. A secret code consists of a number from 0 through 9, followed by a letter in the alphabet, and lastly followed by a number from 0 through 5. How many secret codes are possible?

Write the decimal as a fraction in lowest terms.

11. 0.3

12. 0.22

13. 0.555

14. 0.06

15. 0.1

16. 0.004

Evaluate the factorial.

17. 5!

18. 11!

19. 9!

20. 1!

Permutations and Combinations

Factorials help you count all the different ways to select objects in a group.

⮞ Solving Problems Involving Permutations

DEFINITION

A **permutation** is the number of different ways to arrange a number of objects from a group.

In a permutation, the order of the objects chosen is important. Use the following formula to compute permutations.

PERMUTATION FORMULA

The number of permutations of r objects out of n objects is

$$_nP_r = \frac{n!}{(n-r)!}.$$

▶ **BY THE WAY**

$_nP_r$ is often read as "permutations of n taken r at a time."

▶ **NOTATION**

An alternate notation for $_nP_r$ is $P(n, r)$.

EXAMPLE 1
Find the value of $_5P_3$.

Solution In the permutation formula, substitute 5 for n and 3 for r.

$$_5P_3 = \frac{5!}{(5-3)!} = \frac{5!}{2!} = 5 \cdot 4 \cdot 3 = 60 \ ■$$

EXAMPLE 2
Seven runners are competing in a race. In how many ways can the runners finish in the top 3 spots? Use a permutation expression to solve.

Solution In this problem, $n = 7$ and $r = 3$. Find $_7P_3$.

$$_7P_3 = \frac{7!}{(7-3)!} = \frac{7!}{4!} = 7 \cdot 6 \cdot 5 = 210$$

The runners can finish in the top 3 spots in 210 ways. ■

Solving Problems Involving Combinations

> **DEFINITION**
>
> A **combination** is the number of different ways to select a number of objects from a group.

In a combination, the order of the objects chosen does not matter. Use the following formula to compute combinations.

> **COMBINATION FORMULA**
>
> The number of combinations of r objects selected out of n objects is
>
> $$_nC_r = \frac{n!}{(n-r)!\,r!}.$$

▶ **BY THE WAY**

$_nC_r$ is often read as "combinations of n taken r at a time."

EXAMPLE 3
Find the value of $_9C_5$.

Solution $\quad _9C_5 = \dfrac{9!}{(9-5)!\,5!} = \dfrac{9!}{4!\,5!} = 126$ ■

▶ **REMEMBER**

$n! = n \cdot (n-1) \cdot (n-2) \cdot \ldots \cdot 1$
and
$0! = 1$

EXAMPLE 4
Your philosophy teacher gives you a list of 6 study questions. Three of the 6 questions will be on the final exam. In how many different ways can your philosophy teacher choose the 3 questions? Use a combination expression to solve.

Solution In this problem, $n = 6$ and $r = 3$. Find $_6C_3$.

$$_6C_3 = \frac{6!}{(6-3)!\,3!} = \frac{6!}{3!\,3!} = 20$$

Your philosophy teacher can choose the 3 questions in 20 ways. ■

▶ **NOTATION**

Alternate notations for $_nC_r$ include $C(n, r)$ and $\binom{n}{r}$.

Determining Whether a Situation Represents a Permutation or a Combination

Ask yourself: Does the *order* of the objects matter? In general, permutations model situations where order matters, and combinations model situations where order does not matter.

> **EXAMPLE 5**
> Determine whether the situation represents a *permutation* or a *combination*.
>
> **A** Five candidates are running to fill two positions on the county board.
>
> **Solution** This situation represents a combination since order does not matter. For instance, the result "Ben and Ed" is the same as the result "Ed and Ben." ▪
>
> **B** In how many ways can the letters in the word **MATH** be ordered?
>
> **Solution** The situation represents a permutation since order matters. The result "HTAM" is different from the result "MTAH." ▪

Problem Set

Find the value of the expression.

> 1. **Stepping Stones** $_7P_2$
>
> $$_7P_2 = \frac{\blacksquare!}{(7-\blacksquare)!} = \frac{7!}{\blacksquare!} = 7 \cdot \blacksquare = \blacksquare$$

2. $_8P_4$

3. $_{11}P_1$

4. $_4P_4$

5. $_7P_0$

6. $_5P_2$

7. $_6P_3$

8. $_9P_8$

Use a permutation expression to solve.

> 9. **Stepping Stones** Hector has 8 books. In how many ways can he place them on a shelf?
>
> $$_\blacksquare P_8 = \frac{\blacksquare!}{(8-\blacksquare)!} = \frac{8!}{0!} = 40,320$$

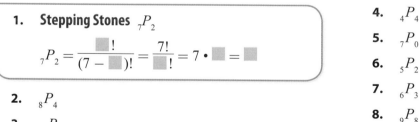

10. For a 30-student speech course, in how many ways can the students be selected to give the first 5 speeches?

11. How many 3-digit code numbers can be made out of these digits: 4, 7, 6, 2, 8, and 1? Assume digits cannot be used more than once.

12. Ms. Murphy has to select 4 swimmers out of 9 swimmers to create a relay team. In how many ways can she create a relay team?

13. A softball coach is determining the batting order for the 9 softball players on the team. In how many ways can the batting order be arranged?

14. In how many ways can a club president select 2 people out of 5 people to give the opening and closing speeches at a conference?

Find the value of the expression.

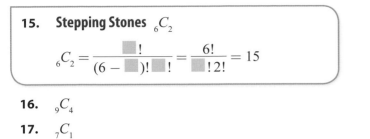

15. Stepping Stones $_6C_2$

$$_6C_2 = \frac{\boxed{}!}{(6 - \boxed{})!\ \boxed{}!} = \frac{6!}{\boxed{}!\ 2!} = 15$$

16. $_9C_4$

17. $_7C_1$

18. $_8C_8$

19. $_6C_3$

20. $_5C_4$

21. $_5C_0$

22. $_3C_1$

Use a combination expression to solve.

23. Stepping Stones Courtney can take 3 of her 6 friends to a movie. In how many ways can she choose who comes?

$$_6C_{\boxed{}} = \frac{\boxed{}!}{(6 - \boxed{})!\ \boxed{}!} = \frac{6!}{\boxed{}!\ 3!} = 20$$

24. Tim must choose 4 graphic novels out of a collection of 13 to take on vacation. In how many ways can he select the graphic novels?

25. Alice wants to work any 2 days in the week, except Sunday. In how many ways can she choose which days to work?

26. Mr. Holloway must choose 5 students from among a class of 30 to serve as tutors. In how many ways can Mr. Holloway choose the students?

27. Turner wants to buy 7 books, but he can buy only 2 of them. In how many ways can he buy 2 books?

28. Ahmad must choose 3 songs for a playlist from a total of 20 songs. In how many ways can Ahmad choose the songs?

Determine whether the situation represents a *permutation* or a *combination*.

29. Stepping Stones Gretchen plays softball, tennis, and soccer. In the summer, she can play only 2 of these sports. In how many ways can she select which sports she will play?

This situation represents a ▢▢▢▢ since order does not matter.

30. Matilda, Tanya, and Renee are auditioning for a play. In how many ways can the girls fill the roles of a grandmother, mother, and daughter?

31. Four people are running in an election that will determine the mayor and deputy mayor. In how many ways can the voters fill these positions?

32. The sergeant major must choose 6 of his squad members to go on a mission. In how many ways can he choose the members?

Probability

Counting outcomes can help you determine the chance that something will or will not happen.

Finding Simple Probabilities

BASIC PROBABILITY OF AN EVENT

The **probability of event A**, written $P(A)$, is computed as

$$P(A) = \frac{\text{number of favorable outcomes}}{\text{total number of possible outcomes}}.$$

Q & A

Q If a member of the 2013 U.S. Senate is chosen at random, what is the probability that the member is a Democrat?

A 53%

EXAMPLE 1
The graph shows the composition, by political party, of the 100 U.S. senators in January 2013. Find the probability.

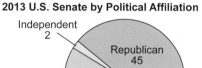

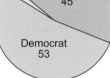

2013 U.S. Senate by Political Affiliation

A If a member of the 2013 U.S. Senate is chosen at random, what is the probability that the member is Republican?

Solution Let A represent the event that the member chosen is Republican.

$$P(A) = \frac{45 \text{ favorable outcomes}}{100 \text{ total outcomes}} = \frac{45}{100} = \frac{9}{20} = 0.45$$

There is a 45% chance that the member chosen is Republican. ▪

B If a member of the 2013 U.S. Senate is chosen at random, what is the probability that the member is Independent?

Solution Let A represent the event that the member chosen is Independent.

$$P(A) = \frac{2 \text{ favorable outcomes}}{100 \text{ total outcomes}} = \frac{2}{100} = \frac{1}{50} = 0.02$$

There is a 2% chance that the member chosen is Independent. ▪

Finding Probabilities of Complementary Events

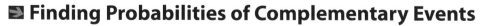

Suppose a jar contains only red marbles and black marbles. One event would be to reach into the jar and draw a red marble, while a second event would be to reach into the jar and draw a black marble. Those two events are known as **complementary events**.

PROBABILITIES OF COMPLEMENTARY EVENTS

If A' represents the complement of event A, then

$$P(A') = 1 - P(A).$$

EXAMPLE 2

Suppose a jar contains only green marbles and blue marbles and it is known that P(drawing a blue marble) $= 0.4$. Find the probability of drawing a green marble.

Solution Because the jar contains only green and blue marbles, the complement of drawing a blue marble is drawing a green marble.

$$P(\text{drawing a green marble}) = 1 - P(\text{drawing a blue marble})$$
$$= 1 - 0.4 = 0.6$$

The probability of drawing a green marble is 0.6. ▪

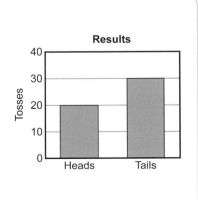

◤ Understanding Theoretical and Experimental Probability

Consider a 6-sided number cube. For any given roll, the probability of rolling an even number is $\frac{1}{2}$. Does that mean that if you roll the number cube 100 times, you'd roll an even number 50 of those times? Not necessarily. The **theoretical probability** of rolling an even number is $\frac{1}{2}$, but the **experimental probability** depends on the actual outcome of rolling the number cube 100 times.

EXPERIMENTAL PROBABILITY OF AN EVENT

The **experimental probability of event A** is

$$\frac{\text{number of times event } A \text{ occurs}}{\text{total number of trials of the experiment}}.$$

▶ BY THE WAY

Data gathered experimentally are sometimes known as **empirical data**.

EXAMPLE 3

Barry tossed a fair coin 50 times and recorded the results in the graph.

Ⓐ What is the theoretical probability of tossing heads?

Solution The theoretical probability of tossing heads is $\frac{1}{2}$. ▪

Ⓑ According to the graph, what is the experimental probability of Barry tossing heads?

Solution The experimental probability of Barry tossing heads is $\frac{20}{50}$ or $\frac{2}{5}$ or 40%. ▪

Results

(Bar graph: vertical axis "Tosses" from 0 to 40; Heads = 20, Tails = 30)

Identifying and Applying the Law of Large Numbers

LAW OF LARGE NUMBERS

As the number of independent trials in an experiment increases, it becomes more likely that the experimental probability of an event gets close to the theoretical probability of the same event.

▶ Q & A

Q Suppose you toss a fair coin 15 times and the coin lands on heads all 15 times. Does that mean that on the 16th toss, it's more likely that the coin will land on tails?

A No, the probability of heads or tails for the next toss is still $\frac{1}{2}$ for each outcome.

EXAMPLE 4
Determine whether the law of large numbers is being used.

Ⓐ If a coin is tossed twice, then one toss will be heads and the other will be tails.

Solution The law of large numbers is not being used because two is not a large number of trials. ▪

Ⓑ If a coin is tossed 500 times, then about 250 of the tosses would be tails.

Solution The law of large numbers is being used. ▪

Problem Set

The graph shows the number of each kind of book in Hero's personal library.

1. **Stepping Stones** If a book is chosen at random, what is the probability that the book is a science fiction book?

   Let A represent the event that the book chosen is a ▮▮▮▮▮ book.

   $$P(A) = \frac{\blacksquare}{\blacksquare} = \frac{7}{\blacksquare} \approx 0.47$$

   The probability that the book chosen is science fiction is ▮ %.

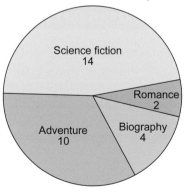

Books in Hero's Library

Science fiction 14
Romance 2
Adventure 10
Biography 4

2. If a book is chosen randomly, what is the probability that the book is a romance book?

3. If a book is chosen randomly, what is the probability that the book is an adventure book?

4. If a book is chosen randomly, what is the probability that the book is a biography?

Find the probability.

5. **Stepping Stones** Suppose a jar contains only brown marbles and yellow marbles, and it is known that $P(\text{drawing a brown marble}) = \frac{3}{7}$. What is the probability of drawing a yellow marble?

Drawing a yellow marble and drawing a brown marble are complementary events.

$P(\text{drawing a yellow marble}) = 1 - P(\text{drawing a } \boxed{} \text{ marble})$

$= \boxed{} - \frac{3}{7} = \frac{4}{7}$

The probability of drawing a yellow marble is $\frac{4}{7}$.

6. Melanie is running for mayor of her town and believes that the probability of her winning the election is $\frac{8}{13}$. What is the probability of her losing the election?

7. On a number cube, the probability of rolling a 5 is $\frac{1}{10}$. What is the probability of *not* rolling a 5?

8. Kurt believes that the probability that he will win the golf tournament is 60%. What is the probability that he will lose the tournament?

Four tiles lettered *M*, *A*, *T*, and *H* are face down on a table. A tile is selected, the letter is recorded, the tile is replaced, and the process is repeated. The results of this experiment are shown in the graph.

9. **Stepping Stones** According to the graph, what is the experimental probability of selecting the letter *A*?

The experimental probability of selecting the letter *A* is $\frac{\boxed{}}{20}$.

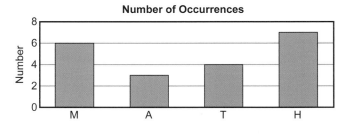
Number of Occurrences

10. According to the graph, what is the experimental probability of selecting the letter *T*?

11. According to the graph, what is the experimental probability of selecting the letter *M*?

12. What is the theoretical probability of selecting the letter *A*?

13. What is the theoretical probability of selecting the letter *T*?

Determine whether the law of large numbers is being used.

14. If a coin is tossed 700 times, then about 350 of the tosses will be heads.

15. If it snowed today, then it will snow tomorrow.

16. If a coin is tossed 4 times, then 2 tosses will be heads and 2 tosses will be tails.

17. If a 6-sided number cube is rolled 600 times, then the number cube will land on 5 about 100 times.

Expected Value

Probability distributions can tell us what to expect when all outcomes are considered.

⮕ Creating a Probability Distribution Table from a Frequency Distribution

HOW TO CREATE A PROBABILITY DISTRIBUTION TABLE

To create a probability distribution table from a frequency table:
Step 1 Find the sum of the frequencies.
Step 2 Divide each frequency by the sum found in Step 1.
Step 3 Replace each frequency in the table with the ratio found in Step 2.
Step 4 Change the label *f* to *P*.

▶ **BY THE WAY**

A frequency table shows the frequency of events.

EXAMPLE 1

In 2013, the Chicago Bears of the National Football League scored 375 points. The frequency distribution table summarizes the number of times the Bears scored points in each of six different ways. Use the frequency table to create a probability distribution table.

Chicago Bears' scoring	Rushing touchdowns	Receiving touchdowns	Returns	Field goals	Extra points	2-Point conversions
f	11	21	10	27	40	1

ESPN.com 2013a

Solution
Step 1 Find the sum of the frequencies.

$$11 + 21 + 10 + 27 + 40 + 1 = 110$$

Step 2 Divide each frequency by the sum found in Step 1.

$$\frac{11}{110} = 0.1, \frac{21}{110} \approx 0.19, \frac{10}{110} \approx 0.09, \frac{27}{110} \approx 0.25, \frac{40}{110} \approx 0.36, \frac{1}{110} \approx 0.01$$

Step 3 Replace each frequency in the table with the ratio found in Step 2.

Step 4 Change the label *f* to *P*.

Chicago Bears' scoring	Rushing touchdowns	Receiving touchdowns	Returns	Field goals	Extra points	2-Point conversions
P	0.1	0.19	0.09	0.25	0.36	0.01

Identifying Properties of Probability Distributions

> **DEFINITION**
>
> A **discrete random variable** is a variable with possible values that can be listed; each value is the numerical outcome of an experiment.

For example, if an experiment is tossing a coin 5 times and determining the number of times the coin lands heads up, then X would be $\{0, 1, 2, 3, 4, 5\}$. The discrete random variable X describes all the possible outcomes of the experiment.

> **PROPERTIES OF PROBABILITY DISTRIBUTIONS**
>
> Every probability distribution for a discrete random variable has the following properties:
> - Each probability is a number between 0 and 1.
> - The sum of all probabilities is equal to 1.

EXAMPLE 2
Explain why the table is not a probability distribution.

A

X	0	1	2	3
P(X)	0.2	0.5	0.1	0.1

Solution The table violates the second property of probability distributions because the sum of all probabilities is 0.9, which is not equal to 1. ∎

B

X	3	6	9	12
P(X)	0.3	0.2	1.1	0.4

Solution The table violates the first property of probability distributions because one of the probabilities, 1.1, is not between 0 and 1. ∎

Understanding Probability Laws and Distributions

A probability distribution can help you solve problems involving probabilities of events.

▶ **TIP**

A probability distribution can also be displayed as a circle graph or a bar graph.

EXAMPLE 3

The table shows an estimate of the percent of the world's population living on each continent in 2010. Use the table to find the probability of event X.

Continent	Africa	North America	South America	Asia	Europe	Oceania
Population distribution	0.15	0.08	0.06	0.6	0.11	0.01

U.S. Census Bureau 2011

A Let X be the event that a person chosen at random from anywhere on earth lived in South America.

Solution $P(X) = 0.06$

The probability that a person chosen at random lived in South America is 6%. ∎

B Let X be the event that a person chosen at random from anywhere on earth lived in either Asia or Oceania.

Solution $P(X) = P(\text{lived in Asia}) + P(\text{lived in Oceania})$
$$= 0.6 + 0.01 = 0.61$$

The probability that a person being chosen at random lived in either Asia or Oceania is 61%. ∎

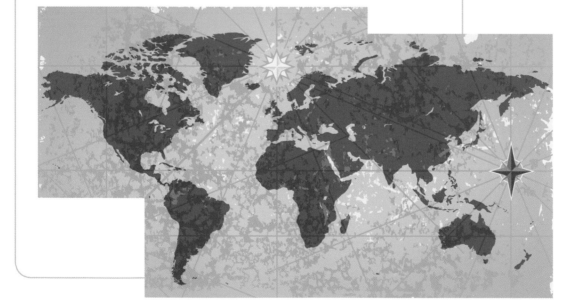

Calculating Expected Value

> **EXPECTED VALUE**
>
> Suppose each outcome of a random variable X is $x_1, x_2, \ldots, x_n$ and has probability $p_1, p_2, \ldots, p_n$ respectively. The **expected value** of X is
>
> $$E(X) = x_1 \cdot p_1 + x_2 \cdot p_2 + \ldots + x_n \cdot p_n.$$

EXAMPLE 4

Suppose there is a 5% chance that a person will consume 1400 mg of sodium per day, a 20% chance that a person will consume 2750 mg of sodium per day, a 25% chance that a person will consume 3100 mg per day, a 30% chance that a person will consume 3800 mg per day, and a 20% chance that a person will consume 4300 mg per day. What is the expected value of sodium intake per day?

$$
\begin{aligned}
E(X) &= x_1 \cdot p_1 + x_2 \cdot p_2 + x_3 \cdot p_3 + x_4 \cdot p_4 + x_5 \cdot p_5 \\
&= 1400 \cdot 0.05 + 2750 \cdot 0.2 + 3100 \cdot 0.25 + 3800 \cdot 0.3 + 4300 \cdot 0.2 \\
&= 70 + 550 + 775 + 1140 + 860 = 3395
\end{aligned}
$$

The expected intake of sodium for a single person is about 3395 mg per day. ■

> ▶ **BY THE WAY**
>
> The recommended amount of sodium intake per day is 1500 mg per person. High sodium consumption raises blood pressure, which is a major risk factor for heart disease and stroke.

Problem Set

Create a probability distribution table.

1. **Stepping Stones**

Atlanta Falcons' scoring	Rushing touchdowns	Receiving touchdowns	Returns	Field goals	Extra points	2-Point conversions
f	12	32	2	33	44	0

ESPN.com 2013b

Step 1 Find the sum of the frequencies.

$$12 + \blacksquare + 2 + 33 + 44 + \blacksquare = \blacksquare$$

Step 2 Divide each frequency by the sum found in Step 1.

$$\frac{\blacksquare}{123} \approx 0.1, \frac{32}{123} \approx 0.26, \frac{2}{123} \approx 0.02, \frac{33}{123} \approx \blacksquare, \frac{44}{123} \approx 0.36, \frac{0}{123} = 0$$

Step 3 Replace each frequency in the table with the ratio found in Step 2.

Step 4 Change the label f to P.

Atlanta Falcons' scoring	Rushing touchdowns	Receiving touchdowns	Returns	Field goals	Extra points	2-Point conversions
P	0.1	$\blacksquare$	0.02	0.27	$\blacksquare$	0

2.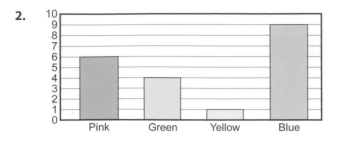

3. The Beavers scored the following points during their first 5 games: {12, 10, 18, 4, 6}.

4. On Monday Sheila sold 20 apples, on Tuesday she sold 12 apples, on Wednesday she sold 20 apples, and on Thursday she sold 28 apples.

Explain why the table is not a probability distribution.

5.

Width (in.)	7	14	21	28
P	0.1	0.3	0.9	0.2

6.

Color	Green	Blue	Yellow	Red
P	1.2	0.5	−0.3	0.4

7.

Number of family members	3	4	5	7
P	0.15	0.25	0.4	0.1

8.

Result	2.1	3.8	5	9.5	10
P	0.2	0.2	0.1	0.6	0.01

Find the probability of the event.

9. Stepping Stones The table shows an estimate of the percent of the world's population that will be living on each continent in 2050.

Continent	Africa	North America	South America	Asia	Europe	Oceania
Population distribution	0.23	0.08	0.06	0.55	0.07	0.01

U.S. Census Bureau 2011

Let X be the event that a person chosen at random from anywhere on earth in 2050 will be living in Europe.

$$P(X) = \blacksquare$$

The probability of a person chosen at random in 2050 living in Europe is ▨ %.

10. Let X be the event that a person chosen at random from anywhere on earth will live in Africa.

11. Let X be the event that a person chosen at random from anywhere on earth will live in either Europe or North America.

12. Let X be the event that a person chosen at random from anywhere on earth will live in either Asia or South America.

13. Let X be the event that a person chosen at random from anywhere on earth will live in North America.

14. Let X be the event that a person chosen at random from anywhere on earth will live in either Asia, Europe, or South America.

Determine the expected value.

15. **Stepping Stones** Renaldo believes that he will score 0 goals in $\frac{1}{3}$ of his soccer games, 1 goal in $\frac{1}{4}$ of his soccer games, and 2 goals in $\frac{5}{12}$ of his soccer games.

$$E(X) = x_1 \cdot p_1 + x_2 \cdot p_2 + x_3 \cdot p_3$$
$$= 0 \cdot \blacksquare + 1 \cdot \frac{1}{4} + 2 \cdot \blacksquare$$
$$\approx 0 + \blacksquare + 0.83$$
$$= 1.08$$

Renaldo should expect to score about $\blacksquare$ goals per game.

16. Maria believes she will get 1 hit in 20% of her softball games, 2 hits in 25% of her games, 3 hits in 50% of her games, and 4 hits in 5% of her games.

17. Meta is entering a 32-player chess tournament. The probability of her playing exactly 1 game is $\frac{3}{16}$, exactly 2 games is $\frac{1}{4}$, exactly 3 games is $\frac{3}{8}$, exactly 4 games is $\frac{1}{8}$, and exactly 5 games is $\frac{1}{16}$.

18.

X	−6	−4	−2	0	2
P	$\frac{1}{6}$	$\frac{1}{6}$	$\frac{1}{3}$	$\frac{1}{12}$	$\frac{1}{4}$

19.

X	0	1	2	3
P	0.2	0.3	0.4	0.1

CHAPTER 3   Review

Choose the answer.

1. Find $_7P_2$.

    A. 7

    B. 9

    C. 21

    D. 42

2. Find $_5C_1$.

    A. 4

    B. 5

    C. 6

    D. 7

3. Six students want to participate in the spelling bee, but there are only 3 spots. In how many ways can a group of 3 students be chosen?

    A. 720

    B. 120

    C. 20

    D. 18

4. A jar contains only red marbles and white marbles. If P(drawing a white marble) $= \frac{2}{7}$, what is the probability of drawing a red marble?

    A. $\frac{1}{7}$

    B. $\frac{3}{7}$

    C. $\frac{5}{7}$

    D. $\frac{6}{7}$

5. An 8-sided number cube is rolled and the result is recorded. What is the probability that the number rolled is a 5?

    A. 0

    B. $\frac{1}{8}$

    C. $\frac{1}{4}$

    D. $\frac{1}{2}$

6. The circle graph shows the makeup of the Riverside Municipal Choir. If a choir member is chosen at random, what is the probability that this member comes from the alto section?

Members in Choir Sections

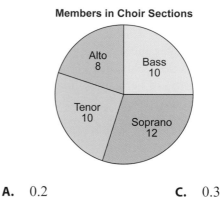

    A. 0.2

    B. 0.25

    C. 0.3

    D. 0.5

7. Use the distribution table to find $P(X \geq 2)$, where X represents the number of free throws Siddiqui makes during a basketball game.

X	0	1	2	3	4
P	0.2	0.1	0.4	0.15	0.15

    A. 0.3

    B. 0.4

    C. 0.55

    D. 0.7

Solve.

8. Carol rolled a 6-sided number cube 60 times and recorded the results in the graph below. According to the graph, what is the experimental probability of rolling a 5?

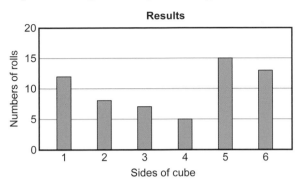

9. At the next city council meeting, the 9 members of the council must pick one person to chair the group. What is the probability that any one member of the council will be chosen?

10. Nyla has 8 movies she wants to watch in one weekend. In how many ways can Nyla arrange the order in which she chooses to watch them?

11. In how many ways can a committee of 6 be chosen from the 100 members of the U.S. Senate?

12. Loretta is a songwriter. The table shows the number of songs she wrote in each of the past 5 months. Use the information in the table to create a probability distribution table.

Month	Jan.	Feb.	Mar.	Apr.	May
Songs	3	5	2	8	2

13. Determine whether the situation represents a permutation or a combination. Cleo wants to take 2 of her 3 brothers to the soccer game on Saturday. In how many ways can she select which of her brothers to take?

14. Explain why the table is not a probability distribution.

Result	0	5	10	15
P	0.2	0.3	−0.3	0.8

15. Explain why the table is not a probability distribution.

Color	Black	White	Brown	Purple
P	0.05	0.35	0.2	0.25

16. Monty enjoys the game of golf. He knows that he will one-putt a green 15% of the time, two-putt 20% of the time, three-putt 35% of the time, and four-putt 30% of the time. Find the expected value for the number of putts Monty will need on any given green.

17. Diva is a race-car driver. The circle graph provides information related to how Diva has finished in each of her races. What is the probability that Diva finished either first or second?

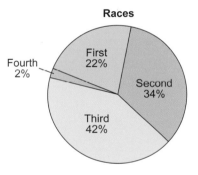

Problem	Topic Lookup
1–3, 10–11, 13	Permutations and Combinations
4–6, 8–9, 17	Probability
7, 12, 14–16	Expected Value

CHAPTER 4 Math Models

Robert Boyle wrote an equation that describes how the pressure, volume, and temperature of a gas relate to each other. Boyle's Law is a useful mathematical model that has helped scientists and engineers solve countless problems. Thanks to Boyle's Law, steam engines can power large locomotives. The first step to solving many real-world problems is figuring out how to write the math that describes what is going on.

In This Chapter

You will learn how various mathematical models, such as direct variation, arithmetic and geometric sequences, matrices, and geometric transformations, can be used to represent real-world situations.

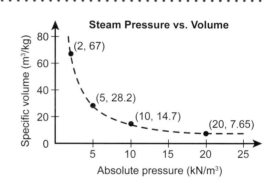

Topic List

Boyle's Law describes how steam can be used to power a train. ►

CHAPTER 4   Introduction

Models can show what objects look like or how ideas relate to each other.

There are many different types of models, and people use models for many different reasons. Inventors can build models, called prototypes, to see if their new ideas can work as planned. Science students can build models of the solar system, showing how the planets revolve around the sun.

Not all models look like their actual or final object, though. You can build a model of the earth's water cycle with jars, rocks, water, and tape. It will show how evaporation works, but it will have little resemblance to clouds and land. Other models are not physical objects. For example, diagrams and graphs can be models of concepts and relationships. In mathematics, it is common to use equations as models of relationships between variables.

Boyle's Law

Boyle's Law states that when a certain amount of gas is kept at a constant temperature, the product of its pressure P and volume V is a constant amount k. The equation $PV = k$ models this relationship. You can use the model to determine how to change the volume of a gas to achieve a certain pressure, or how to change the pressure to achieve a certain volume.

In this chapter, you will learn how to create and use different types of mathematical models.

Preparing for the Chapter

Review the following skills to prepare for the concepts in the chapter: evaluating functions, solving proportions, and describing symmetry.

Evaluating Functions

In a **function**, every input x corresponds to exactly one output y. If the function is written in **function notation**, then $y = f(x)$, where f is the function name.

$$
\underset{\substack{\uparrow \\ \text{input} \\ \text{variable}}}{f}(\underset{}{x}) = \overset{\substack{\text{function} \\ \text{rule}}}{\overbrace{3x + 1}}
$$

function name   function rule

To evaluate a function, substitute a value of the input variable into the function rule and simplify.

EXAMPLE 1

Find $f(5)$ for $f(x) = 3x + 1$.

Solution Substitute 5 for x. Simplify using the order of operations.

$$
\begin{aligned}
f(5) &= 3(5) + 1 \\
&= 15 + 1 \\
&= 16
\end{aligned}
$$

$f(5) = 16$ ∎

Functions can have names other than f and input variables other than x.

EXAMPLE 2

Find $g(4)$ for $g(t) = 5t^2$.

Solution Substitute 4 for t. Simplify using the order of operations.

$$
\begin{aligned}
g(4) &= 5 \cdot (4)^2 \\
&= 5 \cdot 16 \\
&= 80
\end{aligned}
$$

$g(4) = 80$ ∎

Solving Proportions

A **proportion** is an equation stating that two ratios are equal. You can solve a proportion by cross multiplying.

CROSS MULTIPLYING

Given $b \neq 0$ and $d \neq 0$, if $\frac{a}{b} = \frac{c}{d}$, then $a \cdot d = b \cdot c$.

EXAMPLE 3

Solve $\frac{4}{10} = \frac{6}{x}$.

Solution

$$4 \cdot x = 10 \cdot 6 \qquad \text{Cross multiply.}$$
$$4x = 60 \qquad \text{Simplify each side.}$$
$$x = 15 \qquad \text{Divide each side by 4.} \;\blacksquare$$

Describing Symmetry

DEFINITIONS

A figure has **reflection symmetry** if at least one line can be drawn through the figure so that the two resulting sides are mirror images. A line that creates mirror images is called a **line of symmetry**.

EXAMPLE 4

Determine if the rectangle has reflection symmetry. If so, give the number of lines of symmetry.

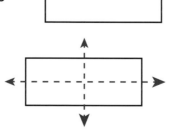

Solution A vertical line drawn through the center creates mirror images.
A horizontal line drawn through the center also creates mirror images.
The rectangle has reflection symmetry.
There are two lines of symmetry. ▪

DEFINITIONS

A figure has **rotation symmetry** if you can rotate it around its center less than one full turn, and the rotated figure looks like the original. The **angle of rotation** is the smallest angle by which the figure can be rotated to look like the original.

A full turn measures 360°. If a figure is a **regular polygon**, then the angle of rotation is 360° divided by the number of sides.

EXAMPLE 5
Determine if the square has rotation symmetry. If so, give the angle of rotation.

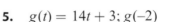

Solution The figure looks like the original after a quarter turn around its center, so it has rotation symmetry. The angle of rotation is $\frac{360°}{4}$, or 90°. ∎

Problem Set

Evaluate the function for the given value.

1. $f(x) = -6x; f(9)$

2. $f(a) = 10a + 8; f(6)$

3. $f(x) = \frac{3}{4}x - 2; f(44)$

4. $g(x) = x - 5.5; g(12)$

5. $g(t) = 14t + 3; g(-2)$

6. $h(m) = m^2 - 3m; h(9)$

Solve the proportion.

7. $\frac{5}{x} = \frac{10}{30}$

8. $\frac{2}{9} = \frac{d}{27}$

9. $\frac{n}{3} = \frac{10}{15}$

10. $\frac{w}{9} = \frac{40}{12}$

11. $\frac{6}{8} = \frac{27}{x}$

12. $\frac{20}{16} = \frac{b}{36}$

For each figure:
A. Determine if the figure has reflection symmetry. If so, give the number of lines of symmetry.
B. Determine if the figure has rotation symmetry. If so, give the angle of rotation.

13.

14.

15.

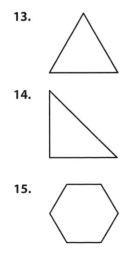

16.

17.

18.

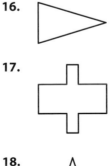

Variation

Many real-world situations involve two variables that relate to each other.

DEFINITIONS

If the relationship between the input x and the output $f(x)$ is a **direct variation**, then you can write the function in the form $f(x) = kx$, where k, the **constant of variation**, is not zero.

For a direct variation, it is common to say that the output *varies directly with* the input.

▶ **BY THE WAY**

You can also say that the output *is proportional to* the input.

◢ Writing and Using Direct Variation Equations

EXAMPLE 1
By Hooke's Law, the distance that a spring stretches varies directly with the mass of the object hanging from the spring. Suppose a 4 kg object hangs from a spring and stretches the spring by 10 cm. How much would a 6 kg object hanging from the spring stretch it by?

Solution
Step 1 Find k.

$$f(x) = kx \qquad \text{Write the general equation.}$$
$$10 = k \cdot 4 \qquad \text{Substitute 10 for } f(x) \text{ and 4 for } x.$$
$$2.5 = k \qquad \text{Divide both sides by 4.}$$

Step 2 Write the specific equation for this variation.

$$f(x) = 2.5x$$

Step 3 Find $f(6)$.

$$f(x) = 2.5x$$
$$f(6) = 2.5 \cdot 6 = 15$$

Hanging a 6 kg object from the spring would stretch it by 15 cm. ▪

▶ **THINK ABOUT IT**

In a direct variation, doubling the input doubles the output, halving the input halves the output, and so on.

⧨ Graphing Direct Variation

EXAMPLE 2
Graph the direct variation equation from Example 1.

Solution Plot ordered pairs and connect them with a straight line.

Mass (kg) (x)	Distance (cm) (f(x))
2	5
4	10

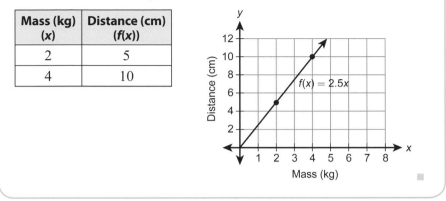

▶ THINK ABOUT IT

The graph of a direct variation equation is a line. You can also graph the line by plotting a point at the y-intercept, 0, and then using the slope, 2.5 or $\frac{5}{2}$, to find another point on the line.

⧨ Writing and Using Inverse Variation Equations

DEFINITIONS

If the relationship between the input x and the output $f(x)$ is an **inverse variation**, then you can write the function in the form $f(x) = \frac{k}{x}$, where k, the **constant of variation**, is not zero.

▶ BY THE WAY

For an inverse variation, you can say that the output *varies inversely with* the input, or that the output *is inversely proportional to* the input.

EXAMPLE 3
By Boyle's Law, the pressure of a gas varies inversely with the volume of the gas. Suppose the pressure of a gas measures 20 kg/cm² when its volume is 400 cm³. What would be the pressure when the volume is decreased to 50 cm³?

Solution
Step 1 Find k.

$$f(x) = \frac{k}{x} \qquad \text{Write the general equation.}$$

$$400 = \frac{k}{20} \qquad \text{Substitute 400 for } f(x) \text{ and 20 for } x.$$

$$8000 = k \qquad \text{Multiply both sides by 20.}$$

Step 2 Write the specific equation for this variation.

$$f(x) = \frac{8000}{x}$$

Step 3 Find $f(50)$.

$$f(x) = \frac{8000}{x} = \frac{8000}{50} = 160$$

Decreasing the volume to 50 cm³ would increase the pressure to 160 kg/cm². ■

Graphing Inverse Variation

▶ THINK ABOUT IT

EXAMPLE 4
Graph the inverse variation equation from Example 3.

Solution Plot ordered pairs and connect them with a smooth curve.

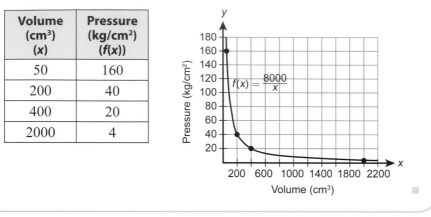

Volume (cm³) (x)	Pressure (kg/cm²) (f(x))
50	160
200	40
400	20
2000	4

In an inverse variation, doubling the input halves the output, halving the input doubles the output, and so on. The graph of an inverse variation equation is a hyperbola.

▶ TIP
The graph of an inverse variation does not touch either axis.

Problem Set

Write the direct variation equation and evaluate the function for the given value.

1. **Stepping Stones** If $f(x)$ varies directly with x and $f(x) = 15$ when $x = 5$, find the value of $f(x)$ when $x = 8$.

   Find k: $f(x) = kx$, so $\blacksquare = 5k$ and $\blacksquare = k$.

   Write the specific equation: $f(x) = \blacksquare x$.

   Find $f(8)$: $f(8) = \blacksquare \cdot 8 = \blacksquare$.

2. If $f(x)$ varies directly with x and $f(x) = 24$ when $x = 2$, find the value of $f(x)$ when $x = 6$.

3. If $h(t)$ varies directly with t and $h(t) = 28$ when $t = 7$, find the value of t when $h(t) = 36$.

4. If $g(a)$ varies directly with a and $g(a) = 3$ when $a = 6$, find the value of a when $g(a) = 10$.

Write the direct variation equation and solve.

5. The cost of a candle varies directly with the volume of the candle. If a candle with a volume of 80 cm³ costs $12, what would be the cost of a candle with a volume of 120 cm³?

6. The mass of an object on Jupiter varies directly with its mass on Earth. A rock that weighs 20 lb on Earth would weigh 42 lb on Jupiter. How much would a rock that weighs 10.5 lb on Jupiter weigh on Earth?

Solve.

7. The graph shows that the distance a wolf spider travels at its top speed varies directly with the number of seconds it has been traveling at that speed.

   A. How far does the spider travel in 4 s?

   B. How long does it take the spider to travel 14 ft?

   C. Give the constant of variation and tell what it represents in this situation.

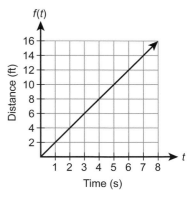

Solve.

8. Write the direct variation equation given $f(x) = 6$ when $x = 4$ and then graph the equation.

Write the inverse variation equation and evaluate the function for the given value.

9. **Stepping Stones** If $f(x)$ varies inversely with x and $f(x) = 4$ when $x = 5$, find the value of $f(x)$ when $x = 2$.

   Find k: $f(x) = \dfrac{k}{x}$, so $\boxed{} = \dfrac{k}{5}$ and $\boxed{} = k$.

   Write the specific equation: $f(x) = \dfrac{\boxed{}}{x}$.

   Find $f(2)$: $f(2) = \dfrac{\boxed{}}{2} = \boxed{}$.

10. If $f(x)$ varies inversely with x and $f(x) = 3$ when $x = 10$, find the value of $f(x)$ when $x = 15$.

11. If $g(x)$ varies inversely with x and $g(x) = 4$ when $x = 2$, find the value of $g(x)$ when $x = 16$.

12. If $g(m)$ varies inversely with m and $g(m) = 3.5$ when $m = 10$, find the value of m when $g(m) = 5$.

Write the inverse variation equation and solve.

13. The time it takes to distribute pamphlets varies inversely with the number of people distributing them. If it takes 40 min for 3 people to distribute the pamphlets, how long would it take if there were 5 people distributing the pamphlets?

14. The time it takes a train to reach its destination varies inversely with its speed. The train takes 3 h to reach its destination when traveling at 50 mph. What must the speed be to make the same trip in 2.5 h?

Solve.

15. The graph shows that the number of pizza slices each person receives varies inversely with the number of people sharing the pizza.

    A. How many slices does each person get when 4 people share the pizza?

    B. How many people are sharing the pizza if each person receives 1 slice?

    C. Give the constant of variation and tell what it represents in this situation.

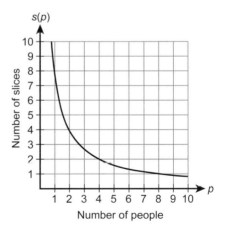

16. Write the inverse variation equation given $f(x) = 3$ when $x = 2$ and then graph the equation.

Sequences

The equation you choose to model a sequence depends on what you are given and what you seek.

A **sequence** is a list of numbers that forms a pattern. Each number in a sequence is a **term**. The notation a_n represents the term in the nth position. In the sequence 4, 6, 8, 10, 12, . . .

$$a_1 = 4 \text{ because the first term is 4, and}$$
$$a_2 = 6 \text{ because the second term is 6, and so on.}$$

In an **arithmetic sequence**, you can find the value of any term after the first term by adding the same number to the previous term. The sequence above is an arithmetic sequence because each term is 2 more than the previous term. The number 2 is the **common difference**.

FORMULA FOR FINDING A COMMON DIFFERENCE

The common difference d in an arithmetic sequence is the difference between consecutive terms.

$$\overset{\text{any term}}{d = a_n - a_{n-1}}$$
previous term

▶ **TIP**

When the terms increase, d is positive. When the terms decrease, d is negative.

➡ Finding Terms in Arithmetic Sequences

With a **recursive formula**, you find the value of a term by using the value of the previous term.

RECURSIVE FORMULA FOR AN ARITHMETIC SEQUENCE

To find the value of any term after the first term, add the common difference to the previous term.

$$\overset{\text{any term} \quad \text{common difference}}{a_n = a_{n-1} + d}$$
previous term

EXAMPLE 1
Find the first four terms in the sequence.

$$a_n = a_{n-1} + 8 \text{ and } a_1 = 25$$

Solution The first term is a_1, which is 25. Because $d = 8$, $a_2 = 25 + 8 = 33$, $a_3 = 33 + 8 = 41$, and $a_4 = 41 + 8 = 49$. The first four terms are 25, 33, 41, and 49. ▪

▶ **THINK ABOUT IT**

$$a_n = a_{n-1} + 8$$
$$a_2 = a_{2-1} + 8$$
$$= a_1 + 8 = 25 + 8 = 33$$

With an **iterative formula**, you can find the value of a term without knowing the value of the previous term.

▶ **BY THE WAY**

An iterative formula is also called an *explicit formula*.

ITERATIVE FORMULA FOR AN ARITHMETIC SEQUENCE

To find the value of the nth term, add the product of $n - 1$ and the common difference to the first term.

any term   common difference

$$a_n = a_1 + (n - 1)d$$

first term

EXAMPLE 2

When Frankie turns a dial, he increases the air pressure inside a container. The pressures after each of four turns are 3 lb/in², 7 lb/in², 11 lb/in², and 15 lb/in². What will the pressure be after Frankie turns the dial 25 times?

Solution

Step 1 Write the iterative formula. The value of the first term is 3 and the common difference is $7 - 3 = 4$. The formula is $a_n = 3 + (n - 1)4$.

Step 2 Substitute 25 for n.

$$a_{25} = 3 + (25 - 1)4 = 3 + (24)4 = 3 + 96 = 99$$

After 25 turns, the pressure will be 99 lb/in². ∎

▶ Analyzing Graphs of Arithmetic Sequences

The graph of an arithmetic sequence is a set of unconnected points that lie along a straight line. The ordered pairs are in the form (n, a_n).

EXAMPLE 3

Write the recursive rule for the sequence shown in the graph.

Solution The point at $(1, 2)$ indicates that the value of the first term is 2. The point at $(2, 5)$ indicates that the value of the second term is 5. So the common difference is $5 - 2 = 3$. To give the complete solution, provide the rule and the first term:
$a_n = a_{n-1} + 3$ and $a_1 = 2$. ∎

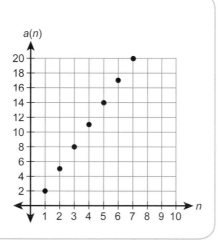

▶ **Q & A**

Q What is the value of the fifth term in the sequence?

A 14

Finding Terms in Geometric Sequences

In a **geometric sequence**, you can find the value of any term, after the first term, by multiplying the same number by the previous term. The sequence

$$3, 6, 12, 24, 48, \ldots$$

is geometric because each term is twice the previous term. The number 2 is the **common ratio**.

FORMULA FOR FINDING A COMMON RATIO

The common ratio r in a geometric sequence is the ratio between consecutive terms.

$$r = \frac{a_n \longrightarrow \text{any term}}{a_{n-1} \longrightarrow \text{previous term}}$$

▶ **TIP**

If the first term is positive, then the terms increase if r is greater than 1, and the terms decrease if r is between 0 and 1.

As with an arithmetic sequence, you can find terms in a geometric sequence by using either a recursive or an iterative formula.

RECURSIVE FORMULA FOR A GEOMETRIC SEQUENCE

To find the value of any term after the first term, multiply the previous term by the common ratio.

any term   previous term

$$a_n = r \cdot a_{n-1}$$

common ratio

EXAMPLE 4
Find the first four terms in the sequence.

$$a_n = 5 \cdot a_{n-1} \text{ and } a_1 = 3$$

Solution The first term is a_1, so the value of the first term is 3. Because $r = 5$, $a_2 = 5 \cdot 3 = 15$, $a_3 = 5 \cdot 15 = 75$, and $a_4 = 5 \cdot 75 = 375$. The first four terms are 3, 15, 75, and 375. ∎

▶ **THINK ABOUT IT**

$$a_n = 5 \cdot a_{n-1}$$
$$a_2 = 5 \cdot a_{2-1}$$
$$= 5 \cdot a_1$$
$$= 5 \cdot 3$$
$$= 15$$

ITERATIVE FORMULA FOR A GEOMETRIC SEQUENCE

To find the value of the nth term, find the product of the first term and the common ratio raised to the $n - 1$ power.

any term   common ratio

$$a_n = a_1 \cdot r^{n-1}$$

first term

EXAMPLE 5

A population of bacteria grows every day. There are 20 bacteria on Day 1, 60 bacteria on Day 2, and 180 bacteria on Day 3. How many bacteria will there be on Day 9?

Solution

Step 1 Write the iterative formula. The first term is 20 and the common ratio is $60 \div 20 = 3$. The formula is $a_n = 20 \cdot 3^{n-1}$.

Step 2 Substitute 9 for n.

$$a_9 = 20 \cdot 3^{9-1} = 20 \cdot 3^8 = 20 \cdot 6561 = 131{,}220$$

There will be 131,220 bacteria on Day 9. ∎

⊵ Analyzing Graphs of Geometric Sequences

EXAMPLE 6

Write the recursive rule for the sequence shown in the graph.

Solution The point at $(1, 8)$ indicates that the first term is 8. The point at $(2, 4)$ indicates that the second term is 4. So the common ratio is $\dfrac{4}{8} = \dfrac{1}{2}$.

The recursive formula is

$a_n = \dfrac{1}{2} \cdot a_{n-1}$ and $a_1 = 8$. ∎

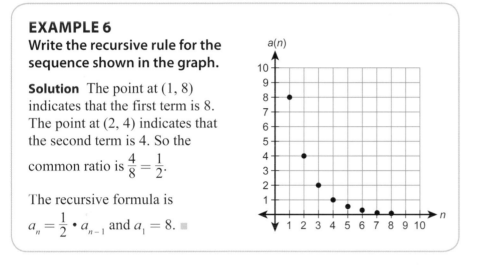

▶ **REMEMBER**

The graph of a geometric sequence is a set of unconnected points that lie along an exponential curve.

⊵ Determining If a Sequence Is Arithmetic, Geometric, or Neither

EXAMPLE 7

Tell if the sequence is arithmetic, geometric, or neither.

Ⓐ 5, 30, 180, 1080, . . .

Solution Look for a common difference: $30 - 5 = 25$ and $180 - 30 = 150$. The differences are not constant.

Look for a common ratio: $\dfrac{30}{5} = 6$, $\dfrac{180}{30} = 6$, and $\dfrac{1080}{180} = 6$. The terms have a common ratio, so the sequence is geometric. ∎

Ⓑ 4, 6, 9, 13, . . .

Solution Look for a common difference: $6 - 4 = 2$ and $9 - 6 = 3$. The differences are not constant.

Look for a common ratio: $\dfrac{6}{4} = 1.5$, $\dfrac{9}{6} = 1.5$, and $\dfrac{13}{9} = 1.\overline{4}$. The ratios are not constant. The sequence is neither arithmetic nor geometric. ∎

Problem Set

Find the first four terms in the arithmetic sequence.

1. **Stepping Stones** $a_n = a_{n-1} + 5$ and $a_1 = 9$

   The first term is 9. Because $d = \blacksquare$, $a_2 = 9 + \blacksquare = 14$, $a_3 = \blacksquare + 5 = \blacksquare$,
   and $a_4 = \blacksquare + \blacksquare = \blacksquare$.

   The first four terms are 9, 14, $\blacksquare$, and $\blacksquare$.

2. $a_n = a_{n-1} + 10$ and $a_1 = 15$

3. $a_n = a_{n-1} + 7$ and $a_1 = -21$

4. $a_n = a_{n-1} - 3$ and $a_1 = 52$

Use an iterative formula to find the indicated term of the arithmetic sequence.

5. **Stepping Stones** 24th term of the sequence 5, 11, 17, 23, . . .

   $a_1 = 5$ and d is $\blacksquare - 5 = 6$. The formula is $a_n = \blacksquare + (n - 1)6$.

   When 24 is substituted for n,
   $a_{24} = 5 + (\blacksquare - 1)6 = 5 + (\blacksquare)6 = 5 + \blacksquare = \blacksquare$.

6. 41st term of the sequence 8, 10, 12, 14, . . .

7. 99th term of the sequence 2, 12, 22, 32, . . .

8. 63rd term of the sequence 20, 15, 10, 5, . . .

Solve.

9. The cans in a display are stacked so there are 2 cans in the top row, 4 cans in the second row, 6 cans in the third row, and so on. There are 22 rows of cans. How many cans are in the bottom row?

10. In a theater, there are 14 seats in the first row, 18 seats in the second row, 22 seats in the third row, and so on. How many seats are in the 18th row?

11. Bryanna's starting salary is \$28,600 per year. If she gets a raise of \$1200 per year, what will her salary be for her 35th year in that job?

12. Write the recursive rule for the sequence 4, 16, 28, 40, ...

13. Write the recursive rule for the sequence whose iterative rule is $a_n = 10 + (n - 1)25$.

14. The graph shows the first five terms in an arithmetic sequence.

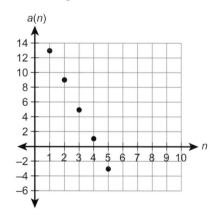

   A. Write the recursive rule for the sequence.

   B. Write the iterative rule for the sequence.

   C. Find the 50th term in the sequence.

Find the first four terms in the geometric sequence.

15. **Stepping Stones** $a_n = 4 \cdot a_{n-1}$ and $a_1 = 5$

The first term is 5. Because $r = \blacksquare$, $a_2 = 4 \cdot \blacksquare = 20$, $a_3 = 4 \cdot 20 = \blacksquare$, and $a_4 = \blacksquare \cdot \blacksquare = \blacksquare$.

The first four terms are 5, 20, $\blacksquare$, and $\blacksquare$.

16. $a_n = 2 \cdot a_{n-1}$ and $a_1 = 3$

17. $a_n = 3 \cdot a_{n-1}$ and $a_1 = -2$

18. $a_n = -2 \cdot a_{n-1}$ and $a_1 = 10$

Use an iterative formula to find the indicated term of the geometric sequence.

19. **Stepping Stones** 9th term of the sequence 2, 8, 32, . . .

$a_1 = 2$ and r is $\blacksquare \div 2 = 4$. The formula is $a_n = \blacksquare \cdot 4^{n-1}$.

When 9 is substituted for n, $a_9 = \blacksquare \cdot 4^{9-1} = \blacksquare \cdot 4^8 = \blacksquare \cdot 65{,}536 = \blacksquare$.

20. 11th term of the sequence 5, 15, 45, . . .

21. 20th term of the sequence 1, 2, 4, 8, . . .

22. 9th term of the sequence 5120, 2560, 1280, . . .

Solve.

23. A computer virus infected 4 computers in the first hour it was released, 8 computers in the second hour, 16 computers in the third, and so on. How many computers were infected with the virus after 24 hours?

24. A population of bacteria is 8500 on Day 1, 9350 on Day 2, and 10,285 on Day 3. What will the population be on Day 30?

25. When a dropped ball hits the ground, it bounces back up 40.5 cm. The height of each successive bounce is two-thirds the height of the previous bounce. How much does the ball bounce up after it hits the ground for the 8th time?

26. Write the recursive rule for the sequence 27, 9, 3, 1, ...

27. Write the recursive rule for the sequence whose iterative rule is $a_n = 15 \cdot 10^{n-1}$.

28. The graph shows the first eight terms in a geometric sequence.

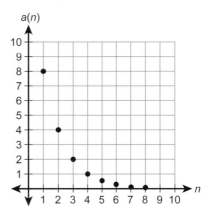

A. Write the recursive rule for the sequence.

B. Write the iterative rule for the sequence.

C. Find the 9th term in the sequence.

Tell if the sequence is arithmetic, geometric, or neither.

29. 6, 11, 10, 15, 14, 19, . . .

30. 9, 36, 144, 576, . . .

31. 12, 15, 18, 21, 24, 27, . . .

32. 10, 5, 0, −5, −10, −15, . . .

Matrices

A matrix is one of several ways you can model a data set with two categories.

Donovan measures and records the pressure of his tires after each car maintenance visit. He could record that data in a table or a spreadsheet.

	Tire pressure (psi)			
	FL	**FR**	**BL**	**BR**
Winter	31.2	29.9	30.5	30.7
Summer	30.8	31.0	31.1	31.3

▶ **BY THE WAY**

The abbreviation *psi* stands for "pounds per square inch."

	A	B	C	D	E
1		FL	FR	BL	BR
2	Winter	31.2	29.9	30.5	30.7
3	Summer	30.8	31.0	31.1	31.3

He could also display the data in a matrix.

DEFINITIONS

A **matrix** is a table of numbers arranged in rows and columns. A capital letter names a matrix.
- The **dimensions** of a matrix are the numbers of rows and columns.
- Each number in the matrix is an **element**.
- The **address** of an element is its location. The address gives the name of the matrix, in lowercase, followed by the element's row and column numbers in subscripts.

▶ **TIP**

Rows are horizontal and columns are vertical.

Consider matrix A.

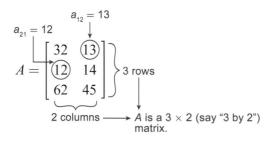

$a_{12} = 13$

$a_{21} = 12$

$$A = \begin{bmatrix} 32 & 13 \\ 12 & 14 \\ 62 & 45 \end{bmatrix}$$ 3 rows

2 columns ⟶ A is a 3 × 2 (say "3 by 2") matrix.

Analyzing a Matrix

EXAMPLE 1

Matrix P shows the pressure in each of Donovan's tires after his winter and summer maintenance visits.

$$P = \begin{bmatrix} 31.2 & 29.9 & 30.5 & 30.7 \\ 30.8 & 31.0 & 31.1 & 31.3 \end{bmatrix}$$

A What are the dimensions of matrix P?

Solution Matrix P has 2 rows and 4 columns, so its dimensions are 2 by 4, written 2×4. ▪

B What is the element with address p_{23}?

Solution Look for the element in row 2, column 3 of matrix P. The element is 31.1. ▪

C What is the address of the element with value 29.9?

Solution The value 29.9 is in row 1, column 2 of matrix P, so the address is p_{12}. ▪

Using a Matrix to Organize Data

EXAMPLE 2

During one year, a car rental agency rented out 330 compact cars, 706 standard-sized cars, and 249 luxury cars on weekends. It rented out 1021 compact cars, 1325 standard-sized cars, and 656 luxury cars on weekdays. Organize this information in a matrix. Name the matrix R.

Solution

Step 1 Determine the two categories. The categories are type of day and type of car.

Step 2 Organize the information in a table. List one category along the left side and the other category along the top.

	Compact	Standard	Luxury
Weekend	330	706	249
Weekday	1021	1325	656

Step 3 Create the matrix by keeping the numbers in the same positions as in the table.

$$R = \begin{bmatrix} 330 & 706 & 249 \\ 1021 & 1325 & 656 \end{bmatrix}$$ ▪

▶ **TIP**

There are two correct matrices. Listing the type of car along the left side and the type of day along the top forms a 3×2 matrix.

$$R = \begin{bmatrix} 330 & 1021 \\ 706 & 1325 \\ 249 & 656 \end{bmatrix}$$

⇥ Interpreting a Matrix

EXAMPLE 3

Matrix S shows the results of a survey in which people in different age groups were asked which type of prize they would prefer to win.

$$\begin{array}{c} \\ 18\text{–}39 \\ 40\text{–}64 \\ 65+ \end{array} \begin{array}{c} \text{Money} \quad \text{Car} \quad \text{Trip} \\ \begin{bmatrix} 15 & 26 & 11 \\ 22 & 14 & 8 \\ 9 & 4 & 18 \end{bmatrix} \end{array} = S$$

A How many people 65 or older prefer to win money?

Solution Look in row 3, column 1. The answer is 9. ▪

B How many people prefer to win a car?

Solution Find the sum of the elements in column 2:

$$26 + 14 + 4 = 44. \ ▪$$

C What percent of people aged 18–39 prefer to win a trip?

Solution Find the sum of the elements in row 1: $15 + 26 + 11 = 52$, which is the total number of people aged 18 to 39. Because 11 of those people prefer to win a trip, divide 11 by 52 and convert the decimal to a percent.

$$\frac{11}{52} \approx 0.21 = 21\% \ ▪$$

⇥ Multiplying a Matrix by a Scalar

A **scalar** is a number that is not an element of a matrix. To multiply a matrix by a scalar, multiply each element in the matrix by the scalar.

EXAMPLE 4

Matrix B shows the costs, in dollars, of a buffet. Find $1.25B$, the matrix that shows the costs after a 25% increase.

$$\begin{array}{c} \\ \text{Breakfast} \\ \text{Lunch} \\ \text{Dinner} \end{array} \begin{array}{c} \text{Child} \quad \text{Adult} \\ \begin{bmatrix} 4 & 7 \\ 5 & 9 \\ 7 & 12 \end{bmatrix} \end{array} = B$$

Solution Multiply each element by 1.25.

$$1.25B = 1.25 \begin{bmatrix} 4 & 7 \\ 5 & 9 \\ 7 & 12 \end{bmatrix} = \begin{bmatrix} 1.25 \cdot 4 & 1.25 \cdot 7 \\ 1.25 \cdot 5 & 1.25 \cdot 9 \\ 1.25 \cdot 7 & 1.25 \cdot 12 \end{bmatrix} = \begin{bmatrix} 5 & 8.75 \\ 6.25 & 11.25 \\ 8.75 & 15 \end{bmatrix} ▪$$

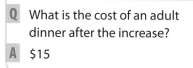

▶ **Q & A**

Q What is the cost of an adult dinner after the increase?

A $15

Adding and Subtracting Matrices

If two matrices have the same dimensions, then you can add or subtract the matrices by adding or subtracting the elements in the same positions. Matrices with different dimensions cannot be added or subtracted.

EXAMPLE 5
Use these matrices to find the sum or difference, if possible.

$$M = \begin{bmatrix} 8 & 10 & 5 \\ 15 & 7 & 3 \end{bmatrix} \quad N = \begin{bmatrix} 2 & 4 & 14 \\ 8 & 9 & 7 \end{bmatrix} \quad P = \begin{bmatrix} 6 & 11 \\ 5 & 0 \\ 12 & 4 \end{bmatrix} \quad Q = \begin{bmatrix} 1 & 8 \\ 7 & 4 \\ 3 & 2 \end{bmatrix}$$

A $M + N$

Both matrices are 2×3 matrices, so they can be added.

Solution $M + N = \begin{bmatrix} 8+2 & 10+4 & 5+14 \\ 15+8 & 7+9 & 3+7 \end{bmatrix} = \begin{bmatrix} 10 & 14 & 19 \\ 23 & 16 & 10 \end{bmatrix}$

> **THINK ABOUT IT**
> Matrix addition is commutative.
> $M + N = N + M$

B $N + P$

Solution Matrix N is a 2×3 matrix. Matrix P is a 3×2 matrix. Because their dimensions are different, the matrices cannot be added.

C $P - Q$

Solution Both matrices are 3×2 matrices, so they can be subtracted.

$$P - Q = \begin{bmatrix} 6-1 & 11-8 \\ 5-7 & 0-4 \\ 12-3 & 4-2 \end{bmatrix} = \begin{bmatrix} 5 & 3 \\ -2 & -4 \\ 9 & 2 \end{bmatrix}$$

> **THINK ABOUT IT**
> Matrix subtraction is **not** commutative.

Problem Set

Use matrix D to solve.

1. **Stepping Stones** What is the element with address d_{31}?

   Look for the element in row ▦, column 1 of matrix D. The element is ▦.

$$D = \begin{bmatrix} 3 & 16 & 1 \\ 20 & 23 & 14 \\ 2 & 7 & 13 \end{bmatrix}$$

2. What is the element with address d_{12}?

3. What is the element with address d_{11}?

4. What is the element with address d_{22}?

5. What is the address of the element with value 1?

6. What is the address of the element with value 14?

7. What are the dimensions of the matrix?

Create the matrix described.

8. A hiking club sponsors several easy hikes: 5 in the winter, 8 in the spring, 11 in the summer, and 14 in the fall. It also sponsors several difficult hikes: 6 in the winter, 6 in the spring, 10 in the summer, and 17 in the fall. Organize the data into a matrix. Name the matrix H.

9. A chess club has 26 original members, of which 11 are girls. It also has 14 new members, of which 6 are boys. Organize the data into a 2×2 matrix. Name the matrix C.

10. The graph shows available apartments for rent. Organize the data into a matrix. Name the matrix A.

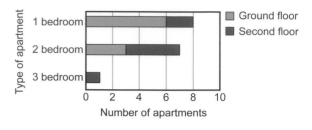

The matrix shows the numbers of ice-cream cones sold at an ice-cream shop one day.

$$\begin{array}{c} \\ \text{Single cone} \\ \text{Double cone} \end{array} \begin{array}{cccc} \text{Chocolate} & \text{Vanilla} & \text{Mint} & \text{Strawberry} \\ \left[\begin{array}{cccc} 84 & 61 & 33 & 40 \\ 68 & 93 & 27 & 15 \end{array}\right] \end{array}$$

11. How many mint cones were sold?

12. Find which is greater: the number of single cones sold or the number of double cones sold. Give the difference.

13. What percent of the single cones sold were chocolate?

14. What percent of the vanilla cones sold were double cones?

The matrix shows the numbers of different types of plants sold at different plant shops.

$$\begin{array}{c} \\ \text{Shop 1} \\ \text{Shop 2} \\ \text{Shop 3} \end{array} \begin{array}{cccc} \text{Herbs} & \text{Flowers} & \text{Shrubs} & \text{Trees} \\ \left[\begin{array}{cccc} 22 & 106 & 87 & 39 \\ 9 & 87 & 91 & 18 \\ 14 & 115 & 122 & 23 \end{array}\right] \end{array}$$

15. How many plants were sold at Shop 1?

16. How many flowers and shrubs did Shop 3 sell?

17. How many more trees were sold at Shop 1 than Shop 2?

18. What is the average number of herbs sold at each shop?

The spreadsheet shows a shop's T-shirt inventory.

19. Which T-shirt color does the shop have the smallest number of?

20. Which T-shirt size does the shop have the smallest number of?

21. How many white or gray shirts in either large or extra large are in stock?

22. Suppose you were to create matrix T by keeping the numbers in the same positions.

    A. What would the dimensions of the matrix be?

    B. What would the element at t_{41} represent?

    C. What would be the addresses of the elements showing there are no T-shirts of that particular size and color?

	A	B	C	D
1		White	Gray	Blue
2	Extra small	2	0	8
3	Small	1	5	4
4	Medium	6	2	6
5	Large	5	1	7
6	Extra large	1	0	3

Use matrices _A_ and _B_ to find the product.

$$A = \begin{bmatrix} 4 & 9 \\ 13 & 5 \end{bmatrix} \quad B = \begin{bmatrix} 20 & 3 \\ 2 & 6 \\ 15 & 14 \\ 11 & 9 \end{bmatrix}$$

23. Stepping Stones $6A$

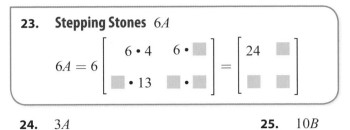

24. $3A$

25. $10B$

26. $2.2B$

Find the sum or difference, if possible.

$$H = \begin{bmatrix} 3 & 1 \\ 0 & 9 \\ 5 & 11 \end{bmatrix} \quad J = \begin{bmatrix} 8 & 1 \\ 5 & 6 \\ 3 & 8 \end{bmatrix} \quad K = \begin{bmatrix} 13 & 7 \\ 25 & 18 \end{bmatrix} \quad L = \begin{bmatrix} 6 & 10 \\ 19 & 18 \end{bmatrix}$$

27. Stepping Stones $K + L$

$$K + L = \begin{bmatrix} 13 + 6 & \blacksquare + 10 \\ 25 + \blacksquare & 18 + \blacksquare \end{bmatrix} = \begin{bmatrix} 19 & \blacksquare \\ \blacksquare & \blacksquare \end{bmatrix}$$

28. $K - L$

29. $H + J$

30. $J + K$

31. $J - H$

Solve.

32. The matrix shows the number of different basketball shots 3 players made in 2 min.

	2-pt	3-pt
Javi	5	1
Victor	3	2
Chris	4	2

The players make it a goal to double these numbers. Create the matrix that shows the players' goals.

33. The matrix shows an airline's costs, in dollars, to its top three destinations when the flight makes no stops, one stop, or two stops.

	No stops	1 stop	2 stop
Destination A	959	868	680
Destination B	1006	940	817
Destination C	684	525	463

Create the matrix that shows the costs after a 10% price increase.

34. The matrices show the number of junior varsity and varsity track team members in different age groups.

	Boys 15–16	17–18		Girls 15–16	17–18
JV	16	21	JV	23	15
Varsity	9	17	Varsity	6	19

A. Create a matrix that shows the total number of junior varsity and varsity track team members in different age groups.

B. Create a matrix by subtracting the boy's matrix from the girl's matrix. Tell what each number in the matrix represents.

Geometric Models

You can find mathematics in art. You can use mathematics to create art, too.

A **transformation** is a change in a figure's position, shape, or size. The **pre-image** is the original figure. The **image** is the result of the transformation.

⮞ Identifying Transformations

> **DEFINITIONS**
>
> An **isometry** changes only a figure's position. There are four isometries.
> - A **translation** slides a figure along a line without turns or flips.
> - A **reflection** flips a figure across a line, creating a mirror image.
> - A **rotation** turns a figure about a given point.
> - A **glide reflection** combines a translation with a reflection. The direction of the translation is parallel to the line of reflection.

> ▶ **TIP**
>
> The footprints you leave behind while walking at a steady pace form a series of glide reflections.

A **strip pattern** is a horizontal pattern that continues indefinitely in both directions. Strip patterns have been used in art and architecture throughout history.

You can translate any strip pattern a certain distance left or right so that the pattern maps onto, or realigns with, itself. Strip patterns may also include glide reflection, reflection symmetry, and rotation symmetry by 180°.

> **EXAMPLE 1**
> **List the transformation, or transformations, that map the strip pattern onto itself.**
>
> **Ⓐ** DDDDDDDDDD
>
> **Solution**
>
> ←DDDDDDDDDD→
>
> The pattern maps onto itself in the following ways:
>
> - a horizontal translation (shortest distance is by one letter)
>
> - a reflection across a horizontal line (line of reflection shown in red) ∎

B

Solution

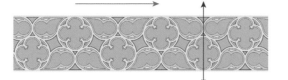

The pattern maps onto itself in the following ways:

- a horizontal translation (blue arrow shows shortest distance)

- a glide reflection (slide half the distance of the translation and flip)

- a 180° rotation (one half turn)

- a reflection across a vertical line (red arrow shows one possible line of reflection) ■

▶ **BY THE WAY**

Strip patterns are also called *frieze patterns* or *border patterns*.

You can also see transformations and symmetry in wallpaper.

This pattern includes vertical and horizontal translations of the same figure. When you look at two rows at a time, you see glide reflections. Also, each figure has vertical symmetry, horizontal symmetry, and 90° rotational symmetry.

≫ Tiling a Plane

To tile a plane is to cover it completely with nonoverlapping figures. If a regular polygon tiles a plane, then the measure of an interior angle divides evenly into 360°.

An equilateral triangle tiles a plane. Each interior angle measures 60°, which divides evenly into 360°.

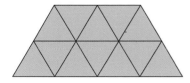

A regular pentagon does not tile a plane. Each interior angle measures 108°, which does not divide evenly into 360°.

▶ **REMEMBER**

The measure of an exterior angle of a regular polygon with n sides is $\frac{360°}{n}$. The measure of an interior angle is 180° minus the measure of its exterior angle.

Naming a Tiling

Sometimes, a set of two or more polygons can be used to tile a plane. The name of a tiling formed by regular polygons is the list of numbers of sides of each polygon that meet at any given vertex. Give the numbers in order, going around the vertex.

EXAMPLE 2
Give the name of the tiling.

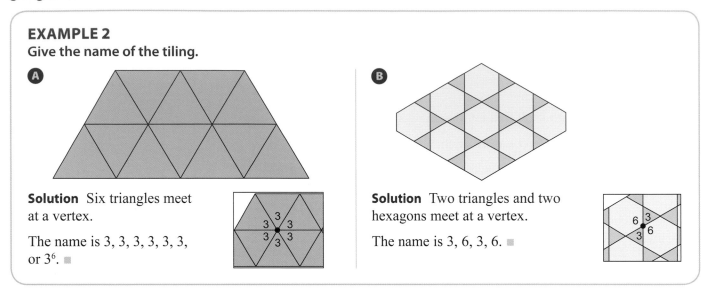

Ⓐ

Solution Six triangles meet at a vertex.

The name is 3, 3, 3, 3, 3, 3, or 3^6. ▪

Ⓑ

Solution Two triangles and two hexagons meet at a vertex.

The name is 3, 6, 3, 6. ▪

A **dilation** is a transformation that changes the size (but not the shape) of a figure.

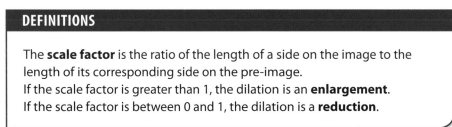

DEFINITIONS

The **scale factor** is the ratio of the length of a side on the image to the length of its corresponding side on the pre-image.
If the scale factor is greater than 1, the dilation is an **enlargement**.
If the scale factor is between 0 and 1, the dilation is a **reduction**.

In a dilation, the pre-image and image are similar. Therefore, you can use proportions to solve problems involving scale factor.

Using Scale Factor with Lengths

EXAMPLE 3
Julie enlarges a 4 in. by 6 in. photo to a 7 in. by 10.5 in. photo. What scale factor did she use?

Solution Divide the length of either side of the image by the length of the corresponding side on the pre-image.

$$\frac{7}{4} = 1.75$$

The scale factor is 1.75, or 175%. ▪

▶ **TIP**

You could also find the scale factor in Example 3 by finding the ratio of the longer side lengths.

$$\frac{10.5}{6} = 1.75$$

EXAMPLE 4
Find the width of the smaller tree.

Solution Write and solve a proportion. Use one ratio for the widths of the trees and one ratio for the heights of the trees.

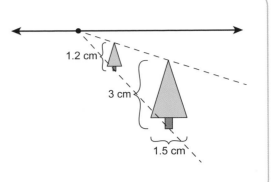

$$\frac{\text{small tree}}{\text{large tree}} \quad \frac{x}{1.5} = \frac{1.2}{3}$$
$$3x = 1.8$$
$$x = 0.6$$

The width of the smaller tree is 0.6 cm. ■

⇒ Using Scale Factor with Areas and Volumes

RATIOS OF AREAS AND VOLUMES OF SIMILAR FIGURES

If two similar figures have a scale factor of $\frac{a}{b}$, then the ratio of their areas is $\frac{a^2}{b^2}$. The ratio of their volumes is $\frac{a^3}{b^3}$.

EXAMPLE 5
The scale factor of an architect's model of a room to the actual room is $\frac{1 \text{ in.}}{8 \text{ ft}}$. The area of the actual room is 432 ft². What is the area of the model?

Solution The ratio of the area of the model to the area of the actual room is $\frac{1^2}{8^2} = \frac{1}{64}$. Use this ratio to write a proportion.

$$\frac{\text{model}}{\text{actual}} \quad \frac{1}{64} = \frac{x}{432}$$
$$432 = 64x$$
$$6.75 = x$$

The area of the model is 6.75 in². ■

EXAMPLE 6
The scale factor of a model rocket to the actual rocket is 1 to 20. Find the volume of the actual rocket if the volume of the model is 1.2 m³.

Solution The ratio of the volume of the model to the volume of the actual rocket is $\frac{1^3}{20^3} = \frac{1}{8000}$. Use the $\frac{\text{model}}{\text{actual}}$ ratio to write a proportion.

$$\frac{1}{8000} = \frac{1.2}{x}$$
$$x = 9600$$

The volume of the actual rocket is 9600 m³. ■

▶ Q & A

Q What is the ratio of the surface area of the model rocket to the surface area of the actual rocket?

A 1 to 400

Problem Set

List the transformation, or transformations, that map the strip pattern onto itself.

1. HHHHHHHHHHH

2. pdpdpdpdpdpdpd

3.

4.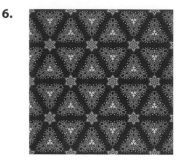

Tell what transformations and symmetries you see in the wallpaper pattern.

5.

6.

Solve.

7. **Stepping Stones** Does a regular decagon tile a plane? Explain.

   Each exterior angle of a regular decagon measures $\frac{360°}{10} = \blacksquare °$.

   Each interior angle measures $180° - \blacksquare ° = \blacksquare °$.

   Because $\blacksquare °$ does not divide into $360°$, a decagon does not tile a plane.

8. Does a regular hexagon tile a plane? Explain.

9. Give the name of the tiling.

10. Give the name of the tiling.

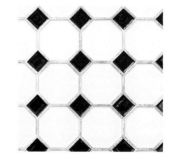

Find the scale factor of the enlargement or reduction.

11. **Stepping Stones** Greg reduces a 21 in. by 27 in. photo to a 14 in. by 18 in. photo.

    Find the ratio of the reduced length to the original length: $\frac{18}{\blacksquare}$.

    Simplify the ratio: $\frac{\blacksquare}{\blacksquare}$.

12. Zaria reduces a 16 in. by 20 in. photo to a 4 in. by 5 in. photo.

13. Sydney enlarges a 5 in. by 7 in. photo to a 15 in. by 21 in. photo.

14. Kurt enlarges a 24 cm by 30 cm photo to a 60 cm by 75 cm photo.

Solve.

15. **Stepping Stones** A 50 cm by 60 cm photograph is reduced so that the length (longer dimension) of the photograph is 48 cm. Find the width of the reduced photograph.

$$\frac{\text{reduced}}{\text{original}} \quad \frac{\blacksquare}{60} = \frac{x}{50}$$

$$\blacksquare = 60x$$

$$\blacksquare = x$$

The width is ▪ cm.

16. Find the height and width of the smaller barn given that it is similar to the larger barn by a scale factor of 60%.

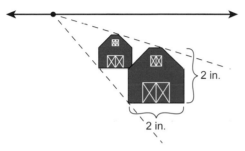

2 in.

2 in.

17. Find the height of the larger figure.

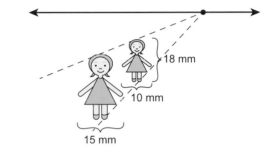

18 mm

10 mm

15 mm

18. A 4 in. by 5 in. photo is enlarged so that its width (shorter dimension) is 5 in. Find the length of the enlarged photo.

Solve the area or volume problem.

19. **Stepping Stones** The scale factor of a model plane to the actual plane is 1 to 25. Find the wing area of the model if the wing area of the actual plane is 300 ft².

The ratio of the wing area of the model to the wing area of the actual plane is $\frac{1^2}{25^2} = \frac{1}{\blacksquare}$.

$$\frac{\text{model}}{\text{actual}} \quad \frac{1}{\blacksquare} = \frac{x}{300}$$

$$300 = \blacksquare x$$

$$\blacksquare = x$$

The wing area of the model is ▪ ft².

20. The scale factor of the model of a garden to the actual garden is 1 to 50. Find the area of the garden if the area of the model is 3 m².

21. The scale factor of the model of an aquarium to the actual aquarium is 1 to 15. If the model holds 2 m³ of water, how much water does the actual aquarium hold?

22. The scale factor of a model boxcar in a train set to the actual boxcar is 1 : 87. What is the volume of the model boxcar if the volume of the actual boxcar is 7.8 million in³?

CHAPTER 4   Review

Choose the answer.

1. What is the constant of variation if $f(x)$ varies directly with x and $f(x) = 9$ when $x = 3$?

   A. $\frac{1}{3}$ C. 12

   B. 3   D. 27

2. The time it takes to wash a truck varies inversely with the number of people washing it. If it takes 30 min for 2 people to wash the truck, how long would it take if there were 3 people washing it?

   A. 12 min   C. 20 min

   B. 15 min   D. 25 min

3. Which sequence is geometric?

   A. 6, 9, 12, 15, 18, 21, . . .

   B. 10, 8, 6, 4, 2, 0, –2, . . .

   C. 3, 4, 6, 9, 13, 18, 24, . . .

   D. 5, 10, 20, 40, 80, 160, . . .

4. What is the common difference in the sequence 16, 8, 0, –8, –16, . . . ?

   A. –8   C. $\frac{1}{2}$

   B. –2   D. 8

5. What is the address of the element with value 1?

$$M = \begin{bmatrix} 18 & 0 & 6 \\ 3 & 10 & 15 \\ -5 & 1 & 3 \\ 7 & 4 & -9 \end{bmatrix}$$

   A. m_{22} C. m_{32}

   B. m_{23} D. m_{33}

6. The matrix shows the numbers of boys and girls who took different types of skiing lessons.

$$\begin{array}{c} \\ \text{Beginner} \\ \text{Intermediate} \\ \text{Advanced} \end{array} \begin{array}{cc} \text{Boys} & \text{Girls} \\ \begin{bmatrix} 15 & 21 \\ 14 & 3 \\ 3 & 8 \end{bmatrix} \end{array}$$

   About what percent of the boys took advanced lessons?

   A. 9%   C. 17%

   B. 25%   D. 73%

7. Which transformation maps the strip pattern onto itself?

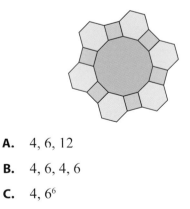

   A. vertical reflection

   B. horizontal reflection

   C. 180° rotation

   D. glide reflection

8. What is the name of the tiling shown?

   A. 4, 6, 12

   B. 4, 6, 4, 6

   C. $4, 6^6$

   D. $4^2, 6^2, 12$

Write the variation equation and evaluate the function for the given value.

9. If $f(x)$ varies directly with x and $f(x) = 96$ when $x = 8$, find the value of $f(x)$ when $x = 3$.

10. If $h(a)$ varies directly with a and $h(a) = 10$ when $a = 5$, find the value of a when $h(a) = 40$.

11. If $g(t)$ varies inversely with t and $g(t) = 9$ when $t = 4$, find the value of $g(t)$ when $t = 2$.

12. If $f(y)$ varies inversely with y and $f(y) = 1$ when $y = 4$, find the value of y when $f(y) = \frac{1}{4}$.

Find the first four terms in the sequence.

13. $a_n = a_{n-1} + 16$ and $a_1 = 10$

14. $a_n = a_{n-1} - 5$ and $a_1 = 100$

15. $a_n = 3 \cdot a_{n-1}$ and $a_1 = 10$

16. $a_n = 5 \cdot a_{n-1}$ and $a_1 = 6$

Use an iterative formula to find the indicated term of the sequence.

17. 71st term of the sequence 5, 7, 9, 11, ...

18. 25th term of the sequence 7, 20, 33, 46, ...

19. 10th term of the sequence 8, 16, 32, 64, ...

20. 15th term of the sequence 1, 3, 9, 27, ...

Use the matrices to find the product, sum, or difference.

$$G = \begin{bmatrix} 8 & 15 \\ 6 & 3 \end{bmatrix} \quad H = \begin{bmatrix} 9 & 14 \\ 21 & 2 \end{bmatrix}$$

21. $2G$

22. $5H$

23. $G + H$

24. $H - G$

Solve.

25. Colin reduces a 15 in. by 21 in. photo to a 5 in. by 7 in. photo. What scale factor did he use?

26. A 24 cm by 30 cm photo is enlarged so that its width (shorter dimension) is 42 cm. Find the length of the enlarged photo.

27. The scale factor of an architect's model of a house to the actual house is 1 to 10. The area of the roof on the actual house is 1450 ft². What is the area of the roof on the model?

28. Lily made a model of her footlocker using a scale of 1 to 5. The model has a volume of 0.09 ft³. What is the volume of the actual footlocker?

CHAPTER 5   Income

Most people get and keep a job so they can make money. It might seem that if you earn $8/h and work for 10 h, then you would end up with $80, but it isn't quite that simple. To understand where the money you earn goes, you need to learn about taxes and other deductions. Once you have money, you can use savings and checking accounts to manage your basic finances.

In This Chapter

You will learn about the math behind gross and net income, and some basics of using bank accounts.

MathGenius, Inc.
2718 Math Ave.
Alpine, UT 84004

Earnings Statement

EMPLOYEE NO.	EMPLOYEE NAME	SOCIAL SECURITY NO.	PERIOD BEG.	PERIOD END	CHECK DATE
1	LEONARD EULER	XXX-XX-5555	04/27/2013	05/12/2013	05/15/2013

EARNINGS	HOURS	RATE	CURRENT AMOUNT	WITHHOLDINGS/ DEDUCTIONS	CURRENT AMOUNT	YEAR TO DATE
REGULAR PAY			1309.00	MEDICARE SSA FED TAX AMT UT STATE TAX	18.98 81.16 164.01 65.45	170.82 730.44 1476.09 589.05

CURRENT AMOUNT	CURRENT DEDUCTIONS	NET PAY	YTD EARNINGS	YTD DEDUCTIONS	YTD NET PAY	CHECK NO.
1309.00	329.60	979.40	11780.97	2966.40	8814.58	37927

UtahStubs.com 2013

Topic List

► Chapter 5 Introduction

► Making Money

► Taxes and Deductions

► Banking

► Chapter 5 Review

When you have a job, you need to understand deductions and how to use bank accounts. ►

CHAPTER 5   Introduction

When you get a job, you want to know how your pay will be determined.

Some types of employees are paid by the hour. They receive the same amount of money for every hour they work. The more hours they work, the more money they are paid. Other types of employees are paid a salary, or a set amount. Putting in a weekend of overtime does not change the amount of their next paycheck.

Employees in the service and sales industries may receive additional income in other ways. For example, it is common for food servers and hairstylists to accept tips from customers. And most car salespeople and real estate agents earn a commission, or a percent of their sales, on top of their regular pay.

Taxes

Both hourly and salaried employees pay taxes, which reduces the amount of their paychecks. These taxes can include Social Security tax, Medicare tax, a federal tax, and a state tax. Because you want to be sure that your income covers your expenses, it is important that you can estimate the amount you will see on your paychecks ahead of time.

◄ In this chapter, you will learn what factors determine the amount of a paycheck.

Preparing for the Chapter

Review the following skills to prepare for the concepts in the chapter: calculating with money, finding the percent one number is of another, and finding the percent of a whole.

Calculating with Money

The smallest amount of money you can give someone in the United States is one penny. One penny is worth 1 cent, written $0.01. Unless you are told otherwise, round money amounts to the nearest hundredth.

HOW TO ROUND TO A GIVEN PLACE VALUE

To round a number to a given place value

Step 1 Identify the digit in the place value you are rounding to.

Step 2 Look at the digit to the right of the digit in the rounding place.

- If the digit to the right is less than 5, round down. To round down, keep the digit in the rounding place as is and change all the digits to the right of the rounding place to zeros.
- If the digit to the right is 5 or greater, round up. To round up, add 1 to the digit in the rounding place and change all the digits to the right of the rounding place to zeros.

EXAMPLE 1
Sunflower seeds cost $1.39/lb. How much would a bag of sunflower seeds weighing 0.78 lb cost?

Solution Multiply the cost per pound by the number of pounds.

$$1.39 \cdot 0.78 = 1.0842$$

Round to the nearest hundredth. The digit 8 is in the hundredths place and 4 is to the right of it. Because $4 < 5$, the number 1.0842 rounds down to 1.08. The bag of seeds would cost $1.08. ∎

In some states, you are required to round the dollar amounts you provide on a tax form to the nearest whole dollar.

EXAMPLE 2
An accountant divides $17,730.43 by 4 and records the quotient, rounded to the nearest dollar, on a tax form. What amount does the accountant record on the form?

Solution Divide.

$$17{,}730.43 \div 4 = 4432.6075$$

Round to the nearest whole number. The digit 2 is in the ones place and 6 is to the right of it. Because $6 > 5$, the number 4432.6075 rounds up to 4433. The accountant records $4433 on the form. ∎

Finding the Percent One Number Is of Another

You can break down a basic percent problem into three components: the part, the whole, and the percent.

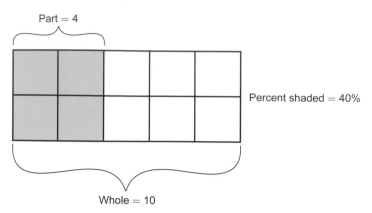

To find what percent the part is of the whole, divide the part by the whole.

> ### EXAMPLE 3
> **What percent of 250 is 145?**
>
> **Solution** The part is 145 and the whole is 250. Divide 145 by 250.
>
> $$145 \div 250 = 0.58$$
>
> Convert the decimal to a percent by moving the decimal point two places to the right: $0.58 = 58\%$.
>
> 58% of 250 is 145. ▪

Finding a Percent of a Whole

To find a percent of a whole, multiply the percent (written as a decimal) by the whole.

> ### EXAMPLE 4
> **What is 70% of $945.34?**
>
> **Solution** Convert the percent to a decimal by dropping the percent sign and moving the decimal point two places to the left.
>
> $$70\% = 0.7$$
>
> Multiply.
>
> $$0.7 \cdot 945.34 = 661.738$$
>
> Because the answer is an amount of money, round to the nearest hundredth. The number 661.738 rounds up to 661.74.
>
> 70% of $945.34 is $661.74. ▪

Problem Set

Solve.

1. Parsley costs $4.68/lb. How much would 0.35 lb of parsley cost?

2. Oatmeal costs $1.73/lb. How much would 2.6 lb of oatmeal cost?

3. A store sells 7 apples for $3. At that rate, how much would the store charge for 1 apple?

4. The cashier at a hotel converts euros to U.S. dollars by multiplying the number of euros by 1.2908. How much, in U.S. dollars, would the cashier give a customer who is exchanging 193 euros?

5. An accountant multiplies $998.02 by 0.06 and records the product, rounded to the nearest dollar, on a tax form. What amount does the accountant record on the form?

6. Mr. Nuñez drove his personal car 95.5 mi for a business trip. His manager said he could charge the company $0.35/mi.

   A. How much would Mr. Nuñez charge the company if he rounded to the nearest dollar?

   B. How much would Mr. Nuñez charge the company if he rounded to the nearest cent?

Find what percent the part is of the whole.

7. What percent of 60 is 12?

8. What percent of $520 is $494?

9. What percent of 1.8 is 40?

10. 15 is what percent of 80?

11. 98 is what percent of 14?

12. $34.50 is what percent of $40?

Find the percent of the whole.

13. What is 50% of 36?

14. What is 10% of $65.40?

15. What is 15% of $141.95?

16. What is 6% of $95?

17. What is 125% of 28?

18. What is 7.75% of $14,298.66?

Making Money

Income is money earned. The income of an employee is determined when he or she is hired.

Calculating Wages

Employees whose incomes are based on the number of hours they work receive **wages**. After hourly employees work more than a certain number of hours per week, usually 40 in the United States, their hourly wage, or hourly rate, becomes an overtime (OT) rate. The overtime rate is usually 1.5 times the regular rate.

Use these formulas to calculate **gross pay**, or pay before deductions.

▶ **TIP**

You can use the words *income* and *pay* interchangeably.

FORMULAS

gross pay (without OT) = hours worked · hourly rate
overtime pay rate = 1.5 · hourly rate
overtime pay = overtime hours · overtime pay rate
gross pay (with OT) = regular pay + overtime pay

EXAMPLE 1
Daniella earns $14/h and worked 47 h last week. She receives overtime pay for hours exceeding 40 h. Find her gross pay for last week.

Solution
Step 1 Find Daniella's regular pay.

$$40 \cdot \$14 = \$560$$

Step 2 Find Daniella's overtime pay rate.

$$1.5 \cdot \$14/h = \$21/h$$

Step 3 Find Daniella's overtime pay. She worked $47 - 40 = 7$ h of overtime.

$$7 \cdot \$21 = \$147$$

Step 4 Add her regular pay and her overtime pay.

$$\$560 + \$147 = \$707$$

Daniella's gross pay is $707. ■

▶ **BY THE WAY**

Some companies pay the overtime pay rate for hours worked on a holiday.

Calculating Salary

An employee who earns a **salary** earns a set amount of money for a given time period. For example, an employee may accept a job offer with an annual, or yearly, salary of $63,550. He or she would receive equal payments throughout the year, based on the company's pay period.

> **DEFINITION**
>
> A **pay period** is the length of time for which an employee gets paid. The most common pay periods are the following:
> - Weekly, occurring 52 times a year
> - Biweekly, or every two weeks, occurring 26 times a year
> - Semimonthly, or twice a month, occurring 24 times a year
> - Monthly, occurring 12 times a year

▶ BY THE WAY

Employees paid semimonthly are usually paid on the first and 15th day of each month.

EXAMPLE 2
Ivan's gross annual salary is $43,725, paid on a biweekly basis. Find his gross pay per pay period.

Solution Because Ivan is paid biweekly, divide his annual salary by 26.

$$\$43,725 \div 26 \approx \$1681.73$$

Ivan's gross pay per pay period is $1681.73. ▪

EXAMPLE 3
Every month, Mrs. Garcia earns $4935 in gross pay. What is her gross annual pay?

Solution Multiply Mrs. Garcia's monthly salary by 12.

$$\$4935 \cdot 12 = \$59,220$$

Mrs. Garcia's gross annual pay is $59,220. ▪

Calculating Tip

Many employees in the service industry earn a portion of their income through tips. These include food servers, food-delivery persons, garage attendants, house cleaners, taxi drivers, barbers, and hairstylists.

▶ BY THE WAY

At a restaurant, it is customary to tip 15% for good service and 20% or more for excellent service.

EXAMPLE 4
A server receives a 20% tip on a meal that costs $84.50. How much is the tip?

Solution Find 20% of $84.50.

$$0.2 \cdot \$84.50 = \$16.90$$

The tip is $16.90. ▪

◥ Calculating Gross Pay with Tips

Tipped employees' **base pay** is their pay before tips are added.

> **EXAMPLE 5**
> One week, Jarrett worked 25 h waiting tables at a restaurant. He received $288.45 in tips. What is his gross weekly pay if his hourly wage is $4.80?
>
> **Solution**
> **Step 1** Find Jarrett's base pay.
> $$25 \cdot \$4.80 = \$120$$
>
> **Step 2** Add the amount of the tips to his base pay.
> $$\$120 + \$288.45 = \$408.45$$
>
> Jarrett's gross weekly pay is $408.45. ■

> ▶ **BY THE WAY**
> The law allows some tipped employees to receive an hourly wage that is less than the minimum wage. The wage differs from state to state.

◥ Calculating Gross Pay with Commission

Many employees in the sales industry earn a **commission**. A commission is money earned for making a sale and is often a percent of an employee's total sales. For employees who earn a commission, their performance determines their pay.

> **EXAMPLE 6**
> Michael earns a gross weekly salary of $634 plus a 4% commission on his furniture sales. What is his gross weekly pay for a week in which he sold $14,130 worth of furniture?
>
> **Solution**
> **Step 1** Determine the commission by finding 4% of $14,130.
> $$0.04 \cdot \$14,130 = \$565.20$$
>
> **Step 2** Add the commission to Michael's salary.
> $$\$634 + \$565.20 = \$1199.20$$
>
> Michael's gross weekly pay is $1199.20. ■

> ▶ **BY THE WAY**
> Michael earns a flat, or straight, commission. A variable commission pays a different percent for different levels of sales.

Problem Set
. . . .

Find the weekly gross pay. Assume overtime pay for time exceeding 40 h.

> 1. **Stepping Stones** hourly rate: $11.25, hours worked: 31
>
> gross pay = hours worked • hourly rate
> = 31 • ▓
> = ▓▓▓▓▓

2. hourly rate: $7.80, hours worked: 28

3. hourly rate: $9.14, hours worked: 48

4. hourly rate: $13.50, hours worked: 52

Find the gross pay per pay period.

5. **Stepping Stones** annual salary: $34,386, pay period: semimonthly

Semimonthly occurs ▮ times per year.

gross pay = $34,386 ÷ ▮

= ▮

6. annual salary: $51,389, pay period: biweekly

7. annual salary: $29,692, pay period: weekly

8. annual salary: $45,080, pay period: monthly

9. annual salary: $71,290, pay period: semimonthly

Solve.

10. If Kira earns $10.48/h, how many full hours must she work to earn at least $375?

11. Jasmin earns a gross weekly salary of $510. What is her gross annual salary?

12. Colby earns a gross biweekly salary of $1430.80. What is his gross annual salary?

13. Antonio earns a gross weekly salary of $534. Sabrina earns a gross annual salary of $26,624. Who has the greater income?

14. Company A offers a semimonthly salary of $1991.62. Company B offers a biweekly salary of $1975.10. Which company offers the greater salary?

15. Brett earns $19.20/h with overtime for hours exceeding 40 per week. How many full hours must he work to earn a gross weekly pay of exactly $1056?

16. **Challenge** Sydney earns a gross yearly salary of $35,984. How much more will she receive in her gross biweekly paycheck after she receives a 3% raise?

Find the amount of the tip when the amount of the bill and the tip percent are given.

17. **Stepping Stones** bill: $41.82, tip percent: 15%

Find 15% of ▮ .

▮ • $41.82 = ▮

The amount of the tip is ▮ .

18. bill: $23.95, tip percent: 20%

19. bill: $63.90, tip percent: 18%

20. bill: $109.66, tip percent: 15%

21. bill: $14.95, tip percent: 25%

Solve.

22. Aubree received a $12 tip on a meal that cost $50. What percent of the meal cost was the tip?

23. Connor earns $2.65/h waiting tables. How much money does he have to receive in tips during an 8 h shift to make $100?

24. A hairstylist earns $12.95/h and works 32 h a week. What is her gross weekly income during a week in which she receives $219 in tips?

25. Sonya earns $3.35/h working at a hotel restaurant that adds a 15% tip to each customer's bill. What is her gross weekly pay for a week in which she works 22 h and serves $1520 worth of food?

26. Christopher earns $9.90/h selling appliances. He also earns a 4% commission on his sales. Find his gross weekly pay for a week in which he worked 30 h and sold $5100 worth of appliances.

27. Victoria earns a gross weekly salary of $450 selling cars. She also receives 25% of the profit made on each car she sells. What is her gross weekly income for a week in which her sales of two cars made profits of $1300 and $850?

28. **Challenge** Gavin earns a gross weekly salary of $320 plus 3% of his first $5000 worth of sales and 4.5% of sales amounts exceeding $5000. Find his gross weekly pay for a week in which he sold $6572 worth of goods.

Taxes and Deductions

Federal, state, and local governments collect taxes to fund agencies and programs.

◥ Understanding a Pay Stub

Every paycheck comes with a stub that explains how the **net pay**, or pay after deductions, was determined. Here is a sample pay stub. Notice that the left side shows the pay period, how the gross pay was determined, and the net pay.

The right side shows the **deductions**. Some of the deductions are **taxes**. Those are not optional. Optional deductions may include money for retirement, health insurance, and life insurance.

The net pay is the gross pay minus all the deductions.

Pay Period: 6/16/13–6/22/13			
EARNINGS		**TAX DEDUCTIONS**	
Regular Hours:	40	Federal Tax:	$97.54
Overtime Hours:	3	Social Security Tax:	$44.14
Regular Pay:	$640	Medicare Tax:	$10.32
Overtime Pay:	$72	State Tax:	$35.60
Gross Pay:	$712	**OTHER DEDUCTIONS**	
Net Pay:	$469.89	Retirement:	$21.26
		Insurance:	$33.25

◥ Finding Net Pay

EXAMPLE 1
Colby worked 18 h for $9.25/h. What was his net pay if he paid $22.81 in federal taxes, $10.32 in Social Security taxes, and $2.41 in Medicare taxes?

Solution

Step 1 Find Colby's gross pay.

$$18 \cdot \$9.25 = \$166.50$$

Step 2 Find the sum of the deductions.

$$\$22.81 + \$10.32 + \$2.41 = \$35.54$$

Step 3 Subtract the deductions from the gross pay.

$$\$166.50 - \$35.54 = \$130.96 \ \blacksquare$$

Federal and state taxes are based on an employee's filing status. For example, tax rates will differ for a single employee with no children and a married employee with three children. Everyone, however, pays the same percent in Social Security and Medicare taxes. Together, these two taxes form the Federal Insurance Contributions Act, known as FICA (FIY-kuh), tax.

▶ **BY THE WAY**

The government uses your Social Security number (SSN) to track your lifetime earnings. This helps determine the Social Security benefits you are entitled to.

▶ **BY THE WAY**

Depending on where you live, you may not have to pay state income tax.

▶ **TIP**

A tax rate is a ratio, such as $15 per every $100 earned. It is sometimes expressed as a percent.

Determining FICA Taxes

FICA TAX FORMULAS

Social Security tax = 6.2% • gross pay
Medicare tax = 1.45% • gross pay
FICA tax = Social Security tax + Medicare tax

▶ BY THE WAY

After year-to-date (YTD) gross pay reaches a certain amount ($113,700 in 2013), Social Security taxes are no longer taken.

EXAMPLE 2

Jennifer's gross weekly pay is $285. How much of her weekly pay will she have taken out for Social Security?

Solution Find 6.2% of $285.

$$0.062 \cdot \$285 = \$17.67$$

Jennifer will have $17.67 taken out for Social Security. ▪

Determining a Take-Home Pay Percent

Net pay is often called take-home pay. Because deductions vary from person to person, the percent of gross pay each employee takes home varies.

EXAMPLE 3

Ivan's gross pay is $166.50 and his net pay is $130.96. What percent of his gross pay is take-home pay?

Solution Divide Ivan's net pay by his gross pay and convert the decimal to a percent.

$$\$130.96 \div \$166.50 \approx 0.78654$$

Ivan's take-home pay is about 79% of his gross pay. ▪

▶ Q & A

Q For the pay stub on the previous page, what percent of the gross pay is take-home pay?

A about 66%

Calculating Annual Deductions

EXAMPLE 4

Amanda earns a gross biweekly salary of $1120. Find the total of her Medicare deductions for the year.

Solution
Step 1 Find Amanda's Medicare deduction for one pay period.

$$0.0145 \cdot \$1120 = \$16.24$$

Step 2 Multiply by the number of pay periods in one year.

$$\$16.24 \cdot 26 = \$422.24$$ ▪

Analyzing a W-2 Form

All the taxes that an employee paid through an employer for a given year are summarized on a **W-2 form**. People who have worked for multiple employers in a year receive multiple W-2 forms, one from each employer.

Here is a sample W-2 form.

22222	a Employee's social security number 999-99-9999	OMB No. 1545-0008		
b Employer identification number (EIN) 99-9999999			1 Wages, tips, other compensation 18,880.64	2 Federal income tax withheld 2360.08
c Employer's name, address, and ZIP code			3 Social security wages 18,880.64	4 Social security tax withheld 1170.60
Company ABC 999 North Street Chicago, IL 60601			5 Medicare wages and tips 18,880.64	6 Medicare tax withheld 273.77
			7 Social security tips	8 Allocated tips
d Control number		9		10 Dependent care benefits
e Employee's first name and initial Last name Suff.		11 Nonqualified plans	12a	
Erin Banks 999 East Ave Chicago, IL 60653		13 Statutory employee Retirement plan Third-party sick pay	12b	
		14 Other	12c	
			12d	
f Employee's address and ZIP code				

15 State Employer's state ID number	16 State wages, tips, etc.	17 State income tax	18 Local wages, tips, etc.	19 Local income tax	20 Locality name
IL 9999999	18,880.64	944.03			

Form **W-2** Wage and Tax Statement   **2013**   Department of the Treasury—Internal Revenue Service
Copy 1—For State, City, or Local Tax Department

▶ BY THE WAY

Boxes 3 and 5 can differ from Box 1 depending on the type of income and the amount of income.

- Box 1 shows the total annual compensation.

- Boxes 2, 4, and 6 show the annual deductions.

- Box 17 shows the state income tax.

Calculating Adjusted Gross Income

Taxes withheld from a paycheck *approximate* the taxes an employee owes the government; the employee might actually owe more money or less money. Employers send out W-2 forms to all their employees every January. Employees have until mid-April, usually April 15, to settle their taxes. They do this by completing a 1040, 1040A, or 1040EZ form.

> **DEFINITIONS**
>
> **Gross income**, or total income, is the sum of job earnings, interest, and dividends.
> **Adjusted gross income (AGI)** is income minus adjustments.

▶ BY THE WAY

Adjustments for AGI include educator expenses, moving expenses, student loan interest, and college tuition.

People receive forms to help determine gross income and AGI. For example, banks send interest information on a 1099-INT form. Interest is part of gross income. Also, colleges send out 1098-T forms, which summarize educational expenses. Adjustments such as college loan interest payments lower gross income, giving former college students a break.

EXAMPLE 5

Garret received a W-2 showing compensation of $44,766.20 and a 1099-INT showing savings account interest of $10.45. His adjustments for educational and moving expenses are $3177.50. Find Garret's AGI.

Solution

Step 1 Find Garret's gross income by adding his compensation from work and his savings account interest.

$$\$44,766.20 + \$10.45 = \$44,776.65$$

Step 2 Subtract adjustments from income to find his AGI.

$$\$44,776.65 - \$3177.50 = \$41,599.15 \ \blacksquare$$

Using a Federal Tax Table

Taxable income is AGI minus exemptions and deductions. The exemptions and deductions are figured out on tax forms. Once a person knows his or her taxable income, the person can use a table to find how much tax he or she owes. Part of a federal tax table is shown.

People who paid more than what is in the table receive a **refund**. People who paid less than what is in the table must pay the difference.

If line 43 (taxable income) is—		And you are—			
At least	But less than	Single	Married filing jointly *	Married filing separately	Head of a household
		Your tax is—			
27,000					
27,000	27,050	3,619	3,184	3,619	3,434
27,050	27,100	3,626	3,191	3,626	3,441
27,100	27,150	3,634	3,199	3,634	3,449
27,150	27,200	3,641	3,206	3,641	3,456
27,200	27,250	3,649	3,214	3,649	3,464
27,250	27,300	3,656	3,221	3,656	3,471
27,300	27,350	3,664	3,229	3,664	3,479
27,350	27,400	3,671	3,236	3,671	3,486
27,400	27,450	3,679	3,244	3,679	3,494
27,450	27,500	3,686	3,251	3,686	3,501
27,500	27,550	3,694	3,259	3,694	3,509
27,550	27,600	3,701	3,266	3,701	3,516
27,600	27,650	3,709	3,274	3,709	3,524
27,650	27,700	3,716	3,281	3,716	3,531
27,700	27,750	3,724	3,289	3,724	3,539
27,750	27,800	3,731	3,296	3,731	3,546
27,800	27,850	3,739	3,304	3,739	3,554
27,850	27,900	3,746	3,311	3,746	3,561
27,900	27,950	3,754	3,319	3,754	3,569
27,950	28,000	3,761	3,326	3,761	3,576

IRS 2012

EXAMPLE 6

Ebony's taxable income is $27,391. She is single and has already paid $3804 in federal taxes. Determine if she overpaid or underpaid, and find the amount she will receive or pay.

Solution Find the row for income that is at least 27,350 but less than 27,400. Then look in the column labeled "Single."

Ebony owes $3671. She has already paid $3804, so she overpaid. She will get a refund of $3804 − $3671, or $133. ∎

At least	But less than	Single
27,000		
27,000	27,050	3,619
27,050	27,100	3,626
27,100	27,150	3,634
27,150	27,200	3,641
27,200	27,250	3,649
27,250	27,300	3,656
27,300	27,350	3,664
27,350	27,400	3,671

Problem Set

Solve.

1. **Stepping Stones** Jacob earns a gross weekly salary of $788.46. What is his weekly net pay if he pays $118.93 in federal taxes, $48.88 in Social Security taxes, $11.43 in Medicare taxes, and $29.03 in state taxes?

    Find the sum of the deductions.

    $118.93 + $48.88 + \boxed{} + \boxed{} = \boxed{}$

    Subtract the deductions from the gross pay.

    $788.46 - \boxed{} = \boxed{}$

2. Ally worked 40 h for $14/h. What was her net pay if she paid $72.80 in federal taxes, $34.72 in Social Security taxes, and $8.12 in Medicare taxes, and she had $30 taken out for retirement savings?

3. Tomas earned $288.59 in net pay for working 33 h. If $66.16 was deducted from his gross pay, what was his hourly wage?

4. Briana's net pay on her biweekly paycheck is $1869.48. If $534.37 was deducted from her gross biweekly pay, what is Briana's gross annual salary?

For each amount of gross pay, find the following:
A. the Social Security tax
B. the Medicare tax

5. **Stepping Stones** $460

    A. The Social Security tax is ▩% of the gross pay.

    ▩ • $460 = \boxed{}

    B. The Medicare tax is ▩% of the gross pay.

    ▩ • $460 = \boxed{}

6. $944

7. $2130.15

8. $1135.88

Solve.

9. **Stepping Stones** Shelby's gross pay is $614.04 and her net pay is $460.05. What percent of her gross pay is take-home pay?

    Divide Shelby's net pay by her gross pay.

    $460.05 ÷ \boxed{} ≈ \boxed{}$

    Convert the decimal to a percent.

    Shelby takes home about ▩% of her gross pay.

10. Colton's gross pay is $1421.50 and his net pay is $973.48. What percent of his gross pay is take-home pay?

11. Earl earned $356 in gross pay. He had $27.23 deducted for FICA taxes and $52.69 deducted for state and federal taxes. What percent of his gross pay did he take home?

12. Antwan estimates he'll take home about 75% of his gross pay. How much must he earn in gross pay if he wants to net at least $650?

Determine the indicated annual deductions.

13. **Stepping Stones** Kim earns a gross weekly salary of $544. Find her annual Medicare deduction.

    Kim's Medicare deduction for one pay period is ▨ • $544 = ▭ .

    Kim is paid weekly, so multiply by ▨ .

    ▨ • ▭ = ▭

14. Jeffrey earns a gross semimonthly salary of $2181.80. Find the total of his Social Security deductions for the year.

15. Kareem earns a gross biweekly salary of $1610. Find the total of his Medicare deductions for the year.

16. Parker earns a gross monthly salary of $6500.

    A. Find the total of his Social Security deductions for the year.

    B. Find the total of his Medicare deductions for the year.

Use this part of Gabriel's W-2 form to answer the questions.

17. What was Gabriel's total compensation?

18. How much federal income tax was withheld?

19. How much FICA tax was withheld?

20. What percent of Gabriel's earnings went toward paying the state tax?

1 Wages, tips, other compensation	2 Federal income tax withheld
31,478.32	4466.83
3 Social security wages	4 Social security tax withheld
31,478.32	1951.66
5 Medicare wages and tips	6 Medicare tax withheld
31,478.32	456.44
7 Social security tips	8 Allocated tips
9	10 Dependent care benefits
Suff. 11 Nonqualified plans	12a
13 Statutory employee / Retirement plan / Third-party sick pay	12b
14 Other	12c
	12d

16 State wages, tips, etc.	17 State income tax	18 Local wages, tips, etc.	19 Local income tax	20 Locality name
31,478.32	1369.31			

Determine each person's adjusted gross income.

21. Tiffany received a W-2 showing compensation of $26,496.03 and has an adjustment of $1024.88 for student loan interest deduction. Find Tiffany's AGI.

22. Sage received two W-2 forms, showing compensation of $14,509.11 and $34,812.30. He also received a 1099-INT form showing interest of $15.08. His adjustment for tuition and fees is $2590. Find Sage's AGI.

Use the 2012 Tax Table on pages A-18 and A-19 to solve.

23. **Stepping Stones** David and Faith are married and filing a joint tax return. Their taxable income is $33,129. Determine their tax.

    Find the row for income that is at least $33,100 but less than ▭ . Then look in the column labeled "Married filing jointly." Their tax is ▭ .

24. Dustin's taxable income is $33,802. He is single and has already paid $4504 in federal taxes. Determine if Dustin overpaid or underpaid, and find the amount he will receive or pay.

25. Ms. McCoy's taxable income is $33,791. She is filing as head of household and has already paid $4655 in federal taxes. Determine if Ms. McCoy overpaid or underpaid, and find the amount she will receive or pay.

26. Mr. Boyd received a refund of $233. His W-2 shows that he had paid $4812 in taxes through payroll deductions. What is his income range if he is married and filing separately?

Banking

A bank is a safe and convenient place to keep your money.

You can deposit your paycheck into a checking account or a savings account. A **checking account** allows you to write checks to pay for things. Most checking accounts come with a **debit card**. Using a debit card at a store is like writing a check that the store immediately cashes.

A **savings account** is an account just for saving money. Money in a savings account generally earns interest, and you cannot use the money to write checks. Both types of bank accounts can come with automatic teller machine (ATM) cards that allow you to withdraw and deposit money.

▶ BY THE WAY

Banks may charge a monthly maintenance fee. Some banks will waive the fee, however, if you have your paycheck directly deposited, or if you maintain a certain minimum balance.

▧ Identifying the Parts of a Check

Carrie Hudson (the payer) wrote this check to the ABC Electric Co. (the payee) in the amount of $110.46. She wrote her account number with the electric company at the bottom left. She signed the check at the bottom right.

The check number appears both at the top of the check, and at the bottom, after the checking account number. This number helps with recordkeeping for both the payer and the payee. The routing number identifies the bank numerically. All banks in the United States have a unique 9-digit routing number.

Check amounts must be written in both numeric and verbal form. When writing the verbal form, replace the decimal point with the word *and*. Write the cents as a fraction with 100 in the denominator. Do not write the word *dollars* because that word is already printed on the check.

▶ TIP

If the verbal form is short, draw a line through the blank space so there is no available space for someone else to change the amount.

Analyzing a Deposit Slip

A deposit slip shows how much money you are depositing into a bank account, and whether it is in the form of cash or checks.

Deposit Ticket		
Carrie Hudson		
999 SW North Ave		
Miami, FL 33130		
Date _May 2, 2013_		
Carrie Hudson		
Sign here if receiving cash*		
✳ **Financial Institution**		
⑆ 456789123 ⑆ 8826304994 ⑈		

Cash			
Check	# 880	35	00
Check	# 1521	516	89
Check	#		
Total from other side			
Subtotal		551	89
*Less cash received		25	00
Total $		526	89

▶ **TIP**

If Carrie were depositing four or more checks, she would continue listing them on the back of the slip.

Carrie deposited two checks: check number 880 for $35, and check number 1521 for $516.89. The sum of the amounts is $551.89. She received $25 back in cash. Notice that Carrie signed the slip because she received cash. The amount deposited into her account was $551.89 − $25 = $526.89.

Analyzing a Register

You can keep track of all your bank transactions for an account in a **register**. In a savings register, you would list deposits, withdrawals, and amounts of interest earned. In a check register, you would include information about checks and debit transactions.

Maintaining a check register can help you avoid an **overdraft**, or having a negative balance. A check returned for insufficient funds, called a **bounced check**, usually results in the person who bounced the check being charged a fee. Here is part of Carrie's check register.

D = Deposit   **AP** = Automatic Payment   **ATM** = Cash Withdrawal   **DC** = Debit Card   **SC** = Service Charge

Date	Code or Check #	Transaction Description	Payment, Fee, Withdrawal (−)		✓	Deposit, Credit (+)		Balance	
								205	21
10/1	305	Phone bill	49	88				−49	88
								155	33
10/3	ATM	Movie	20	00				−20	00
								135	33
10/4	D	Paycheck				345	67	+345	67
								481	00

Carrie brought forward the balance of $205.21 from the previous page of her register to the top of this page. Notice that she used two lines per transaction. For example, she used the first line of the transaction on 10/3 to show that she withdrew $20 from an ATM to see a movie. She used the second line of that transaction to show her updated balance of $135.33.

▶ **Q & A**

Q How much did Carrie deposit on 10/4?

A $345.67

Reconciling a Bank Account

All bank account holders receive a monthly **bank statement**, or account summary, that shows all the transactions for that month. Here is Owen's checking account statement.

Account Number 9827405974			Statement period: 5/2/2013 to 6/3/2013
Beginning Balance	**Total Deposits**	**Total Withdrawals**	**Ending Balance**
$905.16	$215.00	$189.00	$931.16

Date	Ref #	Description	Debits (−)	Credits (+)	Balance
5/4	417	Check	23.95		881.21
5/7		Deposit		50.00	931.21
5/14		Electronic Purchase–Hank's Deli	14.80		916.41
5/16		ATM–123 Main Street	40.00		876.41
5/18	418	Check	110.25		766.16
5/30		Deposit		165.00	931.16

It is a good idea to compare each bank statement you receive to your register to make sure you didn't miss anything and to avoid an overdraft. Here is Owen's register for the same time period as his bank statement above.

D = Deposit   **AP** = Automatic Payment   **ATM** = Cash Withdrawal   **DC** = Debit Card   **SC** = Service Charge

Date	Code or Check #	Transaction Description	Payment, Fee, Withdrawal (−)		✓	Deposit, Credit (+)		Balance	
								905	16
5/1	417	Uniform	23	95	√			881	21
5/7	D	Grad. gift				50	00	931	21
5/14	DC	Hank's	14	80				916	41
5/15	418	Car repairs	110	25	√			806	16
5/16	ATM	Dinner	40	00				766	16
5/30	D	Paycheck				165	00	931	16
5/31	419	Plumber	82	17				848	99

HOW TO RECONCILE A CHECKING ACCOUNT

To reconcile a checking account

Step 1 Identify the ending balance on the bank statement.

Step 2 Subtract check amounts that have not cleared.

Step 3 Add deposit amounts that have not been processed.

Step 4 Compare this amount to the checkbook balance.

▶ **BY THE WAY**

You can choose to receive your bank statements online or offline.

▶ **BY THE WAY**

In this register, each transaction uses only one line. The choice to use one or two lines per transaction is yours.

▶ **TIP**

This process is also known as *balancing a checkbook*.

Here is the reconciliation process for Owen's checking account.

Step 1 The ending balance, shown at the top of the bank statement, is $931.16.

Step 2 Check number 419 did not clear the bank yet. Subtract that amount.

$$\$931.16 - \$82.17 = \$848.99$$

Step 3 Both deposits have been processed. There is nothing to add.

Step 4 Compare $848.99 to the register balance. The amounts are the same. This account is reconciled.

If the amount at the end of Step 3 (adding any unprocessed deposits) does not equal the register amount, check the register for math errors and unrecorded transactions.

> ▶ **TIP**
>
> You can use check marks in a check register to show that a check cleared, meaning that the payee has cashed it.

Problem Set

Use Jason Elliot's check to answer the questions.

```
Jason Elliot                                              227
999 SW Dogwood Ave            Date July 15, 2013
Chicago, IL 60609

PAY TO THE
ORDER OF   Karl Logan                          $  49.70

Forty-nine and 70/100 _____ DOLLARS

✳ Financial Institution

For  Concert Ticket          Jason Elliot

⑆ 987654321 ⑆ 3141592654 ⑈   227
```

1. Who is the payee?

2. Who is the payer?

3. What is the check amount?

4. When did the payer write the check?

5. For what reason did the payer write the check?

6. What is the check number?

7. What is the payer's checking account number?

8. What is the routing number of the bank from which the check is drawn?

Write the verbal form of the amount as it should appear on a check.

9. $35

10. $291.18

11. $1145.96

12. $149.02

Use Darlene Quinn's deposit slip to answer the questions.

Deposit Ticket		
Cash	40	00
Darlene Quinn 999 SW Oak Ave Chicago, IL 60609		
Check # 295	35	75
Check # 1004	102	16
Date June 22, 2013		
Check # 580	59	33
Total from other side		
Sign here if receiving cash*		
Subtotal		
✳ Mytown Bank		
*Less cash received		
I: 321321321 I: 2718281828 I"		
Total $	237	24

13. How many checks did Darlene deposit?

14. What was the total amount of the checks Darlene deposited?

15. How much cash did Darlene deposit?

16. What percent of the total deposit was cash?

17. What is the number of the account that Darlene is depositing into?

18. Why didn't Darlene sign the deposit slip?

Use Shamar Griffin's desposit slip to answer the questions.

Deposit Ticket		
Cash		
Shamar Griffin 999 SW Maple Ave Dallas, TX 75217		
Check # 6782	100	00
Check # 814	75	00
Date Aug. 3, 2013		
Check # 2115	150	00
Shamar Griffin		
Total from other side	625	00
Sign here if receiving cash*		
Subtotal	950	00
✳ Yourtown Bank		
*Less cash received	80	00
I: 987654321 I: 6283185307 I"		
Total $	870	00

19. **Stepping Stones** How much money did Shamar deposit into his account?

Look at the bottom row. Shamar deposited ▢ into his account.

20. What is the sum of the check amounts listed on the front of the deposit slip?

21. What is the sum of the check amounts listed on the back of the deposit slip?

22. Two checks are listed on the back of the slip. One is for $200. What is the amount of the other check?

23. What was the total amount of all the checks Shamar deposited?

24. How much cash did Shamar receive back?

Solve.

25. Laura's balance was $102.35. She then wrote checks for $49.03 and $21.98, made a deposit of $40, and used a debit card for a purchase of $15. What is her new balance?

26. Erik's balance was $89.80. His paycheck of $290.15 was directly deposited into his account. He then withdrew $80 from an ATM machine and wrote checks for $160.14, $45, and $99.50. By how much did Erik overdraw his account?

Use Andy's check register to answer the questions.

D = Deposit	AP = Automatic Payment	ATM = Cash Withdrawal	DC = Debit Card	SC = Service Charge

Date	Code or Check #	Transaction Description	Payment, Fee, Withdrawal (−)	✓	Deposit, Credit (+)	Balance
						68 34
1/15	D	Paycheck			310 58	378 92
1/17	AP	Movie Club	9 95			368 97
1/20	DC	Barber	14 50			354 47
1/24	460	Rent	250 00			104 47
1/30	D	Paycheck			402 71	

27. Stepping Stones What balance did Andy bring forward from the previous page of his register?

Look at the top of the rightmost column. Andy forwarded _____ from the previous page of his register.

28. What is the total amount of the deposits shown?

29. Where did Andy use his debit card, and for how much?

30. What was the check number on the check that Andy used to pay the rent?

31. How much was the automatic payment to the movie club?

32. What amount should Andy write for the balance on January 30?

Use Joy's bank statement to answer the questions.

Account Number 1212343434		Statement period: 6/14/2013 to 7/15/2013	
Beginning Balance	**Total Deposits**	**Total Withdrawals**	**Ending Balance**
$1214.50	$148.00	$295.48	$1067.02

Date	Ref #	Description	Debits (−)	Credits (+)	Balance
6/15		Electronic Purchase–Corner Market	15.44		1199.06
6/19		ATM–Evergreen Mall	40.00		1159.06
6/27	558	Check	84.39		1074.67
6/28	557	Check	130.66		944.01
7/1		Deposit		148.00	1092.01
7/7		Electronic Purchase–Barb's Books	24.99		1067.02

33. Stepping Stones On which day was a deposit processed, and how much was the deposit?

Look for "Deposit" in the Description. A deposit was made on _____ in the amount of _____.

34. How many checks were cashed, and what were their amounts?

35. What was the sum of Joy's electronic purchases?

36. What was Joy's balance *before* she withdrew money from the mall ATM?

37. Joy's register for this statement period shows check number 559 written for $285, check number 560 written for $49, and a deposit on 7/15 of $210.38. The balance in her register is $943.40. Show how Joy would reconcile her account.

CHAPTER 5   Review

Choose the answer.

1. Jordan earns $10.62/h, plus she earns overtime for hours exceeding 40 h per week. What is her gross weekly pay for working 47 h if she gets time and a half for overtime?

   A. $440.73   C. $536.31

   B. $499.14   D. $748.71

2. Trystan accepted a job offer with an annual salary of $33,907, paid on a biweekly basis. What will be his gross pay on each of his paychecks?

   A. $652.06   C. $1412.79

   B. $1304.12   D. $2825.58

3. Which salary results in the greatest annual income?

   A. weekly salary of $681

   B. biweekly salary of $1330

   C. semimonthly salary of $1450

   D. monthly salary of $2895

4. Yasmeen earned a 15% tip on a meal that cost $62.77. What was the tip amount?

   A. $4.18   C. $7.22

   B. $4.78   D. $9.42

5. Lorenzo earns $9.25/h selling televisions. He also earns a 5.5% commission on his sales. What is his gross weekly pay for a week in which he worked 35 h and sold $3294 worth of televisions?

   A. $304.70   C. $504.92

   B. $323.75   D. $628.45

6. Brent worked 40 h one week at a rate of $14.80/h. How much money was deducted from his gross pay for the Social Security tax?

   A. $45.29   C. $9.18

   B. $36.70   D. $8.58

7. Kennedy's gross pay is $972.05 and her net pay is $696.15. About what percent of her gross pay is take-home pay?

   A. 60%   C. 72%

   B. 68%   D. 77%

8. Gina's taxable income is $24,118. She is single and has already paid $3216 in federal taxes. Use the tax table to determine which statement is true.

If line 43 (taxable income) is—		And you are—			
At least	But less than	Single	Married filing jointly *	Married filing sepa-rately	Head of a house-hold
			Your tax is—		
24,000					
24,000	24,050	3,169	2,734	3,169	2,984
24,050	24,100	3,176	2,741	3,176	2,991
24,100	24,150	3,184	2,749	3,184	2,999
24,150	24,200	3,191	2,756	3,191	3,006
24,200	24,250	3,199	2,764	3,199	3,014
24,250	24,300	3,206	2,771	3,206	3,021

IRS 2012

   A. She underpaid by $25.

   B. She underpaid by $32.

   C. She overpaid by $25.

   D. She overpaid by $32.

Solve.

9. Jovani earns a gross weekly salary of $595. What is his gross annual salary?

10. Damien worked 22 h for $13.15/h. The following taxes were deducted from his gross pay: $31.96 in federal taxes, $17.36 in state taxes, and $22.13 in FICA taxes. What was Damien's net pay?

11. Zoey earns a gross semimonthly salary of $1296. Find her annual Medicare deduction.

12. Elvin received a W-2 showing compensation of $34,038 and a 1099-INT for earning $12.41 in interest. He has an adjustment of $1640 for business expenses. Find his AGI.

Use Sandy's deposit slip to answer the questions.

Deposit Ticket

Sandy Moran
999 SW Peach Ave
Sacramento, CA 94235

Date _____ April 9, 2013 _____

_____
Sign here if receiving cash*

✳ Yourtown Bank

⑆ 999273466 ⑆ 847300923 ⑈

Cash		324	00
Check	# 663	768	59
Check	# 818	550	21
Check	#		
Total from other side			
Subtotal			
*Less cash received			
Total $		1642	80

13. How much money in cash did Sandy deposit?

14. How many checks did Sandy deposit?

15. What were the check numbers of the checks that Sandy deposited?

16. What is the total amount of the deposit?

17. What percent of the deposit came from checks?

Use Ashton's check register to answer the questions.

D = Deposit AP = Automatic Payment ATM = Cash Withdrawal DC = Debit Card SC = Service Charge

Date	Code or Check #	Transaction Description	Payment, Fee, Withdrawal (−)	✓	Deposit, Credit (+)	Balance
						146 89
3/16	D	Paycheck			520 81	667 70
3/17	DC	Lunch	17 50			650 20
3/20	419	Phone bill	72 33			577 87
3/21	420	Rent	350 00			227 87
3/23	D	Paycheck			550 56	778 43

18. When did Ashton use his debit card, and for what reason?

19. What was Ashton's balance after he made the debit card purchase?

20. What was the check number of the check that Ashton used to pay the rent, and what was the amount of the check?

21. On what days did Ashton make deposits, and what were the amounts of the deposits?

22. Ashton's next transaction will be an automatic payment of $49 for a gym membership on 3/24. What will he write for the balance after he records this transaction?

Problem	Topic Lookup
1–5, 9	Making Money
6–8, 10–12	Taxes and Deductions
13–22	Banking

CHAPTER 6   Budgeting

Should you drive a car, ride a bike, walk, or take a bus to work? Where should you live? What other expenses will you have, and how much of your income will they take up? Knowing how to budget and how credit works will help you be in control of your finances.

In This Chapter

You will learn about making a budget and managing the basics of credit, and you will spend some time learning about the costs of housing and car ownership.

Income		$ 1,450.00
Rent	-$700.00	
Car	-$325.00	
Utilities	-$150.00	
Misc.	-$95.00	
Monthly Net		$ 180.00

Topic List

Transportation choices, such as whether to bike, drive, or ride public transportation, are important parts of a budget. ▶

CHAPTER 6   Introduction

A budget is a plan—a plan to manage money.

A person's budget is likely to change throughout his or her lifetime. If Juan gets a raise or a new job that pays better than his old job, then he will have more money to spend or save than before. If Marcie takes out a loan for a large purchase, such as a car or a house, then she'll have less money to spend.

Buying a Home

Many people cannot afford to purchase a home outright. Therefore, they take out a loan, called a mortgage. However, banks usually require that homeowners pay a percent of the purchase price as a down payment. According to the U.S. Census Bureau, the median price of a home in April 2013 was $271,600. Even with a small down payment of only 10%, homeowners would have to come up with $27,160 to buy a home at that price. And many banks require a down payment of 20%, which would increase that down payment to $54,320.

How do people save for such a large down payment when they have several expenses, including food, clothing, transportation, rent, insurance, and utilities? They create, and follow, a realistic budget.

◄ In this chapter, you will learn about budgets and loans, and how they play a role in housing and transportation costs.

Preparing for the Chapter

Review the following skills to prepare for the concepts in the chapter: using equations to make predictions, dividing by powers of 10, and computing gross pay amounts.

Using Equations to Make Predictions

EXAMPLE 1

The equation $y = 2.3x + 49.7$ can be used to predict a student's score on an essay question on a test, where x is the number of questions the student answered correctly on the multiple choice part of the test. What does this model predict Casey's score will be on the essay question if he answered 19 questions on the multiple choice part of the test correctly?

Solution Use the equation.

$$y = 2.3x + 49.7$$
$$y = 2.3 \cdot 19 + 49.7 \qquad \text{Substitute 19 for } x.$$
$$y = 43.7 + 49.7 \qquad \text{Multiply.}$$
$$y = 93.4 \qquad \text{Add.}$$

The model predicts that Casey's score on the essay question will be 93. ∎

Dividing by Powers of 10

A shortcut for dividing by a power of 10 is to move the decimal point in the dividend to the left the same number of places as there are zeros in the divisor.

EXAMPLE 2
Find the quotient.

A $345.7 \div 100$

Solution There are 2 zeros in 100, so move the decimal point in 345.7 two places to the left. The quotient is 3.457. ∎

B $\$179{,}500 \div 1000$

Solution There are 3 zeros in 1000, so move the decimal point in $\$179{,}500$ three places to the left. The quotient is $\$179.50$. ∎

Computing Gross Pay Amounts

The number of pay periods an employee has in a year depends on how often the employee is paid.

- There are 52 weekly pay periods in a year.

- There are 26 biweekly pay periods in a year.

- There are 24 semimonthly pay periods in a year.

- There are 12 monthly pay periods in a year.

EXAMPLE 3

Mrs. Reid's gross biweekly salary is $1272. What is her gross annual income?

Solution Multiply Mrs. Reid's biweekly salary by 26.

$$\$1272 \cdot 26 = \$33,072$$

Mrs. Reid's gross annual income is $33,072. ▪

EXAMPLE 4

Patrick earns $17/h and works 40 h a week. What is his gross monthly pay for an average month?

Solution

Step 1 Multiply to find Patrick's gross weekly pay.

$$\$17 \cdot 40 = \$680$$

Step 2 Multiply by 52 to find Patrick's gross annual pay.

$$\$680 \cdot 52 = \$35,360$$

Step 3 Divide by 12 to find Patrick's gross monthly pay.

$$\$35,360 \div 12 \approx \$2946.666667$$

Patrick's gross monthly pay is $2946.67 ▪

Notice that Patrick's gross monthly pay is *not* equal to four times his gross weekly pay. The reason is that there aren't exactly 4 weeks in every month.

Problem Set

· ·

Solve.

1. The equation $y = 0.52x - 345$ can be used to estimate the number of trucks that crossed a certain bridge one day, where x is the number of cars that crossed the bridge that day. According to this model, about how many trucks crossed the bridge on a day when 2496 cars crossed it?

2. The equation $y = 1.4x + 27.6$ can be used to estimate the number of drinks a vendor sells one day, where x is the number of sandwiches she sells that day. According to this model, how many drinks does the vendor sell on a day when she sells 88 sandwiches?

3. The equation $y = 0.448x + 17.62$ can be used to predict the cost of a ticket to a theme park, where x is the number of years since 2000. What is the best prediction for the ticket cost in 2030?

4. The equation $y = 15.7x + 459$ can be used to predict the cost of renting a studio apartment in a certain housing complex, where x is the number of years since 2005. What is the best prediction for the cost of renting a studio apartment in this complex in 2025?

Find the quotient.

5. $54,900 ÷ 10

6. 18,360 ÷ 1000

7. $602.75 ÷ 100

8. 23.99 ÷ 100

9. $933,025 ÷ 1000

10. 6.247 ÷ 10

Solve.

11. Keisha's gross weekly pay is $852. What is her gross annual income?

12. Riley's gross annual income is $47,730. What is his monthly income?

13. DJ earns $16.85/h and works 35 h/wk. What is her gross annual income?

14. Marcel earns $13.40/h and works 40 h/wk. What is Marcel's average gross monthly income?

15. Alan's semimonthly salary is $1760. What is his gross annual salary?

16. Tonya's biweekly salary is $1760. What is her average gross monthly salary?

Budget Basics

Creating a budget is the first step in staying out of
financial trouble and reaching financial goals.

A **budget** helps you determine how you will spend your money over a given
time period, usually monthly. A budget contains different types of expenses.

▣ Classifying Expenses

> **DEFINITIONS**
>
> **Fixed expenses** remain the same from month to month.
> **Living expenses** change from month to month.
> **Annual expenses** occur once a year.

EXAMPLE 1
Tell whether the expense is fixed, living, or annual.

Ⓐ clothing

Solution The amount spent on clothing changes monthly. It is a
living expense. ▪

Ⓑ summer vacation trip

Solution The expense occurs once a year. It is an annual expense. ▪

Ⓒ rent

Solution A rent payment remains the same from month to month.
It is a fixed expense. ▪

To budget for an annual expense, divide the expense amount by 12.

EXAMPLE 2
**Ezra's yearly tuition bill is $1387. How much should he budget
monthly for it?**

Solution Divide $1387 by 12.

$$\$1387 \div 12 \approx \$115.58$$

Ezra should budget $115.58 each month for tuition. ▪

Finding a Percent of Income

EXAMPLE 3
Alice's monthly net pay is $1556. She budgets $650 each month for fixed expenses. What percent of her income is budgeted for fixed expenses?

Solution Divide the amount she budgets for fixed expenses by her monthly net pay.

$$\$650 \div \$1556 \approx 0.4177378$$

About 42% of Alice's income is budgeted for fixed expenses. ◼

▶ Q & A

Q If Alice budgets $125 each month for annual expenses, what percent of her income is budgeted for annual expenses?

A about 8%

Determining Whether a Budget Is Balanced

To determine whether you have a balanced budget, use a **budget sheet** to find the sum of your fixed, annual, and living expenses per month. Then subtract your total monthly expenses from your monthly net income.

DEFINITIONS

In a **balanced budget**, the income equals the expenses.
If a budget has a **surplus**, the income is greater than the expenses.
If a budget has a **deficit**, the income is less than the expenses.

Here is Marlene's monthly budget sheet.

Fixed expenses		Living expenses		Annual expenses ÷ 12	
Rent	$675	Food	$300	Tuition	$55
Car payment	$210	Electricity	$80	Car insurance	$80
Savings	$50	Phone	$75	Renter's insurance	$20
		Gas for car	$120		
		Clothes	$60		
		Car maintenance	$30		
Total Fixed	$935	Total Living	$665	Total Annual	$155
				Total Monthly Expenses	$1755

▶ THINK ABOUT IT

Marlene already divided each of her annual expenses by 12. Her annual expenses total $155 · 12 = $1860.

EXAMPLE 4
Marlene has a semimonthly net income of $854. Determine whether her budget is balanced, shows a surplus, or shows a deficit. If there is a surplus or a deficit, give the amount.

Solution
Step 1 Find Marlene's monthly net income.

$$\$854 \cdot 2 = \$1708$$

Step 2 Subtract Marlene's monthly expenses from her monthly pay.

$$\$1708 - \$1755 = -\$47$$

Marlene's budget shows a deficit of $47. ◼

Predicting Costs

You can use linear equations to predict certain expenses, such as the amount of money that parents spend on raising a child.

▶ BY THE WAY

The U.S. Department of Agriculture creates an annual report on expenditures on children by families.

EXAMPLE 5

The equation $y = 1.55x + 110{,}419$ approximates the total cost, in dollars, of raising a child in the United States from birth to 17 years, given the household's annual income, x. Estimate the total cost of raising a child in a household with an annual income of $47,000.

Solution

$$y = 1.55x + 110{,}419$$
$$y = 1.55 \cdot 47{,}000 + 110{,}419 \qquad \text{Substitute 47,000 for } x.$$
$$y = 72{,}850 + 110{,}419 \qquad \text{Multiply.}$$
$$y = 183{,}269 \qquad \text{Add.}$$

The total cost is $183,269. ∎

Problem Set

Tell whether the expense is fixed, living, or annual.

1. food

2. car payment

3. a flu shot in the fall

4. electric utility service

Determine the monthly amount.

5. **Stepping Stones** Jessie's yearly car insurance bill is $938. How much should she budget monthly for it?

$$\$938 \div \boxed{} \approx \$\boxed{}$$

Jessie should budget $\boxed{}$ each month for her car insurance bill.

6. Mr. Chapman pays $410 per year for a club membership. How much should he budget monthly for it?

7. Veronica pays an annual fee of $355 for a gym membership. How much should she budget monthly for it?

8. For his yearly vacation, Colton plans to spend $350 on train tickets, $200 on food, $150 on accommodations, and $50 on miscellaneous expenses. How much should Colton budget monthly for this vacation?

Determine the percent of income.

9. **Stepping Stones** Ruby budgets $770 each month for living expenses. What percent of her income is that amount if she nets $2120 each month?

$$\$770 \div \$\boxed{} \approx 0.363 \approx \boxed{}\%$$

10. Lizette budgets $375 each month for fixed expenses. What percent of her income is that amount if she nets $1536 each month?

11. Freddy's annual expenses total $2398. What percent of his income does he budget monthly for them if his semimonthly net income is $1707.50?

12. Karlie's monthly fixed expenses consist of a $460 rent payment and a $189 car lease payment. Her annual net income is $20,248. What percent of her income is budgeted for monthly fixed expenses?

13. The graph shows the Genaro family budget for each type of expense per month.

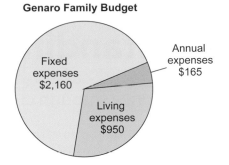

Genaro Family Budget

What percent of the Genaros' income is each expense if their annual net income is $39,600?

Use Griffin's monthly budget sheet to answer the questions.

14. How much did Griffin budget for monthly fixed expenses?

15. How much does Griffin pay annually for home insurance?

16. What percent of Griffin's budget goes toward owning a car?

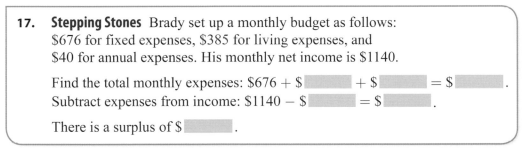

Fixed expenses		Living expenses		Annual expenses ÷ 12	
Mortgage	$1627	Food	$450	Home insurance	$45
Car payment	$323	Electricity	$110	Property taxes	$225
Medicine	$30	Phone	$90	Car insurance	$60
Savings	$75	Gas for car	$200	Life insurance	$15
		Clothes	$50		
		Car maintenance	$20		

Determine whether the monthly budget is balanced, shows a surplus, or shows a deficit. If there is a surplus or a deficit, give the amount.

17. Stepping Stones Brady set up a monthly budget as follows: $676 for fixed expenses, $385 for living expenses, and $40 for annual expenses. His monthly net income is $1140.

Find the total monthly expenses: $676 + $⬚ + $⬚ = $⬚ .
Subtract expenses from income: $1140 − $⬚ = $⬚ .

There is a surplus of $⬚ .

18. Elliot set up a monthly budget as follows: $468 for fixed expenses, $390 for living expenses, and $22 for annual expenses. His monthly net income is $845.

19. Traci budgeted $770 for fixed expenses and $530 for living expenses per month. She has no annual expenses. Her annual net income is $16,752.

The equation $y = 1.55x + 110{,}419$ approximates the total cost, in dollars, of raising a child in the United States from birth to 17 years, given the household's annual income, x.

20. Estimate the total cost of raising a child in a household with an annual income of $82,000.

21. Estimate the total cost of raising a child in a household with a *weekly* income of $1211.

22. Estimate the average *yearly* cost of raising a child in a household with an annual income of $33,000.

23. Estimate a household's annual income if the household's total cost of raising a child is $197,219.

Understanding Credit

Banks lend money through credit cards and loans.

Buying items on **credit**, as you do when you use a **credit card**, is like buying items with a temporary loan of cash with a promise to pay it back. Buying on credit is often called *charging* it.

Credit cards are convenient because you don't have to worry about carrying around enough cash for purchases. But you have to be careful about charging more than you can pay back because interest is added to unpaid balances.

▶ **BY THE WAY**

Most hotels and car rental agencies require that their patrons use a credit card.

⟩ Analyzing a Credit Card Statement

Credit card holders receive a monthly credit card statement. Here is Carrie's statement. It is divided into different sections.

Account Number 3990-4221-9908-1106		Dec. 10, 2013–Jan. 9, 2014	
Summary		**Payments, Credits & Adjustments**	
Previous Balance	$557.65	Dec 15 Payment	$30.00
Payments & Credits	−$90.00	Dec 30 Payment	$60.00
Transactions	$758.85		
Finance Charge	$5.49	**Transactions**	
New Balance	$1231.99	Dec 10 Al's Books	$53.80
		Dec 10 Gas Station 908	$44.76
Minimum Amount Due	$43.12	Dec 15 Health Club	$34.95
Due Date	Feb. 9, 2014	Dec 23 Italia Restaurant	$70.00
		Dec 23 Gas Station 908	$52.95
Total Credit Line	$3000.00	Dec 28 Computer Corner $502.39	
Total Available Credit	$1768.01		

Finance Charges			
Unpaid Balance	Periodic Rate	APR	Finance Charge
$467.65	1.175%	14.1%	$5.49

Carrie's transactions during the statement period are shown on the right side. You can see she made six charges, and the sum of those charges, $758.85, appears in the third line of the summary, which is on the left side. Her payments are listed above her transactions. Carrie made two payments, and the sum of those payments, $90, appears in the second line of the summary.

The summary also shows Carrie's previous balance of $557.65 on the first line, and her **finance charge**, or the amount of interest charged for her unpaid balance, on the fourth line. The bottom section of the statement shows details about this $5.49 charge.

▶ **THINK ABOUT IT**

Carrie's total available credit is the difference between her total credit line and her new balance.

The last five lines of the summary show Carrie's **new balance** or the total amount she owes, the minimum amount she must pay, the date by which she must pay that amount, her total credit line, and how much of that credit line is available for new purchases.

◪ Calculating Balances and Finance Charges

Finance charges are determined by the credit card's annual percentage rate, or **APR**. The credit card company determines that percent.

> ### CREDIT CARD FORMULAS
>
> The **unpaid balance** is the amount left unpaid from the previous month.
>
> $$\text{unpaid balance} = \text{previous balance} - \text{payments and credits}$$
>
> The **periodic rate** is the monthly interest rate.
>
> $$\text{periodic rate} = \frac{\text{APR}}{12}$$
>
> The **finance charge** is the product of the unpaid balance and the periodic rate.
>
> $$\text{finance charge} = \text{unpaid balance} \cdot \text{periodic rate}$$
>
> The **new balance** is the sum of the unpaid balance, the new transaction amounts, and the finance charge.
>
> $$\text{new balance} = \text{unpaid balance} + \text{new transactions} + \text{finance charge}$$

▶ **TIP**

Read credit card offers very carefully. Make sure you know a card's APR, and if, when, and why it would ever increase.

▶ **BY THE WAY**

Fees, such as late fees and over-the-limit fees, can be added to the finance charge.

Returning to Carrie's credit card statement, look at how the amounts on the statement were determined.

Step 1 Determine the unpaid balance.

$$\begin{aligned}
\text{Unpaid balance} &= \text{previous balance} - \text{payments and credits} \\
&= \$557.65 - \$90 \\
&= \$467.65
\end{aligned}$$

Step 2 Determine the periodic rate.

$$\text{periodic rate} = \frac{\text{APR}}{12} = \frac{14.1\%}{12} = 1.175\%$$

Step 3 Determine the finance charge.

$$\begin{aligned}
\text{finance charge} &= \text{unpaid balance} \cdot \text{periodic rate} \\
&= \$467.65 \cdot 0.01175 \\
&\approx \$5.49
\end{aligned}$$

Step 4 Determine the new balance.

$$\begin{aligned}
\text{new balance} &= \text{unpaid balance} + \text{new transactions} + \text{finance charge} \\
&= \$467.65 + 758.85 + \$5.49 \\
&= \$1231.99
\end{aligned}$$

Calculating the Minimum Amount Due

The method for determining the minimum amount due on a credit card is determined by the credit card company. Many companies charge the greater of either a certain dollar amount or a percent of the new balance. Some companies will add the finance charge to the percent of the new balance.

Carrie's credit card company charges either 3.5% of the new balance or $15, whichever is greater. Because 3.5% of $1231.99 is $43.12, that is Carrie's minimum payment. She must pay at least that amount by February 9 to avoid late fees and possible legal action.

▶ **Q & A**

Q Suppose Carrie makes no charges during the next statement period and pays only the minimum amount due. What would her new balance be?

A $1202.84

Calculating Loan Payments and Interest

For large purchases, when a credit card cannot be used, or if using a credit card would be too expensive, it makes sense to take out a **personal loan**.

EXAMPLE 1

Holden took out a loan to buy a used car that cost $12,400. He will pay $229.40 per month for 60 months.

A How much will Holden pay in total for the car?

Solution The total Holden will pay is the monthly payment times the number of months.

$$\$229.40 \cdot 60 = \$13,764$$

Holden will pay a total of $13,764 for the car. ▪

B How much interest will Holden pay?

Solution The amount of interest is the total paid minus the loan amount.

$$\$13,764 - \$12,400 = \$1364$$

Holden will pay $1364 in interest. ▪

EXAMPLE 2

Maddie's total payment for her student loan was $7,303.20. She paid it off after making equal monthly payments for 4 years. What was Maddie's monthly student loan payment?

Solution Divide the total payment by the number of months. There are 48 months in 4 years.

$$\$7303.20 \div 48 = \$152.15$$

Maddie's monthly payment was $152.15. ▪

Using Loan Tables

Loan officers may choose to use a **rate table** when working with customers and discussing the type of loan that best suits their needs.

A loan officer can use the rate table to find the amount of interest that will be charged for every $100 borrowed, given the APR and the number of months to pay back the loan.

	Interest per $100				
Months	**7% APR**	**9% APR**	**11% APR**	**13% APR**	**15% APR**
3	1.75	2.25	2.75	3.25	3.75
6	3.50	4.50	5.50	6.50	7.50
9	5.25	6.75	8.25	9.75	11.25
12	7.00	9.00	11.00	13.00	15.00
15	8.75	11.25	13.75	16.25	18.75
18	10.50	13.50	16.50	19.50	22.50

> **TIP**

Not everyone who applies for a loan gets one. Loan officers use several factors, including a person's salary and credit history, to determine if the person gets a loan, and at what APR.

EXAMPLE 3
Quincy will borrow $2750 at 9% APR. He will pay it back in 15 months. How much interest will he pay?

Solution

Step 1 Determine the interest per $100.

In the table, locate the intersection of the column with 9% APR and the row with 15 months. The interest is $11.25 per $100.

Step 2 Determine the number of hundreds borrowed.

$$\$2750 \div \$100 = 27.5$$

Step 3 Multiply the interest per $100 by the number of hundreds.

$$\$11.25 \cdot 27.5 = \$309.375$$

Quincy will pay $309.38 in interest. ∎

> **Q & A**

Q What will Quincy's total payment be?

A $3059.38

> **Q & A**

Q What will Quincy's monthly payment be?

A $203.96

For loan amounts that will take longer to pay back, loan officers can use a table that determines the monthly payment amount per $100 borrowed.

	Monthly Payment per $100		
Years	**11.5% APR**	**12.5% APR**	**13.5% APR**
2	4.684	4.731	4.778
3	3.298	3.345	3.394
5	2.199	2.251	2.301

EXAMPLE 4

Ms. Pena will borrow $12,000 at 11.5% APR and pay it back in 5 years.

A What will Ms. Pena's monthly payment be?

Solution

Step 1 Find the monthly payment per $100.

In the table, locate the intersection of the column with 11.5% APR and the row with 5 years. The monthly payment per $100 is $2.199.

Step 2 Determine the number of hundreds borrowed.

$$\$12,000 \div \$100 = 120$$

Step 3 Multiply the monthly payment per $100 by the number of hundreds.

$$\$2.199 \cdot 120 = \$263.88$$

Ms. Pena's monthly payment will be $263.88. ◾

B How much interest will Ms. Pena pay?

Solution

Step 1 Find her total payment. There are 60 months in 5 years.

$$\$263.88 \cdot 60 = \$15,832.80$$

Step 2 Subtract the loan amount from the total payment.

$$\$15,832.80 - \$12,000 = \$3832.80$$

Ms. Pena will pay $3832.80 in interest. ◾

▶ **TIP**

The dollar values in the table have three decimal places. Do not round these values. Save rounding until after you multiply by the appropriate number of hundreds.

Problem Set

Use Jason's credit card statement to answer the questions.

1. What is the statement period?

2. What is the minimum amount due?

3. How many transactions did Jason make?

4. How much was Jason's most expensive transaction?

5. What is the APR on this card?

6. How much greater is the amount Jason paid than the amount he charged?

7. What percent of the minimum amount due is the finance charge?

8. What percent of his previous balance did Jason pay?

Account Number 5546-0904-6389-1048		Oct. 6, 2013–Nov. 2, 2013	
Summary		**Payments, Credits & Adjustments**	
Previous Balance	$3302.81	Oct 9 Payment	$145.00
Payments & Credits	−$145.00		
Transactions	$138.95	**Transactions**	
Finance Charge	$42.08	Oct 7 Coffee Shack	$9.07
New Balance	$3338.84	Oct 16 Gas n Go	$67.76
		Oct 20 Movie Download—	
Minimum Amount Due	$108.86	Ref 39075446	$3.99
Due Date	Dec. 2, 2013	Nov 1 Gas n Go	$58.13
Total Credit Line	$10,000.00		
Total Available Credit	$6661.16		

Finance Charges			
Unpaid Balance	Periodic Rate	APR	Finance Charge
$3157.81	1.3325%	15.99%	$42.08

Solve the credit card problem.

9. Stepping Stones Cora's unpaid balance is $846.32 and her APR is 16.5%. What is her finance charge?

Divide to determine the periodic rate:
$$\frac{APR}{12} = \frac{16.5\%}{12} = \boxed{}\%.$$

Multiply the unpaid balance by the periodic rate: $846.32 \cdot \boxed{} \approx \$\boxed{}$.

10. Maya's unpaid balance is $205.16. Her APR is 14.4% and she has $82.10 in new transactions. What is her new balance?

11. Jon's statement shows a previous balance of $676.00, a payment of $250, and a new transaction of $843.18. His APR is 10.2%. What is Jon's new balance?

12. Doug's minimum payment is 1.5% of his new balance. What is his minimum payment if his new balance is $616.00?

Solve the loan problem.

13. Stepping Stones Leslie took out a loan for $2300. To pay it back, she will make 24 monthly payments of $121.85. How much will she pay in interest?

Multiply to determine the total payment: $121.85 \cdot \boxed{} = \$\boxed{}$.

Subtract the loan amount from the total payment to find the interest:
$\boxed{} - \$2300 = \$\boxed{}$.

14. Asaph took out a loan for $17,550. To pay it back, he will make 60 monthly payments of $437. How much will he pay in interest?

15. Mr. Dixon paid a total of $29,902.32 for his car. What was his monthly payment if he paid off his loan after making 72 monthly payments?

16. Jasmin made monthly payments for a year and a half to pay off her loan. If she paid a total of $1963.08, then how much were her monthly payments?

Use the interest rate table on page 143 to answer the questions.

17. Stepping Stones Myles will borrow $1300 at 13% APR. He will pay it back in 6 months. How much interest will he pay?

Use the table to determine the amount of interest per hundred: $6.50.

Divide to determine the number of hundreds borrowed: $1300 \div \$100 = \boxed{}$.

Multiply the interest per $100 by the number of hundreds: $\boxed{} \cdot \boxed{} = \$\boxed{}$.

18. Darlene will borrow $2200 at 15% APR. She will pay it back in 12 months. How much interest will she pay?

19. Lia will borrow $675 at 11% APR. She will pay it back in 9 months. What will her monthly payment be?

20. Rocco needs to borrow $820. He was approved for a loan with a 9% APR. He was going to pay it off in 18 months, but then switched it to 9 months. How does this switch change his monthly payment?

Use the monthly payment rate table on page 143 to answer the questions.

21. Stepping Stones Gabriel will borrow $7500 at 12.5% APR. What will his monthly payment be if he chooses to pay it back in 3 years?

Monthly payment per hundred: $\boxed{}$

Divide to determine the number of hundreds borrowed: $7500 \div \$100 = 75$.

Multiply the payment per $100 by the number of hundreds: $\boxed{} \cdot 75 \approx \$\boxed{}$.

22. Maribel will borrow $6250 at 13.5% APR. What will her monthly payment be if she chooses to pay it back in 2 years?

23. Eddie will borrow $9000 at 11.5% APR. How much does he save in interest by choosing to pay it off in 3 years instead of 5 years?

Housing

You can either rent a home or buy a home.

As an adult, when you live in a home that you do not own, you are expected to pay **rent**. Most landlords require that the rent be paid monthly. To help avoid a deficit in your budget, you can use a formula to determine the maximum amount you should pay in rent.

▶ **BY THE WAY**

The owner of a rental property is called the landlord, landlady, or lessor. The person renting the property is called the tenant or lessee.

▧ Determining a Maximum Rent Amount

MAXIMUM MONTHLY RENT FORMULA

One rule of thumb says that your monthly rent should be no more than 28% of your gross monthly income.

$$\text{monthly rent} \leq 0.28 \cdot \text{gross monthly income}$$

EXAMPLE 1
Jeffrey's gross annual salary is $29,365. To the nearest dollar, what is the maximum amount of rent he can afford to pay?

Solution

Step 1 Divide by 12 to find Jeffrey's gross monthly salary.

$$\$29{,}365 \div 12 \approx \$2447.08$$

Step 2 Find 28% of $2447.08.

$$0.28 \cdot \$2447.08 \approx \$685.18$$

The maximum amount of rent that Jeffrey can afford to pay is $685. ▪

▶ **THINK ABOUT IT**

The amount of rent is not the only cost of renting a home. You will usually be expected to pay for at least some of the utilities, such as gas, electricity, television service, and water.

▧ Finding the Move-In Cost

When you move in to a rental property, you must sign a **lease**. The lease is your contract. It states the rent amount, when the rent is due, and the length of time you will rent, as well as restrictions and responsibilities.

You may also be required to pay a **security deposit** and the first and last months' rent. The security deposit, less the cost of any damages you made to the property, is returned to you when you move out.

▶ **BY THE WAY**

Paying the last month's rent ahead of time gives the landlord some assurance that you won't move out without giving proper notice.

EXAMPLE 2

Jeffrey found an apartment renting for $650 per month. How much will Jeffrey pay to move in if he must pay a $300 security deposit and the first and last months' rent?

Solution Find the sum of the security deposit and 2 months' rent.

$$\$300 + 2(\$650) = \$300 + \$1300 = \$1600$$

Jeffrey will pay $1600 to move into the apartment. ■

You can take out a loan, called a **mortgage**, to buy a home. You can use a formula to ensure you do not borrow more than you should.

◢ Determining a Maximum Mortgage Amount

MAXIMUM MORTGAGE FORMULA

One common rule of thumb is that your mortgage should be no more than twice your gross annual income.

mortgage ≤ 2 • gross annual income

▶ **REMEMBER**

weekly = 52 times/year
biweekly = 26 times/year
semimonthly = 24 times/year
monthly = 12 times/year

EXAMPLE 3

Stacy's gross biweekly income is $1564. What is the maximum mortgage amount she can afford to borrow?

Solution

Step 1 Multiply by 26 to find Stacy's gross annual salary.

$$\$1564 \cdot 26 = \$40{,}664$$

Step 2 Multiply $40,664 by 2.

$$2 \cdot \$40{,}664 = \$81{,}328$$

The maximum mortgage amount Stacy can afford to borrow is $81,328. ■

◢ Computing Monthly Mortgage Payments

As with other types of loans, the amount you pay back to the bank depends on your interest rate and the length of the loan, shown here in years. You can use a table like this one to determine monthly mortgage payments.

Monthly Mortgage Payment per $1000 Borrowed				
Rate	**15-year**	**20-year**	**25-year**	**30-year**
5.00%	7.908	6.600	5.846	5.368
5.25%	8.039	6.738	5.992	5.522
5.50%	8.171	6.879	6.141	5.678
5.75%	8.304	7.021	6.291	5.836
6.00%	8.439	7.164	6.443	5.996

▶ **TIP**

You can find the complete table, with rates from 3% to 8%, on page A-17.

EXAMPLE 4

Mr. Castro is buying a home for $215,990. He is making a 15% down payment and financing the rest with a 30-year loan at 5.5% interest.

Ⓐ How much will Mr. Castro borrow?

Solution

Step 1 Find the amount of Mr. Castro's down payment, which is 15% of $215,990.

$$0.15 \cdot \$215,990 = \$32,398.50$$

Step 2 Subtract the down payment from the cost of the home.

$$\$215,990 - \$32,398.50 = \$183,591.50$$

Mr. Castro will borrow $183,591.50. ▪

Ⓑ How much will Mr. Castro's monthly mortgage payment be?

Solution

Step 1 Find the monthly payment per $1000.

In the table, locate the intersection of the column for a 30-year loan and the row with 5.5% interest. The monthly payment per $1000 is $5.678.

Step 2 Determine the number of thousands borrowed.

$$\$183,591.50 \div \$1000 = 183.5915$$

Step 3 Multiply the monthly payment per $1000 by the number of thousands.

$$\$5.678 \cdot 183.5915 = \$1042.432537$$

Mr. Castro's monthly mortgage payment will be $1042.43. ▪

Ⓒ What will Mr. Castro's total payment be for the home?

Solution

Step 1 Find the total amount repaid to the bank. Mr. Castro will make a total of 30 • 12, or 360, monthly payments.

$$\$1042.43 \cdot 360 = \$375,274.80$$

Step 2 Add the down payment to the amount repaid to the bank.

$$\$375,274.80 + \$32,398.50 = \$407,673.30$$

Mr. Castro will pay a total of $407,673.30 for the home. ▪

Ⓓ How much interest will Mr. Castro pay?

Solution

Subtract the amount borrowed from the total repaid.

$$\$375,274.80 - \$183,591.50 = \$191,683.30$$

Mr. Castro will pay $191,683.30 in interest. ▪

> ▶ **THINK ABOUT IT**
>
> You can also determine Mr. Castro's total payment for the home by adding the amount of interest, $191,683.30, to the price of the home, $215,990.

Understanding Amortization

Amortization is the process of paying off an interest-bearing loan by making equal payments. Part of Mr. Castro's monthly mortgage payment will go toward paying off interest. The remainder will go toward reducing his balance. Each month, the amount applied to interest decreases because the interest rate is being applied to a lesser balance.

The table shows how Mr. Castro's balance changes after each of his first five payments. Notice that even though he is paying $1042.43 per month, his balance decreases only by the amount applied to the principal. Over time, Mr. Castro will begin to see his balance decrease more rapidly as more and more of each payment gets applied to the principal.

| Payment | Starting balance | Monthly payment $1042.43 | | New balance |
		Applied to interest	Applied to principal	
1	$183,591.50	$841.46	$200.97	$183,390.53
2	$183,390.53	$840.54	$201.89	$183,188.64
3	$183,188.64	$839.61	$202.82	$182,985.82
4	$182,985.82	$838.69	$203.74	$182,782.08
5	$182,782.08	$837.75	$204.68	$182,577.40

▶ **BY THE WAY**

Mr. Castro's bank can supply him with the table for all 360 payments. This table is called the *amortization schedule*.

Predicting a Future Home Value

Home values fluctuate, but most homes tend to **appreciate**, or increase in value, over time.

FORMULA FOR THE VALUE OF A HOME WITH APPRECIATION

The formula gives the predicted value of a home P where
- V is the original value of the home,
- r is the rate of appreciation, and
- Y is the number of years in the future.

$$P = V(1 + r)^Y$$

EXAMPLE 5

Mr. Castro bought his home for $215,990. A local real estate agent predicts that the home will appreciate in value 3% each year.

A Predict the value of Mr. Castro's home in 30 years.

Solution

$$\begin{aligned} P &= V(1 + r)^Y \\ &= 215{,}990(1 + 0.03)^{30} \\ &= 215{,}990(1.03)^{30} \\ &= 215{,}990 \cdot 2.42726247 \\ &\approx 524{,}264.42 \end{aligned}$$

Substitute 215,990 for V, 0.03 for r, and 30 for Y.
Add inside the parentheses.
Evaluate the power.
Multiply.

The predicted value of Mr. Castro's home in 30 years is about $524,264. ∎

▶ **TIP**

Do not round until the last step. Leave the value of 1.03^{30} in the calculator, and then multiply by 215,990.

> **B** By how much is Mr. Castro's home predicted to appreciate in 30 years?
>
> **Solution** Subtract the original value of the home from the predicted future value.
>
> $$\$524{,}264 - \$215{,}990 = \$308{,}274$$
>
> Mr. Castro's home is predicted to appreciate \$308,274 in 30 years. ■

Mr. Castro will pay a total of \$407,673.30 for his home. He will pay property taxes and be responsible for all maintenance and repairs. But after 30 years his home may be worth far more than what he put into it.

Problem Set

Find the maximum amount of rent the person can afford. Round to the nearest dollar.

1. **Stepping Stones** Drew's gross semimonthly salary is \$1650.

   Find Drew's gross monthly salary:
   $\$1650 \cdot 2 = \$\underline{}$.

   Find 28% of Drew's gross monthly salary:
   $0.28 \cdot \$\underline{} = \$\underline{}$.

2. Isaac's gross annual salary is \$56,953.

3. Gavin's gross biweekly salary is \$1120.

4. Paul's gross weekly salary is \$456.

5. Alana works 40 h/wk, earning \$9.75/h.

6. **Challenge** What is the minimum *hourly wage* that Brendella must earn to afford an apartment that rents for \$820/month?

Solve the rent problem.

7. **Stepping Stones** Jeron is signing a lease for a one-bedroom apartment that rents for \$635/month. How much will Jeron pay to move in if he must pay the first and last months' rent, a \$400 security deposit, and a \$75 pet deposit?

   Find the cost of 2 months' rent:
   $2 \cdot \$\underline{} = \$1270$.

   Find the sum of the deposits:
   $\$400 + \$75 = \$\underline{}$.

   Combine the rents and the deposits:
   $\$1270 + \$\underline{} = \$\underline{}$.

8. Blake is signing a lease for a studio apartment that rents for \$425/month. How much will Blake pay to move in if he must pay the first and last months' rent and a security deposit equal to 50% of his monthly rent?

9. Mr. Lee is signing a lease for an apartment that rents for \$985/month plus \$10/month per pet. Mr. Lee has two dogs. How much will he pay to move in if he must pay the first and last months' rent, a \$600 security deposit, and a \$150 pet deposit?

10. Mrs. Doyle hired a real estate agent to help her find an apartment. The agent's fee is 75% of the monthly rent. How much will Mrs. Doyle pay to move into an apartment if the rent is \$1200/month and she must pay the first and last months' rent, her agent's fee, and a security deposit equal to 1 month's rent?

For each person, find the following amounts:
A. the maximum mortgage amount that he or she can afford to borrow
B. the maximum amount that he or she can spend on a home

11. **Stepping Stones** Hadley's gross monthly salary is $4840. She has $13,600 saved for a down payment.

    A. Find Hadley's gross annual salary and double it: $4840 • ░░░ = $58,080, and 2 • $58,080 = $ ░░░ .

    B. Add the down payment amount to the maximum mortgage amount:
    $ ░░░ + $13,600 = $ ░░░ .

12. Cristal's gross semimonthly salary is $2968.50. She has $25,000 saved for a down payment.

13. Mr. Nichols works 40 h/wk, earning $23/h. He has $14,700 saved for a down payment.

14. Dr. Garza's biweekly salary is $5932. She has $65,000 saved for a down payment.

For each person, find the following amounts:
A. the mortgage amount that he or she will borrow
B. his or her monthly mortgage payment (use the mortgage payment table on page A-17)
C. his or her total payment for the house
D. the amount of interest that he or she will pay

15. Spencer is buying a home for $152,800. He is making a 20% down payment and financing the rest with a 15-year loan at 3.75% interest.

16. Veronica is buying a home for $262,300. She is making an 8% down payment and financing the rest with a 25-year loan at 4% interest.

17. Mr. McDaniel is buying a home for $189,000. He is making a 20% down payment and financing the rest with a 30-year loan at 6.5% interest.

18. Kendall is buying a home for $119,000. She is making a 12% down payment and financing the rest with a 20-year loan at 4.5% interest.

Solve.

19. **Stepping Stones** Marissa bought her house for $196,800. A local real estate agent predicts that the house will appreciate in value 4% each year. Predict the value of Marissa's house in 20 years.

$$P = V(1 + r)^Y$$
$$= 196,800(1 + 0.04)^{20}$$
$$= 196,800(\text{░░})^{20}$$
$$\approx 196,800 \cdot \text{░░░}$$
$$\approx \text{░░░}$$

    The predicted value of Marissa's house in 20 years is about $ ░░░ .

20. Brock bought his house for $135,200. A local real estate agent predicts that the house will appreciate in value 5% each year. Predict the value of Brock's house in 25 years.

21. Mr. and Mrs. Benson bought a condominium for $92,000. A local real estate agent predicts that the condo will appreciate in value 3.5% each year. By how much is the Bensons' condominium predicted to appreciate in 30 years?

Owning a Car

Many people need a car to get around.

You may choose to take out an automobile loan to pay for a car.

▶ **BY THE WAY**

When you finance a car, the lender holds the title until it is paid off. In other words, the lender legally owns it while you are still making payments.

EXAMPLE 1
Eli is buying a car for $16,450. The dealer will give him a trade-in allowance of $3100 for his old car, and he will make a $2500 down payment. How much will Eli finance with an auto loan?

Solution
Subtract the trade-in allowance and down payment from the price.

$$\$16,450 - \$3100 - \$2500 = \$10,850$$

Eli will finance $10,850 with an auto loan. ▪

⬛ Computing Monthly Auto Payments

You can use a table like this one to determine monthly auto payments.

Monthly Car Loan Payment per $1000 Borrowed				
APR	**2-year loan**	**3-year loan**	**4-year loan**	**5-year loan**
3.0%	42.981	29.081	22.134	17.969
3.5%	43.203	29.302	22.356	18.192
4.0%	43.425	29.524	22.579	18.417

▶ **TIP**

You can find more rates in the car loan table on page A-17.

EXAMPLE 2
Mollie has decided to buy a car for $12,400. She will finance $8900 of it with a 5-year auto loan at 3.5% APR.

Ⓐ What will Mollie's monthly auto payment be?

Solution
Step 1 Find the monthly payment per $1000.

In the table, locate the intersection of the 5-year loan column and the 3.5% APR row. The monthly payment per $1000 is $18.192.

Step 2 Determine the number of thousands borrowed.

$$\$8900 \div \$1000 = 8.9$$

Step 3 Multiply the payment per $1000 by the number of thousands.

$$\$18.192 \cdot 8.9 = \$161.9088$$

Mollie's monthly auto payment will be $161.91. ▪

B How much interest will Mollie pay?

Solution

Step 1 Find the total amount repaid to the bank. Mollie will make $5 \cdot 12 = 60$ payments.

$$\$161.91 \cdot 60 = \$9714.60$$

Step 2 Subtract the amount financed from the amount repaid.

$$\$9714.60 - \$8900 = \$814.60$$

Mollie will pay $814.60 in interest. ▪

C What is Mollie's total cost for the car?

Solution

Add the amount of interest Mollie will pay to the car price.

$$\$12,400 + \$814.60 = \$13,214.60$$

Mollie's total cost for the car is $13,214.60. ▪

▶ Predicting a Future Car Value

Most cars **depreciate**, or decrease in value, over time.

FORMULA FOR THE VALUE OF A CAR WITH DEPRECIATION

The formula gives the predicted value of a car P where
- V is the original value of the car,
- r is the rate of depreciation, and
- Y is the number of years in the future.

$$P = V(1 - r)^Y$$

EXAMPLE 3

Victor is buying a new car valued at $17,630. It is expected to depreciate an average of 13% each year during the first 5 years. Predict the value of Victor's car in 5 years.

Solution

$$\begin{aligned}
P &= V(1 - r)^Y \\
&= 17,630(1 - 0.13)^5 \\
&= 17,630(0.87)^5 \\
&= 17,630 \cdot 0.4984209207 \\
&\approx 8787
\end{aligned}$$

Substitute 17,630 for V, 0.13 for r, and 5 for Y.
Subtract inside the parentheses.
Evaluate the power.
Multiply.

The predicted value of Victor's car in 5 years is about $8787. ▪

◪ Calculating Gas Mileage and Travel Costs

Operating a car involves several costs. One of those is the cost of gasoline. The Environmental Protection Agency (EPA) rates each car's gas consumption, and that rating, given in miles per gallon (mpg), is listed on the car's window sticker. The EPA rating gives the expected **gas mileage** for both city and highway driving. Actual gas mileage for each trip will vary.

MPG FORMULA

To determine a vehicle's gas mileage, divide the number of miles driven by the number of gallons used to drive that distance.

$$\text{mpg} = \frac{\text{number of miles driven}}{\text{number of gallons used}}$$

EXAMPLE 4

Reuben recorded the odometer reading of 27,835 before filling his car with gas. The next time he filled his car, the odometer reading was 28,122. He needed 11.2 gal of gas to fill his car. Find Reuben's gas mileage, rounded to the nearest mpg.

Solution

Step 1 Find the number of miles driven.

$$28{,}122 - 27{,}835 = 287$$

Step 2 Use the formula.

$$\text{mpg} = \frac{\text{number of miles driven}}{\text{number of gallons used}} = \frac{287}{11.2} = 25.625$$

Reuben's gas mileage was about 26 mpg. ▪

> ▶ **BY THE WAY**
>
> A vehicle's odometer shows the total distance the vehicle has traveled from the time it left the factory.

EXAMPLE 5

Sabrina is planning a trip in which she will drive 630 mi. Her car gets an average of 32 mpg, and the cost of gas is about $3.89/gal. Estimate the driving cost of the trip.

Solution

Step 1 Divide the total number of miles by the number of miles per gallon to find the number of gallons of gas that Sabrina will use.

$$630 \div 32 = 19.6875$$

Step 2 Multiply the number of gallons by the cost per gallon.

$$19.6875 \cdot \$3.89 = \$76.584375$$

The driving cost of Sabrina's trip will be about $77. ▪

Determining Insurance Premiums

Most U.S. states require that drivers carry auto insurance.

> **DEFINITIONS**
>
> **Liability insurance** pays for injuries to others, and damages to their property, in the event you cause an accident.
> **Collision insurance** pays for damages to your car, in the event you cause an accident.
> **Comprehensive insurance** pays for damages to your car not caused by an accident. Such causes could be fire, theft, vandalism, or weather.

Liability coverage has three parts:

- the maximum bodily injury coverage per person
- the maximum bodily injury coverage per accident
- the maximum property damage coverage per accident

For example, if you get 100/300/50 liability insurance, the insurance company will pay up to $100,000 per injured person, up to $300,000 for all injured persons, and up to $50,000 in property damage.

The cost of an insurance policy is called a **premium**. An insurance company may use tables to determine a base premium. The premium depends on the deductible (how much you have to pay before insurance pays) you choose.

The total premium is determined by multiplying the base premium by a rating factor. The bottom table factors in the age and gender of a driver, for drivers aged 17 to 29.

Oopsy-Daisy Insurance Company Annual Base Premiums

Liability Insurance		
Type	**Amount**	**Premium**
Bodily injury	25/50	$220
	50/100	$310
	100/300	$450
Property damage	25	$175
	50	$245
	100	$375

Collision and Comprehensive Premiums		
Deductible	**Coll.**	**Comp.**
$100	$215	$129
$250	$185	$102
$500	$148	$85

Rating Factor		
Age	**Male**	**Female**
17–20	3.0	1.45
21–24	2.15	1.2
25–29	1.55	1.0

> **► TIP**
>
> The higher the deductible, the lower the premium.

> **EXAMPLE 6**
> A 24-year-old male driver buys 25/50/25 liability insurance, collision insurance with a $250 deductible, and comprehensive insurance with a $100 deductible. Find his total annual premium.
>
> **Solution**
> **Step 1** Use the tables to determine each base premium.
>
> bodily injury: $220, property damage: $175, collision: $185, comprehensive: $129
>
> Find the sum: $220 + $175 + $185 + $129 = $709
>
> **Step 2** Multiply the base premium of $709 by the rating factor for a 24-year-old male.
>
> $$\$709 \cdot 2.15 = \$1524.35$$
>
> The annual premium will be $1524.35. ■

Problem Set

For each person, find the following amounts:
A. his or her monthly car payment (use the car loan payment table on page A-17)
B. the total amount of interest he or she will pay
C. his or her total payment for the car

1. Dominic is buying a car for $15,995. He will finance $13,000 of it with a 4-year auto loan at 4.3% APR.

2. Mr. and Mrs. Wallace have decided to buy a car for $21,600. They will finance $15,000 of it with a 5-year auto loan at 2.9% APR.

3. Augusto is buying a car for $16,395. He will make a $2700 down payment and finance the rest of it with a 4-year auto loan at 5.2% APR.

4. Rudy has arranged to buy a car for $10,240. He has a $3000 trade-in allowance and will make a $2000 down payment. He will finance the rest with a 3-year auto loan at 3.4% APR.

Solve. Use the car loan payment table on page A-17.

5. Alyssa is getting a 3-year auto loan for $8,995. By how much will her monthly payment decrease if she can get a loan at 2.5% APR instead of at 5.5% APR?

6. Vadim is approved for a $13,000 auto loan at 4.7% APR. How much more total interest will he pay if he takes out a 5-year loan instead of a 4-year loan?

Find the predicted value.

7. **Stepping Stones** Marta is buying a new car valued at $22,445. It is expected to depreciate an average of 12% each year during the first 6 years. Predict the value of Marta's car in 6 years.

$$P = V(1 - r)^Y$$
$$= 22{,}445(1 - 0.12)^6$$
$$= 22{,}445(\quad)^6$$
$$\approx 22{,}445 \cdot \rule{2cm}{0.4pt}$$
$$\approx \rule{2cm}{0.4pt}$$

The predicted value of Marta's car in 6 years is about $\rule{1.5cm}{0.4pt}$.

8. Stefan is buying a new car valued at $18,210. It is expected to depreciate an average of 14% each year during the first 4 years. Predict the value of Stefan's car in 4 years.

9. Lina is buying a used car valued at $6,880. It is expected to depreciate an average of 7% each year. Predict the value of Lina's car in 5 years.

10. **Challenge** Yutaka is buying a new car valued at $34,900. It is expected to depreciate an average of 15% each year during the first 5 years, and an average of 8% each year after that. Predict the value of Yutaka's car in 10 years.

Solve.

11. **Stepping Stones** Jenny drove 264 mi on 8.2 gal of gas. She paid $3.56/gal.

   A. Find her gas mileage, rounded to the nearest mpg.

   $$\text{mpg} = \frac{\text{number of miles driven}}{\text{number of gallons used}} = \frac{\boxed{}}{8.2} \approx \boxed{}$$

   Jenny's gas mileage was about ▢ mpg.

   B. Find the driving cost of the trip, rounded to the nearest dollar.

   Multiply the number of gallons by the cost per gallon:
   $8.2 \cdot \$\boxed{} \approx \$\boxed{}$.

   The driving cost of the trip was $▢.

12. Luis drove 308 mi on 21 gal of gas. Find his gas mileage, rounded to the nearest mpg.

13. Sandra recorded the odometer reading of 55,009 before filling her car with gas. The next time she filled her car, the odometer reading was 55,468. She needed 16.4 gal of gas to fill her car. Find Sandra's gas mileage, rounded to the nearest mpg.

14. Sabrina is planning a 1830-mi driving trip. Her car gets an average of 24 mpg, and the cost of gas is about $4.09/gal. Estimate the driving cost of the trip.

15. Tenisha and Marc each drove from their home in Philadelphia to their grandparents' home in Miami, a distance of 1195 mi. Tenisha's car gets 28 mpg and Marc's car gets 41 mpg. Assuming gas costs $3.70/gal, how much more did Tenisha pay for gas than Marc?

16. Mrs. Knight recorded the odometer reading of 110,765 mi before filling her car with gas. The next time she filled her car, the odometer reading was 111,277. Her dashboard display showed that the average gas mileage for the trip was 38.5 mpg. How much did it cost her to fill her tank if gas costs $3.93/gal?

Find the total annual premium. Use the tables on page 155.

17. **Stepping Stones** A 19-year-old female driver buys 50/100/50 liability insurance, and collision and comprehensive insurance, each with $500 deductibles.

   Find the base premium:
   $310 + $▢ + $148 + $▢ = $788.

   Find the total premium: $788 • ▢ = $▢.

18. A 17-year-old male driver buys 50/100/25 liability insurance, collision insurance with a $500 deductible, and comprehensive insurance with a $250 deductible.

19. A 29-year-old male driver buys 100/300/100 liability insurance and collision and comprehensive insurance, each with $250 deductibles.

20. A 21-year-old female driver buys 25/50/50 liability insurance, collision insurance with a $500 deductible, and comprehensive insurance with a $250 deductible.

21. A 26-year-old female driver buys 50/100/25 liability insurance, and collision and comprehensive insurance, each with $100 deductibles.

CHAPTER 6   Review

Choose your answer.

1. In a budget, what type of expense is entertainment?

    A. fixed

    B. living

    C. annual

2. Lance has an annual $3145 tuition bill and an annual $1262 car insurance bill. What percent of his income does he budget monthly for them if his semimonthly net income is $1493?

    A. about 12%

    B. about 18%

    C. about 25%

    D. about 34%

3. Bobby's credit card statement shows a previous balance of $1607.80, a payment of $166.87, and new transactions totaling $98.40. What is Bobby's new balance if his APR is 13.5%?

    A. $1357.63

    B. $1457.14

    C. $1555.54

    D. $1733.86

4. Alexia took out a loan for $7500. To pay it back, she will make monthly payments in the amount of $149.74 for 6 years. How much will she pay in interest?

    A. $3606.25

    B. $3281.28

    C. $1484.40

    D. $1274.96

5. Martina is signing a lease for an apartment that rents for $540/month. How much will she pay to move in if she must pay the first and last months' rent and a security deposit equal to 75% of one month's rent?

    A. $945

    B. $1080

    C. $1485

    D. $1890

6. Mr. Ortega bought his home for $242,800. It is predicted to appreciate in value by 4.5% each year. Which is the best prediction for the value of Mr. Ortega's home in 15 years?

    A. $406,690

    B. $469,887

    C. $1,092,600

    D. $1,638,900

7. Which driver got the best gas mileage?

    A. Roy drove 606 mi on 21.2 gal of gas.

    B. Kole drove 358 mi on 18.7 gal of gas.

    C. Sydney drove 341 mi on 15.8 gal of gas.

    D. Yvette drove 463 mi on 14.5 gal of gas.

8. Ramon is buying a used car valued at $9800. It is expected to depreciate an average of 5% each year. Which is the best prediction for the value of Ramon's car in 8 years?

    A. $3920

    B. $4219

    C. $6502

    D. $7448

Solve.

9. The equation $y = 1.55x + 110{,}419$ approximates the total cost, in dollars, of raising a child in the United States from birth to 17 years, given the household's annual income, x. Predict the total cost of raising a child in a household with an annual income of $27,000.

10. Keisha set up a monthly budget as follows: $740 for fixed expenses, $355 for living expenses, and $65 for annual expenses. Her monthly net income is $1145. Determine whether her monthly budget is balanced, shows a surplus, or shows a deficit. If there is a surplus or deficit, give the amount.

11. Mr. Wheeler's minimum credit card payment is the greater of either 2% of the new balance or $20. What is his minimum payment if his new balance is $1164.87?

12. Jenna will borrow $2000 at 13% APR. She will pay it back over 9 months. Use the Interest per $100 rate table on page 143 to answer the questions.

    A. How much interest will she pay?

    B. What will her total payment be?

    C. What will her monthly payment be?

13. Kurt will borrow $3600 at 12.5% APR. He will pay it back in 2 years. Use the Monthly Payment per $100 rate table on page 143 to answer the questions.

    A. What will his monthly payment be?

    B. What will his total payment be?

    C. How much interest will he pay?

14. Linda's gross annual salary is $33,696. What is the maximum amount she can afford in rent?

15. Mr. Lee's gross weekly salary is $1204. What is the maximum amount he can spend on a home if he has $21,000 saved for a down payment?

16. Rickey is buying a home for $178,300. He is making a 20% down payment and financing the rest with a 25-year loan at 6.25% interest. Use the mortgage payment table on page A-17 to answer the questions.

    A. How much will he borrow?

    B. What will his monthly mortgage payment be?

    C. What will his total payment for the home be?

    D. How much interest will he pay?

17. Ms. Estrada is buying a car for $16,230. She will finance $12,000 of it with a 5-year loan at 4.8% APR. Use the car loan payment table on page A-17 to answer the questions.

    A. What will her monthly auto payment be?

    B. How much interest will she pay?

    C. What will her total payment for the car be?

18. An 18-year-old male driver buys 25/50/25 liability insurance, and collision and comprehensive insurance, each with $100 deductibles. Use the tables on page 155 to find his annual premium.

Problem	Topic Lookup	Problem	Topic Lookup
1, 2, 9, 10	Budget Basics	5, 6, 14–16	Housing
3, 4, 11–13	Understanding Credit	7, 8, 17,18	Owning a Car

CHAPTER 7   Saving Money

There are many ways to invest money. Stocks, bonds, and insurance can all be important parts of planning for your financial future. When you understand investment options, you will be able to make wise investments and watch your money grow.

In This Chapter

You will learn how you can use mathematics to help you make good, long-term financial plans.

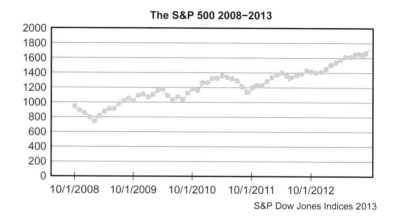

The S&P 500 2008–2013

S&P Dow Jones Indices 2013

Topic List

► Chapter 7 Introduction

► Interest

► Insurance

► Investments

► Chapter 7 Review

At stock exchanges, traders try to make money for investors.

CHAPTER 7   Introduction

Your budget should include a savings plan. That way you'll have money for short-term needs and goals, as well as for retirement.

If you hear that people live "from paycheck to paycheck," it means that their money from one paycheck runs out just before their next paycheck arrives. Because they do not put money into savings, they are unable to pay for unexpected emergencies. And if they lose their job, they have no money until they are able to find another one.

People living paycheck to paycheck can gain the ability to save by reducing their expenses or increasing their income. Ways of reducing expenses include moving to a less expensive home and spending less money on clothes and entertainment. Ways of increasing income include working more hours and finding a better-paying job.

Retirement

It can be hard to save when you are just starting out. But people should start saving as much money as they can, as soon as they can. Interest on retirement accounts is compounded. Therefore, there is a big difference in the amount of money people will have in their retirement if they start saving in their 20s instead of in their 30s or 40s.

◀ In this chapter, you will learn ways to protect your money and make it grow.

Preparing for the Chapter

Review the following skills to prepare for the concepts in the chapter: estimating values on a graph, simplifying exponential expressions, and solving multiplication equations.

Estimating Values on a Graph

EXAMPLE 1
Use the graph to answer the questions.

A What is y when $x = 30$?

Solution Find 30 on the x-axis and move up until you reach the graph. Look left to the y-axis to see that y is between 400 and 450, but slightly closer to 400.

When x is 30, $y \approx 420$. ∎

B What is x when $y = 250$?

Solution Find 250 on the y-axis and move right until you reach the graph. Look down to the x-axis to see that x is about a third of the way between 10 and 15.

When y is 250, $x \approx 11.5$. ∎

Simplifying Exponential Expressions

Follow the order of operations when simplifying an expression.

ORDER OF OPERATIONS

Step 1 Perform operations within grouping symbols.
Step 2 Evaluate powers.
Step 3 Multiply and divide from left to right.
Step 4 Add and subtract from left to right.

EXAMPLE 2
Simplify $45(3 + 0.05)^7$.

Solution

$$45(3 + 0.05)^7 = 45(3.05)^7 \qquad \text{Add inside the parentheses.}$$
$$\approx 45(2455.267841) \qquad \text{Raise 3.05 to the seventh power.}$$
$$\approx 110{,}487.0528 \qquad \text{Multiply.} \ ∎$$

Solving Multiplication Equations

To solve a multiplication equation, use the inverse operation, which is division.

EXAMPLE 3
Solve. Round to the nearest hundredth.

A $156.04 = 21.5x$

Solution The variable is being multiplied by 21.5, so divide each side by 21.5.

$$\frac{156.04}{21.5} = \frac{21.5x}{21.5}$$
$$7.257674419 \approx x$$

The value of x is about 7.26. ∎

B $31,000x = 1095$

Solution The variable is being multiplied by 31,000, so divide each side by 31,000.

$$\frac{31,000x}{31,000} = \frac{1095}{31,000}$$
$$x \approx 0.0353225806$$

The value of x is about 0.04. ∎

Problem Set

Use the graph to answer the questions.

1. What is y when $x = 10$?

2. What is y when $x = 40$?

3. What is y when $x = 75$?

4. What is x when $y = 50$?

5. What is x when $y = 100$?

6. What is x when $y = 140$?

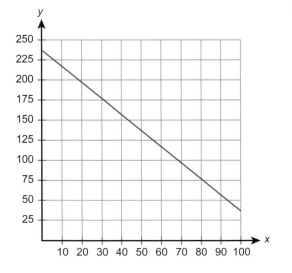

7. What is h when $t - 1$?

8. What is h when $t = 10$?

9. What is h when $t = 6$?

10. What is t when $h = 18$?

11. What is t when $h = 15$?

12. What is t when $h = 10$? Be careful. There could be more than one answer.

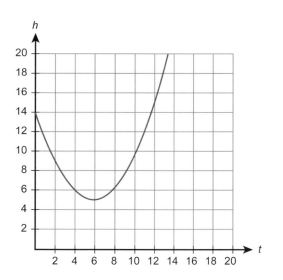

Simplify.

13. $(2.7 + 1.35)^4$

14. $600(1 + 0.03)^{12}$

15. $95.5(2 - 1.95)^4$

16. $7(4.1 + 0.03)^{(5 \cdot 2)}$

17. $412.75\left(5 + \dfrac{21}{8}\right)^8$

18. $350\left(1 + \dfrac{0.18}{4}\right)^{(4 \cdot 3)}$

Solve. Round to the nearest hundredth.

19. $6.74x = 94.9$

20. $5.3g = 4$

21. $45 = 0.02m$

22. $27.8 = 1.55y$

23. $3.6b = 18.905$

24. $24.1 = 104.9w$

Interest

You can make your money work for you by depositing it into an account that earns interest.

Simple interest is interest that is calculated only on the **principal**.

⤳ Using the Simple Interest Formula

> **SIMPLE INTEREST FORMULA**
>
> To find the interest I, where P is the principal, r is the annual interest rate, and t is the time in years, use the formula
>
> $$I = Prt.$$

> **EXAMPLE 1**
> **Elijah deposited $800 into a savings account that pays a simple annual interest rate of 1.75%.**
>
> **A** How much interest will he earn after 3 years?
>
> **Solution** Substitute 800 for P, 0.0175 for r, and 3 for t.
>
> $$\begin{aligned} I &= Prt \\ &= 800 \cdot 0.0175 \cdot 3 \\ &= 42 \end{aligned}$$
>
> Elijah will earn $42 in interest. ◾
>
> **B** If he makes no other deposits or withdrawals, what will the total amount be in his account after 3 years?
>
> **Solution** Add the interest earned to the principal.
>
> $$\$800 + \$42 = \$842$$
>
> Elijah will have $842 in his account. ◾

EXAMPLE 2

Marley deposited money into a savings account that pays a simple annual interest rate of 2.1%. How much did she deposit if she earned $25.83 after 9 months?

Solution Substitute 25.83 for I, 0.021 for r, and 0.75 for t.

$$I = Prt$$
$$25.83 = P \cdot 0.021 \cdot 0.75$$
$$25.83 = P \cdot 0.01575 \qquad \text{Simplify the right side.}$$
$$1640 = P \qquad \text{Divide both sides by 0.01575.}$$

Marley deposited $1640. ∎

▶ **TIP**

Because r is an annual rate, t must be given as a number of years. Nine months equals $\frac{9}{12}$, or $\frac{3}{4}$ of a year, and $\frac{3}{4} = 0.75$.

▶ Using the Compound Interest Formula

When you earn **compound interest**, new interest is based on your principal *plus* any interest already earned. Therefore, you earn more money with compound interest than with simple interest.

COMPOUND INTEREST FORMULA

To find the total amount A in an account earning compound interest, where P is the principal, r is the annual interest rate, t is the time in years, and n is the number of compounding intervals per year, use the formula

$$A = P\left(1 + \frac{r}{n}\right)^{nt}.$$

EXAMPLE 3

Mrs. Vargas deposited $3620 into a savings account for which interest is compounded quarterly at a rate of 3.1%.

A Assuming she makes no other deposits or withdrawals, how much will be in her account after 5 years?

Solution Substitute 3620 for P, 0.031 for r, 4 for n, and 5 for t.

$$A = P\left(1 + \frac{r}{n}\right)^{nt}$$
$$= 3620\left(1 + \frac{0.031}{4}\right)^{4 \cdot 5}$$
$$= 3620\left(1 + 0.00775\right)^{4 \cdot 5} \qquad \text{Simplify inside the parentheses.}$$
$$= 3620\left(1.00775\right)^{20} \qquad \text{Simplify.}$$
$$\approx 3620 \cdot 1.166960448 \qquad \text{Evaluate the power.}$$
$$\approx 4224.39682 \qquad \text{Multiply.}$$

Mrs. Vargas will have $4224.40 in her account. ∎

B How much interest will she earn after 5 years?

Solution Subtract the principal from the total amount.

$$\$4224.40 - \$3620 = \$604.40$$

Mrs. Vargas will earn $604.40 in interest. ∎

▶ **TIP**

semiannually = 2 times/year
quarterly = 4 times/year
monthly = 12 times/year
weekly = 52 times/year
daily = 365 times/year

▶ **Q & A**

Q How much interest would Mrs. Vargas have earned if her account paid an annual simple interest rate of 3.1% instead?

A $561.10

EXAMPLE 4

Phoenix deposited money into an account in which interest is compounded weekly at a rate of 2.82%. How much did he deposit if the total amount in his account after 3 years was $1523.56, and he made no other deposits or withdrawals?

Solution Substitute 1523.56 for A, 0.0282 for r, 52 for n, and 3 for t.

$$A = P\left(1 + \frac{r}{n}\right)^{nt}$$

$$1523.56 = P\left(1 + \frac{0.0282}{52}\right)^{52 \cdot 3}$$

$1523.56 \approx P\,(1.000542308)^{52 \cdot 3}$ Simplify within the parentheses.

$1523.56 \approx P\,(1.000542308)^{156}$ Simplify.

$1523.56 \approx P \cdot 1.088256712$ Evaluate the power.

$1400.000555 \approx P$ Divide to isolate P.

Phoenix deposited about $1400. ∎

⬛ Analyzing Graphs of Interest Earned

Simple interest grows linearly. Compound interest grows exponentially. Look at the graph. The solid red line shows the total amount in an account that pays simple interest. The principal is $1000 and the interest rate is 3.7%. The dashed blue curve shows the total amount in another account that has the same principal and interest rate. The interest in that account, however, is compounded daily.

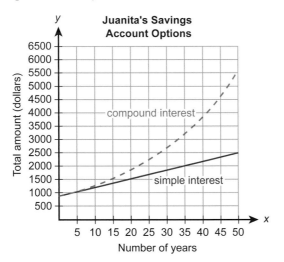

Juanita's Savings Account Options

▶ **THINK ABOUT IT**

The benefit of compounding increases as the number of years increases.

EXAMPLE 5

After 35 years, how much more would Juanita have earned in the account that earns compound interest compared with the account that earns simple interest? Use the graph to solve.

Solution

Step 1 Estimate the amount of compound interest.

Look at the graph. The total amount in the account earning compound interest after 35 years would be about $3300. Because the principal was $1000, the amount of interest would be about $2300.

Step 2 Estimate the amount of simple interest earned.

Look at the graph. The total amount in the account earning simple interest after 35 years would be about $2000. Because the principal is $1000, the amount of interest would be about $1000.

Step 3 Subtract the interest amounts.

$$\$2300 - \$1000 = \$1300$$

After 35 years, Juanita would have earned about $1300 more in the account that earns compound interest than in the account that earns simple interest. ■

Problem Set

Solve the simple interest problem.

1. **Stepping Stones** Naomi deposited $1625 into a savings account that pays a simple annual interest rate of 1.44%. How much interest will she earn after 4 years?

   $$I = Prt$$
   $$= 1625 \cdot \boxed{} \cdot 4$$
   $$= \boxed{}$$

   Naomi will earn $\boxed{}$ in interest after 4 years.

2. Corey deposited $700 into a savings account that pays a simple annual interest rate of 2.9%. How much interest will he earn after 3 months?

3. Tori deposited $3100 into a savings account that pays a simple annual interest rate of 3.38%. How much interest will she earn after 18 months?

4. Jasper deposited $1822 into a savings account that pays a simple annual interest rate of 1.95%. If he makes no other deposits or withdrawals, what will the total amount be in his account after 7 years?

5. Denver deposited $315 into a savings account that pays a simple annual interest rate of 2.45%. If he makes no other deposits or withdrawals, what will the total amount be in his account after 6 months?

6. Andrew and Jenna each deposited $500 into savings accounts that earn simple interest. Andrew's account has an annual rate of 1.875%, and Jenna's has an annual rate of 3.05%. If neither one makes any other deposits or withdrawals, how much more money will Jenna have in her account after 10 years?

Find the principal.

7. **Stepping Stones** Sherelle deposited money into a savings account that pays a simple annual interest rate of 3.72%. How much did she deposit if she earned $31.62 after 2 years?

$$I = Prt$$
$$31.62 = P \cdot 0.0372 \cdot \blacksquare$$
$$31.62 = P \cdot \blacksquare$$
$$\blacksquare = P$$

Sherelle deposited $ ▮ .

8. Ms. Juarez deposited money into a savings account that pays a simple annual interest rate of 1.6%. How much did she deposit if she earned $38.88 after 3 years?

9. Tobias deposited money into a savings account that pays a simple annual interest rate of 2.2%. How much did he deposit if he earned $7.70 after 21 months?

The first four rows of an amortization table for a loan are shown. Each row shows how much of each monthly payment of $357.90 is applied to the principal of $19,000. Complete the table by using a simple annual interest rate of 8.9%. The calculations for the first month are shown in parentheses.

	Payment	Starting balance	Monthly payment $357.90		New balance
			Applied to interest	**Applied to principal**	
	1	$19,000	$140.92 ($19,000 • 0.089 • $\frac{1}{12}$)	$216.98 ($357.90 − $140.92)	$18,783.02 ($19,000 − $216.98)
10.	2	$18,783.02			
11.	3				
12.	4				

Solve the compound interest problem.

13. **Stepping Stones** Clark deposited $1500 into a savings account in which interest is compounded monthly at a rate of 2.4%. Assuming he makes no other deposits or withdrawals, how much will be in his account after 3 years?

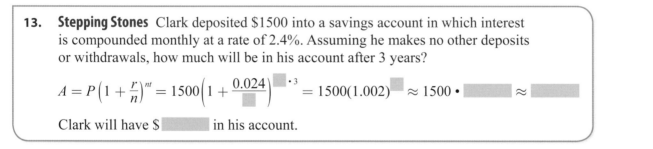

$$A = P\left(1 + \frac{r}{n}\right)^{nt} = 1500\left(1 + \frac{0.024}{\blacksquare}\right)^{\blacksquare \cdot 3} = 1500(1.002)^{\blacksquare} \approx 1500 \cdot \blacksquare \approx \blacksquare$$

Clark will have $ ▮ in his account.

14. Nigel deposited $7000 into a savings account in which interest is compounded semiannually at a rate of 2.38%. Assuming he makes no other deposits or withdrawals, how much will be in his account after 14 years?

15. Sage deposited $2260 into a savings account in which interest is compounded daily at a rate of 3.6%. Assuming she makes no other deposits or withdrawals, how much will be in her account after $2\frac{1}{2}$ years?

16. Willow deposited $950 into a savings account in which interest is compounded weekly at a rate of 2.93%. How much interest will she earn after 6 years?

17. Mr. Downs deposited $5000 into a savings account in which interest is compounded quarterly at a rate of 3.15%. How much interest will he earn after 1 year?

18. Payton deposited $675 into an account in which interest is compounded monthly at a rate of 2.7%. How much more interest will he earn during the second year than the first year?

Find the principal.

19. **Stepping Stones** Lizette deposited money into an account in which interest is compounded quarterly at a rate of 3.2%. How much did she deposit if the total amount in her account after 5 years was $4837.65, and she made no other deposits or withdrawals?

$$A = P\left(1 + \frac{r}{n}\right)^{nt}$$

$$4837.65 = P\left(1 + \frac{\boxed{}}{4}\right)^{4 \cdot \boxed{}}$$

$$4837.65 = P \cdot \boxed{}^{20}$$

$$4837.65 = P \cdot \boxed{}$$

$$\boxed{} = P$$

Lizette deposited $\boxed{}$.

20. Gianni deposited money into an account in which interest is compounded monthly at a rate of 4.5%. How much did he deposit if the total amount in his account after 9 months was $1820.30, and he made no other deposits or withdrawals?

21. Karley deposited money into an account in which interest is compounded daily at a rate of 2.13%. How much did she deposit if the total amount in her account after 3 years was $1002.02, and she made no other deposits or withdrawals?

The graph shows the total amounts in two accounts with the same principal and annual interest rate. Use the graph to solve.

22. What is the principal?

23. How much simple interest is earned after 20 years?

24. How much compound interest is earned after 25 years?

25. What is the difference in the amounts of interest earned after 45 years?

26. **Challenge** What is the annual interest rate?

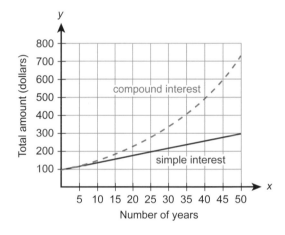

The graph shows the total amounts in two accounts with the same principal of $500. Both earn interest that is compounded semiannually. Use the graph to solve.

27. Which account has the greater interest rate? How do you know?

28. How much interest does Account A earn after 20 years?

29. How long does it take for the total amount in Account B to double its principal?

30. What is the difference in the amounts of interest earned after 45 years?

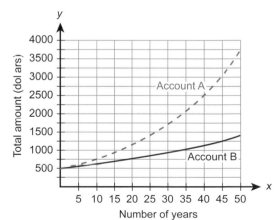

Insurance

Insurance can provide financial peace of mind.

Many employers offer **health insurance**, a benefit that covers medical expenses. The cost of insurance is called a **premium**. Most employers pay for part of the premium, and employees pay the rest of the premium.

▶ **BY THE WAY**

Some companies offer health insurance only to full-time employees. And those that offer health insurance to part-time employees may pay a smaller percentage of the premium.

▶ Calculating a Health Insurance Premium

EXAMPLE 1
The total premium for Anita's health insurance is $7810. Anita's employer pays 75% of the premium and deducts the remainder from her paycheck. Anita is paid semimonthly.

Ⓐ How much does Anita pay annually for health insurance?

Solution Anita's employer pays 75% of the annual premium, so Anita pays 25% of the premium. Find 25% of $7810.

$$0.25 \cdot \$7810 = \$1952.50$$

Anita pays $1952.50 annually for health insurance. ∎

Ⓑ How much is deducted from each of her paychecks for health insurance?

Solution Divide the amount Anita pays annually by 24.

$$\$1952.50 \div 24 \approx \$81.35$$

For health insurance, $81.35 is deducted from each of Anita's paychecks. ∎

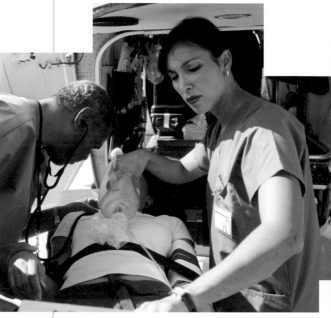

▶ Calculating Your Share of a Medical Bill

You may have to first pay a deductible before the insurance company makes any payments. Your policy will state your deductibles, **co-payments**, and coverage amounts or percentages.

▶ **BY THE WAY**

Co-payments, or co-pays, for office visits tend to range from $0 to $35.

EXAMPLE 2

The health insurance company that insures Celeste pays 80% of the cost of an MRI after she pays a $50 deductible. How much will Celeste pay for an MRI that costs $890?

Solution

Step 1 Subtract the deductible from the cost of the MRI.

$$\$890 - \$50 = \$840$$

Step 2 The insurance company pays 80% of the cost after the deductible, so Celeste pays 20% of it. Find 20% of $840.

$$0.20 \cdot \$840 = \$168$$

Step 3 Add Celeste's portion after the deductible to the deductible.

$$\$50 + \$168 = \$218$$

Celeste will pay $218 for the MRI. ∎

EXAMPLE 3

The health insurance company that insures Janet will pay 80% of the cost after Janet pays a $25 co-pay. The cost of the visit to the doctor is $195. How much does Janet pay?

Solution

Step 1 The insurance company pays for 80% of the cost of the visit, so Janet pays 20% of the visit. Find 20% of $195.

$$0.20 \cdot \$195 = \$39$$

Step 2 Janet pays a co-pay of $25. Add the co-pay to the cost of the visit.

$$\$25 + \$39 = \$64$$

Janet pays $64 dollars. ∎

⮞ Calculating a Life Insurance Premium

Life insurance provides money to another person, called a **beneficiary**, if the insured person, the policyholder, dies.

Term life insurance provides protection for a given time period. For example, a policy may cover the next 10 years or 20 years. Term life insurance is the most common, and most affordable, type of life insurance.

An insurance agent may use a table like this one to find an annual premium.

Fly-by-Night Life Insurance Company			
Age at issue		Annual premium per $1000 of term	
Male	Female	10-year	20-year
20–24	23–27	$2.50	$3.80
25–29	28–32	$3.25	$5.84
30–34	33–37	$3.82	$7.93
35–39	38–42	$4.55	$10.33
40–44	43–47	$5.78	$13.68
45–49	48–52	$7.53	$17.56

EXAMPLE 4

Stefan, a 36-year-old male, bought a $150,000, 10-year life insurance policy from Fly-by-Night Life Insurance through his employer. Stefan is paid weekly.

Ⓐ What is Stefan's annual premium?

Solution

Step 1 Find the annual premium per $1000.

In the table, locate the row for males aged 35–39. Look to the right under the 10-year column. The annual premium per $1000 is $4.55.

Step 2 Determine the number of thousands purchased.

$$\$150,000 \div \$1000 = 150$$

Step 3 Multiply the premium per $1000 by the number of thousands.

$$\$4.55 \cdot 150 = \$682.50$$

Stefan's annual premium is $682.50 ∎

▶ **BY THE WAY**

Women in many countries, including the United States, tend to live longer than men.

▶ **Q & A**

Q What would the annual premium be for a 36-year-old female buying the same policy as Stefan did?

A $573

B How much is deducted from each of his paychecks for life insurance?

Solution Divide Stefan's annual premium by 52.

$$\$682.50 \div 52 \approx \$13.13$$

For life insurance, $13.13 is deducted from each of Stefan's paychecks. ∎

Problem Set

For each person, find the following amounts:
A. how much he or she pays annually for health insurance
B. how much is deducted from his or her paycheck for health insurance

1. **Stepping Stones** The total annual premium for health insurance for Hugo is $7800. His employer pays 90% of the premium and deducts the remainder from his paycheck. Hugo is paid biweekly.

   A. The employer pays 90% of the premium, so Hugo pays ▓% of the premium. Find 10% of $7800: ▓ • $7800 = $▓.

   B. Divide the amount Hugo pays annually by 26.

   $$\$▓ \div 26 = \$▓$$

2. The total annual premium for health insurance for Qing is $9115. Her employer pays 65% of the premium and deducts the remainder from her paycheck. Qing is paid weekly.

3. The total annual premium for health insurance for Trenton is $8512. His employer pays 85% of the premium and deducts the remainder from his paycheck. Trenton is paid semimonthly.

4. The total annual premium for health insurance for Ms. Everett is $12,304. Her employer pays 70% of the premium and deducts the remainder from her paycheck. Ms. Everett is paid monthly.

Find the person's share of his or her medical bill.

5. **Stepping Stones** The health insurance company that insures Zelda pays 85% of an emergency room visit after Zelda pays a $100 deductible. The cost of her emergency room visit is $4089. How much will Zelda pay for the visit?

   Subtract the deductible from the cost: $4089 − $▓ = $3989.

   The insurance company pays ▓% of the cost after the deductible, so Zelda pays 15% of the cost.

   Find ▓% of $3989: 0.15 • $3989 = $▓.

   Add Zelda's portion after the deductible to the deductible: $100 + $▓ = $▓.

6. The health insurance company that insures Peter pays 80% of nutritional counseling after Peter pays a $50 deductible. The cost of his counseling was $1060. How much did Peter pay for his nutritional counseling?

7. Kenny must pay a co-pay of $20 to visit the doctor. Then the insurance company pays 90% of the cost of the visit. How much did Kenny pay to see the doctor if the cost of the visit was $379?

8. Mattie must pay a $15 co-pay for each of her visits to a chiropractor. Then the insurance company pays 60% of the cost of the visit. After her accident, she made 12 visits to the chiropractor, each costing $305. How much, in total, did Mattie pay for her chiropractor visits?

Solve the health insurance problem.

9. Lindsey and Carter each went to a doctor for a vaccine. Lindsey had no co-pay, and her insurance company pays 75% of vaccine costs. Carter paid a $10 co-pay, and his insurance company pays 80% of vaccine costs. Who paid more for the vaccine, and by how much, if the cost of the vaccine is $132?

10. When Mrs. Flynn had her baby, the insurance company paid 95% of prenatal visit costs and 100% of the delivery cost. Her prenatal visits cost a total of $5302, and the cost of the delivery was $3698. How much did the insurance company pay?

11. A health insurance company pays 90% of the cost of prescription medicines for Dale. If Dale paid $14.28 for his prescription medicine, then how much would someone without insurance pay for the same medicine?

12. **Challenge** Camille's employer pays 95% of her health insurance premium. She is single and has $11.25 deducted from her weekly paycheck for health insurance. If she marries and adds insurance coverage for her husband on her policy, her annual premium will increase by 70%. How much will Camille then pay annually for health insurance?

For each person, find the following amounts:
A. his or her annual life insurance premium (Use the Fly-by-Night Life Insurance Company table on page 173.)
B. how much is deducted from his or her paycheck for life insurance

13. **Stepping Stones** Vanessa, a 29-year-old female, bought a $125,000, 20-year life insurance policy through her employer. Vanessa is paid semimonthly.

    A. Use the table. The annual premium per $1000 is $▮.

    Determine the number of thousands purchased:
    $125,000 ÷ $1000 = ▮.

    Multiply the annual premium per $1000 by the number of thousands:
    $▮ • 125 = $▮.

    B. Divide Vanessa's annual premium by 24: $▮ ÷ 24 ≈ $▮.

    For life insurance, $▮ is deducted from each of Vanessa's paychecks.

14. Henry, a 41-year-old male, bought a $100,000, 10-year life insurance policy through his employer. Henry is paid biweekly.

15. Antonio, a 26-year-old male, bought a $200,000, 20-year life insurance policy through his employer. Antonio is paid monthly.

16. Karen, a 52-year-old female, bought a $75,000, 20-year life insurance policy through her employer. Karen is paid weekly.

17. Rosemary, a 33-year-old female, bought a $180,000, 10-year life insurance policy through her employer. Rosemary is paid semimonthly.

Solve the life insurance problem. Use the Fly-by-Night Life Insurance Company table on page 173.

18. Nikos, a 39-year-old male, bought a $300,000, 20-year life insurance policy. If he keeps it for all 20 years, what is the total amount he will pay for it?

19. Annually, how much more would a 41-year-old male pay for a $130,000, 20-year life insurance policy than a 41-year-old female?

20. Annually, how much more would a 47-year-old male pay for a $275,000, 20-year life insurance policy than for a $275,000, 10-year life insurance policy?

Investments

The greater the risk, the greater the possible reward.

Different types of investments have different risk factors and different growth rates, called **rates of return**.

▶ **THINK ABOUT IT**

Homes are investments because homes tend to appreciate in value.

DEFINITIONS

Three common types of investments are stocks, bonds, and mutual funds.

- A **stock** is a paper that represents a fraction of ownership, or **share**, in a company.
- A **bond** is a loan to a company or a government (called the issuer) for a given time period. Investors buy bonds for a given value, called the *face value*. The bond issuer pays back the face value when the loan becomes due, or matures. The bond issuer also pays interest semiannually on the bond. A bond's annual interest rate is called its **coupon rate**.
- A **mutual fund** is a collection of financial securities (often a mix of stocks, bonds, and/or real estate) managed by a firm for its investors.

⇒ Estimating Time and Growth on Investments

There is a rule to estimate how long it will take invested money to double.

THE RULE OF 72

By the **Rule of 72**, the approximate number of years it takes for an investment to double in value is 72 divided by the expected annual rate of return, written as a percent.

$$\text{number of years to double} \approx \frac{72}{\text{rate of return (\%)}}$$

EXAMPLE 1

The value of an investment grew from $5000 to $10,000 in 10 years. What was the annual rate of return?

Solution The investment doubled in value, so use the Rule of 72.

$$10 \approx \frac{72}{r} \qquad \text{Substitute the value into the formula.}$$
$$10r \approx 72 \qquad \text{Cross multiply.}$$
$$r \approx 7.2 \qquad \text{Divide both sides by 10.}$$

The annual rate of return was about 7.2%. ■

▶ **TIP**

When using this rule, do *not* convert the percent to a decimal.

➡ Buying and Selling Stock

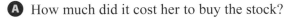

EXAMPLE 2

Kathie bought 300 shares of a company's stock for $21.86/share. She pays a broker a 1% commission to buy and sell stock.

Ⓐ How much did it cost her to buy the stock?

Solution

Step 1 Multiply the number of shares by the cost per share.

$$300 \cdot \$21.86 = \$6558$$

Step 2 Determine the broker's commission by finding 1% of $6558.

$$0.01 \cdot \$6558 = \$65.58$$

Step 3 Add the commission to the cost of the shares.

$$\$6558 + \$65.58 = \$6623.58$$

It cost Kathie $6623.58 to buy the stock. ■

Ⓑ After one year, Kathie sold all her shares of the stock, when they were worth $26.09/share. What was her net gain or loss?

Solution

Step 1 Multiply the number of shares by the selling price per share.

$$300 \cdot \$26.09 = \$7827$$

Step 2 Determine the broker's commission by finding 1% of $7827.

$$0.01 \cdot \$7827 = \$78.27$$

Step 3 Subtract the commission from the selling price of the shares.

$$\$7827 - \$78.27 = \$7748.73$$

Step 4 Subtract the amount Kathie paid for the shares from the amount she received from selling the shares.

$$\$7748.73 - \$6623.58 = \$1125.15$$

Kathie's net gain was $1125.15. ■

Ⓒ What was Kathie's rate of return?

Solution Divide Kathie's net gain by her total cost.

$$\$1125.15 \div \$6623.58 \approx 0.17$$

Kathie's rate of return was about 17%. ■

> **▶ TIP**
>
> Stock values fluctuate. There is no guarantee you will make money buying and selling stocks.

Determining the Interest on a Bond

► BY THE WAY

Bonds are traded like stocks and can be purchased for more or less than their face value.

EXAMPLE 3
Jonah bought a bond with a face value of $2000 and a coupon rate of 8%. The bond will mature in 10 years. What is the total amount of interest he will receive?

Solution Use the formula $I = Prt$.

$$I = 2000 \cdot 0.08 \cdot 10$$
$$= 1600$$

Jonah will receive a total of $1600 in interest. ■

Because the interest on a bond is paid semiannually, Jonah will receive payments of $1600 \div 20 = $80, every 6 months for 10 years.

Calculating Retirement Contributions

Social Security payments will cover only some of your retirement expenses. You should have a retirement plan in place to ensure you can retire comfortably. Most retirement plans are mutual funds that are designed to decrease in risk as you get closer to your retirement age.

DEFINITIONS

A **401(k)** is a retirement account in which your employer deducts a percent of your paycheck to contribute to the account. Your employer may match that amount, up to a certain percent.
A **403(b)** works the same as a 401(k), but it is for employees of tax-exempt organizations, such as public schools.
An **individual retirement account**, or **IRA**, is a retirement account that you set up with your bank yourself. You decide how often, and how much, to contribute.

► BY THE WAY

In 2013, the yearly maximum amount that someone younger than 50 could contribute to a 401(k) or 403(b) was $17,500. For an IRA, the amount was $5500.

EXAMPLE 4
Mena's gross annual income is $51,207. She is paid biweekly and has 4% deducted from each paycheck for her 401(k). Her employer matches her deduction, up to 4%.

A How much does Mena have deducted from each paycheck for her 401(k)?

Solution
Step 1 Determine Mena's gross paycheck amount.

$$\$51,207 \div 26 = \$1969.50$$

Step 2 Find 4% of the gross paycheck amount.

$$0.04 \cdot \$1969.50 = \$78.78$$

Mena has $78.78 deducted from each paycheck for her 401(k). ■

B How much money is deposited into Mena's 401(k) each payday?

Solution Mena's employer fully matches her deduction. Therefore, 2 • $78.78, or $157.56, is deposited into her 401(k) each payday. ▪

► **TIP**

An employer match is "free money." It is recommended to have at least as much money deducted as your employer will match, if possible.

⮕ Determining How Much You Should Save

Because of inflation, everything will be more expensive when you retire. As a general rule of thumb, you should have 10 times your gross annual pay saved up by the time you retire.

EXAMPLE 5
Evan's gross semimonthly pay is $1980. To maintain his current way of life, how much should he save up by the time he retires?

Solution
Step 1 Determine Evan's gross annual salary.

$$\$1980 \cdot 24 = \$47,520$$

Step 2 Multiply his gross annual salary by 10.

$$10 \cdot \$47,520 = \$475,200$$

Evan should save up $475,200 by the time he retires. ▪

Problem Set

Use the Rule of 72 to solve.

1. **Stepping Stones** You invest $7500 into a mutual fund that is expected to earn 7% per year. How long will it take the fund to be worth $15,000?

   You are looking for when the investment will double, so use the Rule of ▨.

   $$\text{number of years to double} \approx \frac{72}{▨} \approx ▨$$

   It will take about ▨ years for the mutual fund to be worth $15,000.

2. You invest $6500 into a mutual fund that is expected to earn 6% per year. How long will it take the fund to be worth $13,000?

3. The value of an investment doubled in 15 years. What was the annual rate of return?

4. The value of an investment grew from $800 to $1600 in 8 years. What was the annual rate of return?

For each person, find the following:
A. how much it cost to buy the stock
B. the net gain or loss
C. the rate of return

5. **Stepping Stones** Roger bought 800 shares of a company's stock for $15.34/share. He pays a broker a commission of $20 to buy and sell stock. After one year, Roger sold all his shares, when they were worth $18.77/share.

   A. Find Roger's cost to buy the shares: 800 • $▇ = $▇.

   Add the commission to the cost of the shares: $▇ + $20 = $▇.

   B. Multiply the number of shares by the selling price per share: 800 • $18.77 = $▇.

   Subtract the commission from the price of the shares: $▇ − $20 = $▇.

   Subtract the amount Roger paid for the shares from the amount he received from selling the shares: $▇ − $▇ = $▇.

   C. Divide Roger's net gain by his total cost: $▇ ÷ $▇ ≈ ▇.

   Roger's rate of return was about ▇%.

6. Mrs. Trujillo bought 400 shares of a company's stock for $42.98/share. She pays a broker a commission of $16 to buy and sell stock. After one year, she sold all her shares, when they were worth $56.13/share.

7. Yasmin bought 800 shares of a company's stock for $6.82/share. She pays a broker a 1.2% commission to buy and sell stock. After one year, she sold all her shares, when they were worth $6.90/share.

8. Conrad bought 7200 shares of a company's stock for $27.80/share. He pays a broker a 1% commission to buy and sell stock. After one year, he sold all his shares, when they were worth $25.85/share.

9. Sylvia bought 200 shares of a company's stock for $9.35/share. She pays a broker a commission of $8 to buy and sell stock. After one year, she sold all her shares, when they were worth $20.33/share.

10. **Challenge** Jake bought 6100 shares of a company's stock for $39/share. The broker's commission Jake pays for buying and selling stock is $40 for the first 5000 shares plus 0.5% of the value of the remaining shares. After one year, Jake sold all his shares of the stock, when they were worth $47.29/share.

For each person, find the following amounts:
A. total amount of interest he or she will receive
B. amount of interest he or she will receive semiannually

11. **Stepping Stones** Natasha bought a bond with a face value of $1000 and a coupon rate of 6%. The bond will mature in 20 years.

    A. $I = Prt = \$1000 \cdot ▇ \cdot 20 = \$▇$

    B. $\$▇ \div 40 = \$▇$

12. Sal bought a $1000 bond that has a coupon rate of 7%. The bond will mature in 10 years.

13. Mr. Merritt bought a $10,000 bond that has a coupon rate of 9%. The bond will mature in 30 years.

14. Daphne bought a $5000 bond that has a coupon rate of 5.5%. The bond will mature in 5 years.

For each person, find the following amounts:
A. how much is deducted from his or her paycheck for a retirement plan
B. how much is deposited into his or her retirement plan each payday

15. **Stepping Stones** Mr. Lane's gross paycheck amount is $744.27. He has 6% deducted from his paychecks for his 403(b). His employer matches his deduction, up to 3%.

   A. Find 6% of the paycheck amount: ▧ • $744.27 ≈ $▧ .

      Mr. Lane has $▧ deducted from each paycheck.

   B. The employer matches up to 3% of the deduction. That is half of what Mr. Lane is contributing, so his employer is contributing $▧ to his retirement plan. His employer's contribution plus his own contribution equals a total deposit of $▧ contributed to his 403(b) each payday.

16. Rylie's gross paycheck amount is $1305.60. She has 4% deducted from her paychecks for her 401(k). Her employer matches her deduction, up to 4%.

17. Kane's gross annual income is $61,458. He is paid semimonthly and has 5% deducted from his paychecks for his 401(k). His employer matches his deduction, up to 5%.

18. Nancy's gross annual income is $46,905. She is paid monthly and has 9% deducted from her paychecks for her 403(b). Her employer matches her deduction, up to 3%.

19. Tanner's gross annual income is $72,378. He is paid biweekly and has 7% deducted from his paychecks for his 401(k). His employer matches his deduction, up to 5%.

Solve the IRA problem.

20. Karl contributes 5% of his net pay to his IRA. How much does Karl contribute to his IRA after one year if his net weekly pay is $530?

21. In a year in which the maximum contribution to an IRA was $5500, Phoebe deposited 10% of her net monthly pay to her IRA. Her net monthly pay was $3478. How much more could she have contributed per month?

Determine the needed savings before retirement to maintain the person's current way of life.

22. Corbin's gross biweekly pay is $1788.

23. Dr. Sandoval's gross semimonthly pay is $8580.

24. Royce's gross weekly pay is $760.

25. Jennifer's gross monthly pay is $5645.

CHAPTER 7   Review

Choose your answer.

1. Jada deposited $867 into a savings account that pays a simple annual interest rate of 0.89%. How much interest will she earn after 15 months?

   A. $1.93

   B. $5.14

   C. $9.65

   D. $13.35

2. Gary deposited $1490 into a savings account in which interest is compounded weekly at a rate of 2.15%. Assuming he makes no other deposits or withdrawals, how much will be in his account after 3 years?

   A. $1522.38

   B. $1558.45

   C. $1586.11

   D. $1589.25

3. Carly's employer pays 95% of her health insurance premium and deducts the remainder from her paycheck. How much is deducted from each of her paychecks if she is paid biweekly and the annual premium is $10,818?

   A. $20.80

   B. $22.54

   C. $395.27

   D. $428.21

4. The health insurance company will pay 90% of the knee replacement surgery for Mrs. Pollard, after she pays a $500 deductible. The cost of her surgery is $31,700. How much will Mrs. Pollard pay for the surgery?

   A. $2670

   B. $3170

   C. $3220

   D. $3620

5. Freddie, a 32-year-old male, bought a $140,000, 10-year life insurance policy. What is Freddie's annual premium? (Use the table on page 173.)

   A. $455.00

   B. $534.80

   C. $817.60

   D. $1110.20

6. Deborah invested $3000 into a fund that is expected to earn 8.2% per year. If you use the Rule of 72, about how long will it take the fund to be worth $6000?

   A. 3 years

   B. 9 years

   C. 11 years

   D. 27 years

7. Omar bought 1000 shares of a company's stock for $15.23/share. If he pays a broker a 0.75% commission to buy and sell stock, then what is his net gain if he sells all his shares when they are worth $18.78/share?

   A. $3294.92

   B. $3435.77

   C. $3479.00

   D. $3514.50

8. Natalie's gross annual income is $44,905. She is paid biweekly and has 6% deducted from her paychecks for her 401(k). How much money is deposited into her 401(k) each payday if her employer fully matches her deduction?

   A. $103.63

   B. $112.26

   C. $207.26

   D. $224.52

Solve the interest problem.

9. Dylan deposited $450 into a savings account that pays a simple interest rate of 1.45%. If he makes no other deposits or withdrawals, what will the total amount be in his account after 4 years?

10. Stephanie deposited money into a savings account that pays a simple annual interest rate of 2.3%. How much did she deposit if she earned $322 after 5 years?

11. Raven deposited $5600 into a savings account in which interest is compounded daily at a rate of 3.9%. How much interest will she earn after 7 years?

12. Marcus deposited money into an account in which interest is compounded quarterly at a rate of 3.3%. How much did he deposit if the total amount in his account after 21 months was $4369.20, and he made no other deposits or withdrawals?

Solve the insurance problem.

13. Allen's employer pays 85% of his health insurance premium and deducts the remainder from his paycheck. He is paid weekly and the annual premium is $9604.

    A. How much does Allen pay annually for health insurance?

    B. How much is deducted from each of his paychecks for health insurance?

14. Mackenzie must pay a $10 co-pay to visit the doctor. Then her insurance company pays 80% of the cost of the visit. How much did Mackenzie pay to see her doctor if the cost of the visit was $258?

15. Kate, a 47-year-old female, bought a $75,000, 20-year life insurance policy through her employer. If she is paid semimonthly, how much does her employer deduct from each of her paychecks for life insurance? (Use the table on page 173.)

Solve the investment problem.

16. The value of an investment grew from $4000 to $8000 in 20 years. By the Rule of 72, what was the estimated annual rate of return?

17. Tyris bought 3000 shares of a company's stock for $8.33/share. How much did it cost him to buy the stock if he pays a broker a commission of $18 to buy stock?

18. Mr. Mercado bought a bond with a face value of $5000 and a coupon rate of 7.5%. The bond will mature in 15 years. How much interest will he receive semiannually?

19. Calista's gross annual income is $39,036. She is paid monthly and has 6% deducted from her paychecks for her 403(b). If her employer matches her deduction up to 4%, how much is deposited into her retirement plan each payday?

20. Malik's gross biweekly pay is $2720. To maintain his current lifestyle, how much should he save by the time he retires?

Problem	Topic Lookup
1, 2, 9–12	Interest
3–5, 13–15	Insurance
6–8, 16–20	Investments

CHAPTER 8   More Math Models

Did you know that music is related to fractions and symmetry? Did you know that you can use an equation to describe the path of a pendulum? Mathematics can help you understand everything from music to carpentry.

In This Chapter

You will learn about mathematical models of growth, decay, and music. You'll also see how trigonometric ratios and periodic functions can help you solve many real-world problems.

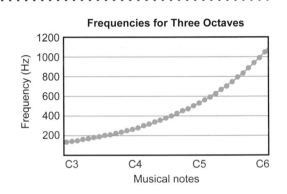

Topic List

▶ Chapter 8 Introduction

▶ Growth and Decay

▶ Trigonometric Ratios

▶ Periodic Functions

▶ Math and Music

▶ Chapter 8 Review

The length and weight of each string in a piano determine the string's frequency when it is struck.

▶

CHAPTER 8 Introduction

Mathematics can show up in some fairly unexpected places.

As you become acquainted with more math models, it will become easier to notice math all around you. For example, when you see a crowd of people in a city, you may think about how you can use a formula to predict the city's population in 50 years. When you see a tree, you may think about how you can use trigonometry to determine the height of the tree. Even listening to the radio may spark thoughts of math.

Music

Math and music are closely related. We commonly use numbers and other math concepts to read, write, and play music. For example, musical pieces often have repeating choruses or bars, which are musical patterns. This and other relationships are fundamental to mathematics and create an essential link between math and music.

In this chapter, you will see math models used in a variety of real-world situations.

Preparing for the Chapter

Review the following skills to prepare for the concepts in the chapter: converting percents to decimals, simplifying fractions, and identifying transformations.

Converting Percents to Decimals

The % sign means *per 100*. Therefore, to convert a percent to a decimal, remove the % sign, and divide by 100. The shortcut for dividing a number by 100 is moving the decimal point two places to the left.

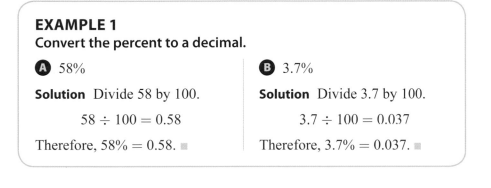

EXAMPLE 1
Convert the percent to a decimal.

A 58%

Solution Divide 58 by 100.

$$58 \div 100 = 0.58$$

Therefore, 58% = 0.58. ■

B 3.7%

Solution Divide 3.7 by 100.

$$3.7 \div 100 = 0.037$$

Therefore, 3.7% = 0.037. ■

Simplifying Fractions

A fraction is simplified when the numerator and denominator have no common factors other than 1.

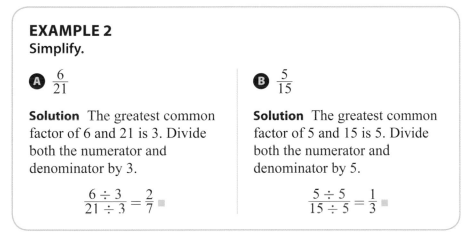

EXAMPLE 2
Simplify.

A $\frac{6}{21}$

Solution The greatest common factor of 6 and 21 is 3. Divide both the numerator and denominator by 3.

$$\frac{6 \div 3}{21 \div 3} = \frac{2}{7} \ ■$$

B $\frac{5}{15}$

Solution The greatest common factor of 5 and 15 is 5. Divide both the numerator and denominator by 5.

$$\frac{5 \div 5}{15 \div 5} = \frac{1}{3} \ ■$$

Identifying Transformations

DEFINITIONS

A **transformation** is a change in a figure's position, shape, or size.
- A **translation** slides a figure along a line without turns or flips.
- A **reflection** flips a figure across a line, creating a mirror image.
- A **rotation** turns a figure about a given point.
- A **glide reflection** combines a translation with a reflection.
  The direction of the translation is parallel to the line of reflection.

▶ BY THE WAY

These four transformations only change a figure's position. They are also called isometries.

EXAMPLE 3
Name the transformation that maps the pre-image (red) onto the image (blue).

Ⓐ P

ᴚ

Solution The pre-image maps onto the image after a quarter turn about a point.

P- ˎ
  ˎ
 •   ↓
     ᴚ

The transformation is a rotation. ▪

Ⓑ P

P

Solution The pre-image maps onto the image after a slide down and to the right.

P ˎ
  ˎ ↘
     P

The transformation is a translation. ▪

Ⓒ P

Ꮽ

Solution The pre-image maps onto the image after a flip over a horizontal line.

P
← – – →
Ꮽ

The transformation is a reflection. ▪

Ⓓ P

Ꮽ

Solution The pre-image maps onto the image after (1) a slide to the right and (2) a flip over a horizontal line.

P —①→ P
            ②
← – – – – →
Ꮽ

The transformation is a glide reflection. ▪

Problem Set

Convert the percent to a decimal.

1. 125%

2. 18%

3. 7%

4. 0.06%

5. 3000%

6. 4.12%

Simplify.

7. $\dfrac{6}{60}$

8. $\dfrac{4}{14}$

9. $\dfrac{15}{20}$

10. $\dfrac{12}{42}$

11. $\dfrac{56}{64}$

12. $\dfrac{30}{45}$

Name the transformation that maps the pre-image (red) onto the image (blue).

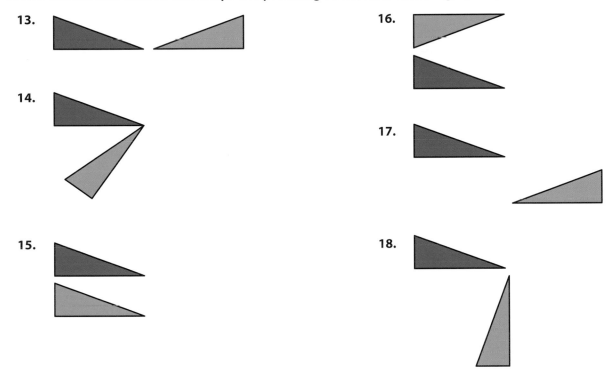

13.

14.

15.

16.

17.

18.

Growth and Decay

When a population grows exponentially, it increases by progressively larger amounts.

⬛ Predicting a Population: Exponential Growth

> **EXPONENTIAL GROWTH FORMULA**
>
> Find the total amount y, where b is the initial amount, r is the rate of growth, and t is the time.
>
> $$y = b(1 + r)^t$$

> ▶ **THINK ABOUT IT**
>
> Both the formula for the value of a home with appreciation and the compound interest formula are exponential growth formulas.

> **EXAMPLE 1**
> According to the U.S. Census Bureau, the population of Texas in 2010 was 25,145,561, and it was growing at an annual rate of 1.8%.
>
> **Ⓐ** Write a formula that can be used to predict the population of Texas for any year after 2010.
>
> **Solution** Substitute 25,145,561 for b and 0.018 for r.
>
> $$\begin{aligned} y &= 25{,}145{,}561(1 + 0.018)^t && \text{Substitute.} \\ &= 25{,}145{,}561(1.018)^t && \text{Add.} \end{aligned}$$
>
> The formula is $y = 25{,}145{,}561(1.018)^t$. ▪
>
> **Ⓑ** Use the formula to predict the population of Texas in 2025.
>
> **Solution** The year 2025 is 15 years after the year 2010, so substitute 15 for t.
>
> $$\begin{aligned} y &= 25{,}145{,}561(1.018)^{15} \\ &\approx 25{,}145{,}561 \cdot 1.306822701 && \text{Evaluate the power.} \\ &\approx 32{,}860{,}789.94 && \text{Multiply.} \end{aligned}$$
>
> The predicted population of Texas in 2025 is 32,860,790. ▪

> ▶ **TIP**
>
> Leave the value of 1.018^{15} in your calculator, and then multiply by 25,145,561.

Making Predictions with Exponential Growth

EXAMPLE 2
Predict when the population of Texas will reach 40,000,000.

Solution
Step 1 Substitute 40,000,000 for y and isolate the power.

$$40,000,000 = 25,145,561(1.018)^t \qquad \text{Substitute.}$$
$$1.590738023 \approx 1.018^t \qquad \text{Divide both sides by 25,145,561.}$$

Step 2 Use the guess-and-check strategy to solve for t.

$$\text{Try 26: } 1.018^{26} \approx 1.59017 \qquad \text{too low}$$
$$\text{Try 27: } 1.018^{27} \approx 1.61879 \qquad \text{too high}$$

t is between 26 and 27. The population of Texas is predicted to reach 40,000,000 a bit more than 26 years after 2010, or during 2036. ▪

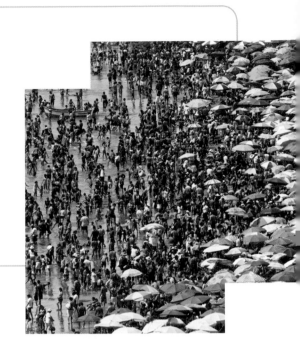

Analyzing a Graph: Exponential Growth

EXAMPLE 3
The graph shows the growth of an insect population during a field study.

Ⓐ Estimate the insect population on Day 40 of the study.

Solution Find 40 on the x-axis and move up on the graph. Look left to see that the population was between 750 and 1000, but much closer to 750. The insect population on Day 40 was about 800. ▪

Ⓑ How many days did it take for the insect population to reach 3000?

Solution Find 3000 on the y-axis and move right on the graph. Look down to see that the number of days was between 90 and 95, but slightly closer to 95. It took about 93 days for the insect population to reach 3000. ▪

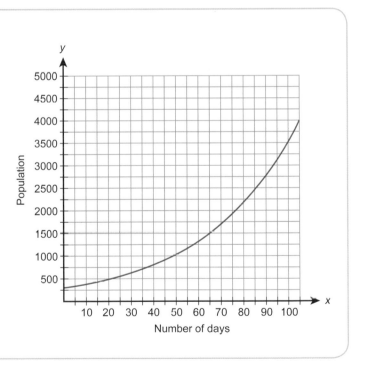

⮩ Making Predictions with Exponential Decay

When a population decays exponentially, it decreases by progressively smaller amounts.

▶ **THINK ABOUT IT**

The formula for the value of a car with depreciation is an exponential decay formula.

EXAMPLE 4
A study finds that the population of toads in an area is about 3800, and that it is decreasing at a rate of 5.5% each year.

🅐 Write a formula that can be used to predict the toad population in the area for any number of years after the study.

Solution Substitute 3800 for b and 0.055 for r.

$$y = 3800(1 - 0.055)^t \qquad \text{Substitute.}$$
$$= 3800(0.945)^t \qquad \text{Subtract.}$$

The formula is $y = 3800(0.945)^t$. ■

🅑 Predict the toad population in the area 10 years after the study.

Solution Substitute 10 for t.

$$y = 3800(0.945)^{10}$$
$$\approx 3800 \cdot 0.5679604376 \qquad \text{Evaluate the power.}$$
$$\approx 2158.249663 \qquad \text{Multiply.}$$

The predicted toad population 10 years after the study is 2158. ■

▶ **BY THE WAY**

In 2013, the U.S. Geological Survey reported that, on average, the rate of decline of all the amphibian populations the agency studied was 3.7%, with the rate of decline for the more-threatened species being 11.6%.

EXAMPLE 5
Predict when the toad population will reach half its initial value.

Solution
Step 1 Substitute 1900 for y and isolate the power.

$$1900 = 3800(0.945)^t \qquad \text{Substitute.}$$
$$0.5 \approx 0.945^t \qquad \text{Divide both sides by 3800.}$$

Step 2 Use the guess-and-check strategy to solve for t.

Try 10: $0.945^{10} \approx 0.56796$ too high
Try 13: $0.945^{13} \approx 0.47931$ too low
Try 12: $0.945^{12} \approx 0.50720$ slightly too high

t is between 12 and 13. The toad population will reach half its initial value during the 12th year after the study. ■

▶ **TIP**

The initial population is 3800, so substitute half of 3800, which is 1900, for y. Then solve for t.

A **half-life** is the time it takes for a quantity to decrease by one-half. So the half-life of the toad population is about 12 years.

Solving a Radioactive Decay Problem

Half-life is a common measure used with radioactive substances. Cobalt-60 has a half-life of about 5 years. That means that half of the initial amount decays in 5 years. Then it takes another 5 years for half of that remaining amount to decay. So, after 10 years, the amount of cobalt-60 remaining is one-fourth the initial amount.

HALF-LIFE FORMULA

Find the remaining amount of a substance y, where b is the initial amount, t is the time, and h is the half-life.

$$y = b(0.5)^{\frac{t}{h}}$$

EXAMPLE 6

Cobalt-60 has a half-life of about 5 years. After 30 years, how many grams of a 400 g sample will remain?

Solution Substitute 400 for b, 30 for t, and 5 for h.

$$
\begin{aligned}
y &= 400(0.5)^{\frac{30}{5}} && \text{Substitute.} \\
&= 400(0.5)^6 && \text{Simplify the exponent.} \\
&= 400 \cdot 0.015625 && \text{Evaluate the power.} \\
&= 6.25 && \text{Multiply.}
\end{aligned}
$$

After 30 years, 6.25 g of the sample will remain. ■

Problem Set

For each problem:
A. Write a formula to model the situation.
B. Use the formula to make the desired prediction.

1. **Stepping Stones** According to the U.S. Census Bureau, the population of Hawaii in 2010 was 1,360,301, and it was growing at an annual rate of 1.2%. Predict the population of Hawaii in 2032.

   A. $y = b(1 + r)^t = 1{,}360{,}301(1 + \boxed{})^t$
   $$= 1{,}360{,}301(\boxed{})^t$$

   B. $y = 1{,}360{,}301(\boxed{})^{22} \approx 1{,}360{,}301 \cdot \boxed{}$
   $$\approx \boxed{}$$

   The predicted population of Hawaii in 2032 is $\boxed{}$.

2. An experiment starts with a population of 35 bacteria. It is expected to grow at a rate of 300% each day. Predict the population after 8 days.

3. There were 15 members in a photography group when the group was formed. The group is expected to grow at an annual rate of 20%. Predict the number of members in the photography group 10 years after it was formed.

4. A population of 500 beetles is expected to grow at a rate of 70% per week. Predict the population after 15 weeks.

5. Jordan bought a 1930s painting that is expected to appreciate in value by 12% each year. She bought the painting for $1700. Predict the value of Jordan's painting 20 years after she purchased it.

Make the desired prediction.

6. A rat population is estimated to be 420, and it is growing at a weekly rate of 10%. Predict when the rat population will reach 3500.

7. In 2000, a city's population was 36,238 and it was growing at a rate of 0.85%. Predict when the city's population will reach 40,000.

Use the graph that shows a city's expected population for numbers of years after a census to solve.

8. Predict the city's population 25 years after the census.

9. Predict when the city's population will reach 500,000.

10. Predict when the city's population will reach 625,000.

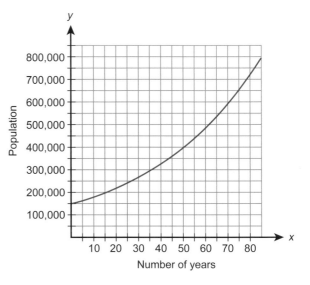

For each problem:
A. Write a formula to model the situation.
B. Use the formula to make the desired prediction.

11. **Stepping Stones** A man-made lake is stocked with 10,000 fish. This population is expected to decline by an annual rate of 15%. Predict the fish population 5 years after the lake is stocked.

A. $y = b(1 - r)^t = 10{,}000(1 - \boxed{})^t$
$= 10{,}000(\boxed{})^t$

B. $y = 10{,}000(\boxed{})^5 \approx 10{,}000 \cdot \boxed{}$
$\approx \boxed{}$

The predicted fish population 5 years after the lake is stocked is $\boxed{}$.

12. In 2010, a town's population was 23,211, and it was decreasing by an annual rate of 0.5%. Predict the town's population in 2040.

13. At its peak, Tristan's blog had 1810 monthly visitors. Since then, the number of monthly visitors has been declining at a rate of 4% per month. Predict the number of monthly visitors 1 year after the blog's peak month.

14. A population of 80,000 toads is expected to shrink at a rate of 9.2% per year. Predict the toad population in 20 years.

15. Mrs. Wong purchased a computer for $779 when she started her own business. The value of her computer depreciates at a rate of 22% per year. Predict the value of Mrs. Wong's computer 5 years after she started her business.

Make the desired prediction.

16. In 2010, a city's population was 1,405,233, and it was decreasing at a rate of 1.1%. Predict when the city's population will first be below 1,200,000.

17. Mr. Mosley purchased a new motor home for $78,000. It is expected to depreciate an average of 17% each year. Predict when the value of Mr. Mosley's motor home will first be below $10,000.

Use the graph that estimates the number of disease-free trees in a park for numbers of years after a tree study to solve.

18. Predict the number of disease-free trees in the park 70 years after the study.

19. Predict when the number of disease-free trees in the park will first be below 100,000.

20. Predict when the number of disease-free trees in the park will first be below 40,000.

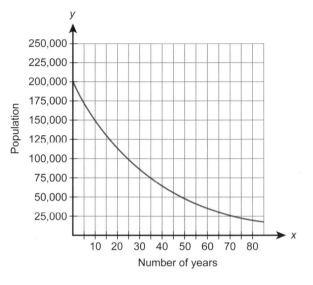

Number of years

Solve.

21. **Stepping Stones** Iodine-125 has a half-life of about 60 days. After 180 days, how many milligrams of a 200 mg sample will remain?

$$y = b(0.5)^{\frac{t}{h}}$$

$$y = 200(0.5)^{\frac{180}{\blacksquare}}$$

$$= 200(0.5)^{\blacksquare}$$

$$= 200 \cdot \blacksquare$$

$$= \blacksquare$$

After 180 days, ▇ mg of the sample will remain.

22. Strontium-90 has a half-life of about 28 years. After 112 years, how many grams of a 50 g sample will remain?

23. Cobalt-60 has a half-life of about 5 years. After 13 years, how many grams of a 30 g sample will remain?

24. Sodium-24 has a half-life of 15 hours. How much time has passed if 12.5 g of an initial 50 g sample remain?

25. Uranium-238 has a half-life of about 4.5 billion years. How long will it take for about 97% of a sample to decay?

Trigonometric Ratios

Trigonometry looks at how the angle measures and side lengths in a triangle are related.

A right triangle has one right angle. The side opposite the right angle is called the hypotenuse. In $\triangle ABC$, c is the hypotenuse. The other two sides, a and b, are the legs of the right triangle.

The sides opposite the acute angles are referred to as the *opposite* and *adjacent* sides, depending on which acute angle you are referring to.

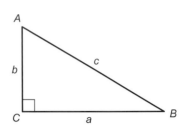

➲ Finding Trigonometric Ratios

A **trigonometric ratio** is a ratio of two side lengths in a right triangle.

DEFINITIONS

The **sine** of an angle, abbreviated sin, is the ratio of the length of the opposite side to the length of the hypotenuse.

$$\sin A = \frac{\text{opposite}}{\text{hypotenuse}}$$

The **cosine** of an angle, abbreviated cos, is the ratio of the length of the adjacent side to the length of the hypotenuse.

$$\cos A = \frac{\text{adjacent}}{\text{hypotenuse}}$$

The **tangent** of an angle, abbreviated tan, is the ratio of the length of the opposite side to the length of the adjacent side.

$$\tan A = \frac{\text{opposite}}{\text{adjacent}}$$

▶ **REMEMBER**

In this triangle, in reference to $\angle A$, a is the opposite side, and b is the adjacent side. In reference to $\angle B$, b is the opposite side, and a is the adjacent side. The hypotenuse is the longest side of a right triangle.

▶ **TIP**

The adjacent side is always a leg. It is never the hypotenuse.

EXAMPLE 1
Use $\triangle FGH$ to write each trigonometric ratio as a simplified fraction and as a decimal. Round to four decimal places.

A $\sin F$

Solution

$\sin F = \dfrac{\text{opp}}{\text{hyp}}$

$= \dfrac{12}{13}$

≈ 0.9231 ■

B $\cos F$

Solution

$\cos F = \dfrac{\text{adj}}{\text{hyp}}$

$= \dfrac{5}{13}$

≈ 0.3846 ■

C $\tan F$

Solution

$\tan F = \dfrac{\text{opp}}{\text{adj}}$

$= \dfrac{12}{5}$

$= 2.4$ ■

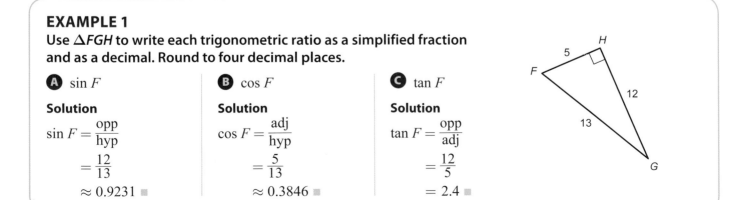

EXAMPLE 2
Identify the trigonometric ratio that is shown for the angle.

A $\angle M, \dfrac{8}{17}$

Solution The side of length 8 is opposite $\angle M$, and the side of length 17 is the hypotenuse. The ratio is the sine ratio. ■

B $\angle N, \dfrac{15}{8}$

Solution The side of length 15 is opposite $\angle N$, and the side of length 8 is adjacent to $\angle N$. The ratio is the tangent ratio. ■

Trigonometric ratios for right triangles with the same acute angle measures are equal. Here, $\triangle ABC$ and $\triangle DEF$ are similar, so the corresponding angles have equal measures.

$$m\angle B = m\angle E$$
$$\tan B = \frac{AC}{CB} = \frac{6}{8} = 0.75$$
$$\tan E = \frac{DF}{FE} = \frac{3}{4} = 0.75$$

Use your calculator to find a trigonometric ratio for any angle measure. First make sure you are in Degree mode. On a TI-83/84 graphing calculator, press 2nd CATALOG, scroll down to Degree, and press ENTER.

```
CATALOG      ▯
 dbd(
 ▸Dec
▸Degree
 DelVar
 DependAsk
 DependAuto
 det(
```

```
Degree
              Done
sin(45)
          .7071067812
tan(18)
          .3249196962
```

▶ **TIP**
Some calculators have a button that toggles among Degree (D), Radian (R), and Gradian (G) modes. Consult your user's manual.

⬛ Finding an Unknown Side Length

You can use a trigonometric ratio to find an unknown side length.

EXAMPLE 3
Find the value of *x*. Round to the nearest hundredth.

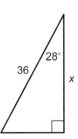

Solution In relation to the 28° angle, the unknown length is the adjacent side. The known length is the hypotenuse. Use the cosine ratio.

$$\cos 28° = \frac{x}{36}$$ $\quad \cos \angle = \dfrac{\text{adjacent}}{\text{hypotenuse}}$

$36 \cdot \cos 28° = x$ Multiply both sides by 36.

$36 \cdot 0.8829 \approx x$ Use a calculator for the cosine.

$31.79 \approx x$ Simplify the left side. ■

◤ Application: Safety

EXAMPLE 4
OSHA requires that portable ladders be set up so that they make a 75° angle with the ground. A painter wants the top of his ladder to reach 24 ft up the side of a building. How far away should the base of his ladder be from the base of the building?

Solution Draw a sketch to help determine which trigonometric ratio to use.

Assume the building forms a 90° angle with the ground. The ladder, ground, and side of the building form a right triangle.

In relation to the 75° angle, the unknown length is the adjacent side. The known length is the opposite side. Use the tangent ratio.

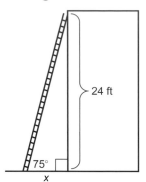

$$\tan 75° = \frac{24}{x} \qquad \tan \angle = \frac{\text{opposite}}{\text{adjacent}}$$

$$x \cdot \tan 75° = 24 \qquad \text{Multiply both sides by } x.$$

$$x = \frac{24}{\tan 75°} \qquad \text{Divide both sides by } \tan 75°.$$

$$x \approx 6.4308 \qquad \text{Simplify the right side.}$$

The ladder should be about 6.4 ft from the base of the building. ◾

▶ BY THE WAY

OSHA is the Occupational Safety and Health Administration. It is part of the U.S. Department of Labor and enforces safety standards in the workplace.

▶ REMEMBER

A calculator was used to obtain the tangent and sine ratios in Examples 4 and 5. You will usually need a calculator when you solve trigonometric ratio problems.

◤ Application: Flight

EXAMPLE 5
For the first 3 mi after takeoff, an airplane climbs steadily at a 12° angle of elevation. What is the airplane's altitude after its first 3 mi of travel?

Solution Draw a sketch to help determine which trigonometric ratio to use.

The altitude, or height, of the airplane is its perpendicular distance to the ground.

In relation to the 12° angle, the unknown length is the opposite side. The known length is the hypotenuse. Use the sine ratio.

$$\sin 12° = \frac{x}{3} \qquad \sin \angle = \frac{\text{opposite}}{\text{hypotenuse}}$$

$$3 \cdot \sin 12° = x \qquad \text{Multiply both sides by 3.}$$

$$0.6237 \approx x \qquad \text{Simplify the left side.}$$

The airplane's altitude is about 0.6 mi. ◾

▶ TIP

An *angle of elevation* is an angle made with the ground, or parallel to the ground, as if a person were in the angle, looking up. An *angle of depression* is an angle made with a line parallel to the ground and an object on the ground below. If a person looks down from a window at a flower on the ground, the angle of depression is the angle at which the person is looking down.

Problem Set

Use $\triangle PQR$ to write the trigonometric ratio as a decimal. Round to four decimal places.

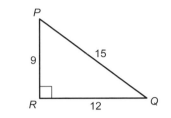

1. Stepping Stones $\sin P$

$$\sin P = \frac{\text{opp}}{\text{hyp}}$$

$$= \frac{12}{\boxed{}}$$

$$= \boxed{}$$

2. $\cos P$

3. $\tan P$

4. $\sin Q$

5. $\cos Q$

6. $\tan Q$

Identify the trigonometric ratio that is shown for the angle in $\triangle DEF$.

7. Stepping Stones $\angle E, \frac{24}{25}$

The side of length 24 is adjacent to $\angle E$, and the side of length 25 is the \boxed{}. This ratio is the \boxed{} ratio.

8. $\angle E, \frac{7}{25}$

9. $\angle D, \frac{24}{7}$

10. $\angle D, \frac{24}{25}$

11. $\angle D, \frac{7}{25}$

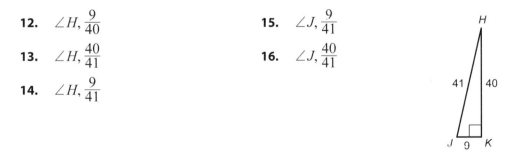

Identify the trigonometric ratio that is shown for the angle in $\triangle HJK$.

12. $\angle H, \frac{9}{40}$

13. $\angle H, \frac{40}{41}$

14. $\angle H, \frac{9}{41}$

15. $\angle J, \frac{9}{41}$

16. $\angle J, \frac{40}{41}$

Find the value of x. Round to the nearest hundredth.

17. Stepping Stones

$$\sin \boxed{}° = \frac{x}{15}$$

$$\boxed{} \cdot \sin 54° = x$$

$$\boxed{} \approx x$$

(triangle with 54° at top, 15 as hypotenuse, right angle at bottom left, x along the bottom)

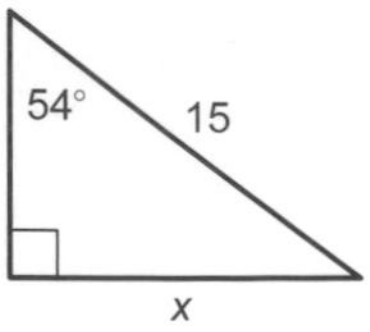

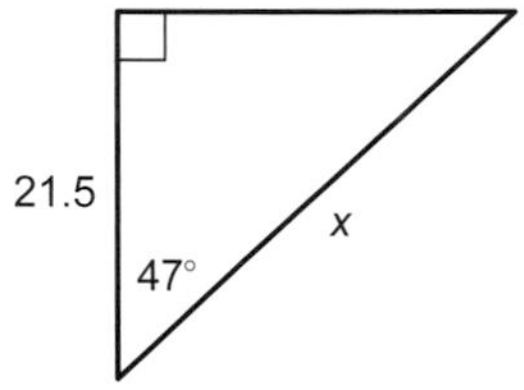

18.

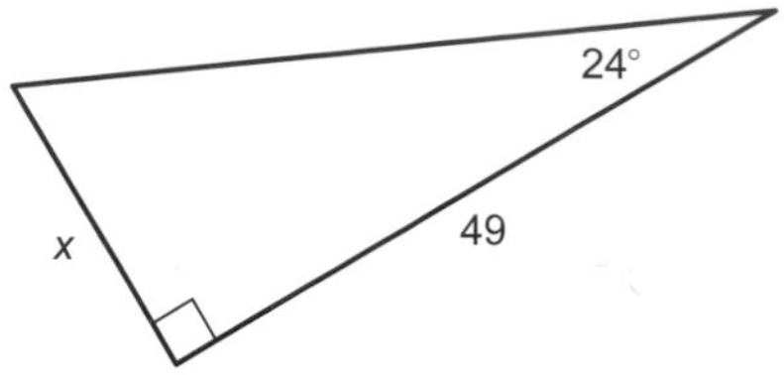

(triangle with 24° angle, side 49, side x, right angle at bottom)

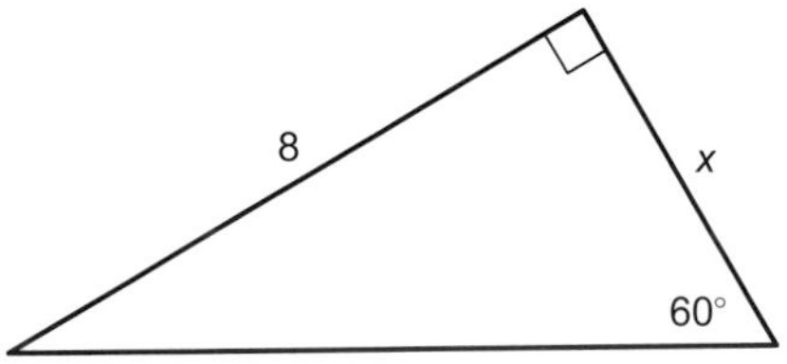

21.

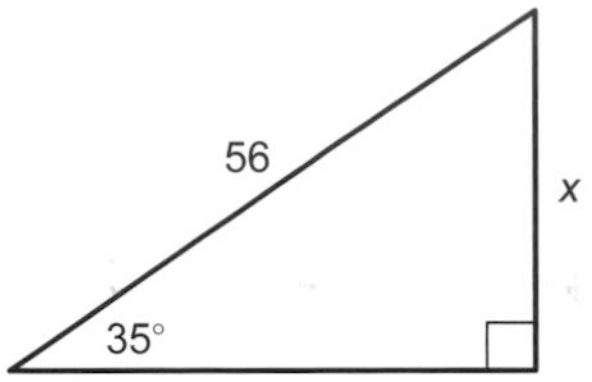

(triangle with 56, x, 35° angle, right angle at bottom right)

19.

(triangle with right angle top, 21.5, x, 47°)

22.

(triangle with 81.9, 65°, x, right angle)

20.

(triangle with right angle top, 8, x, 60°)

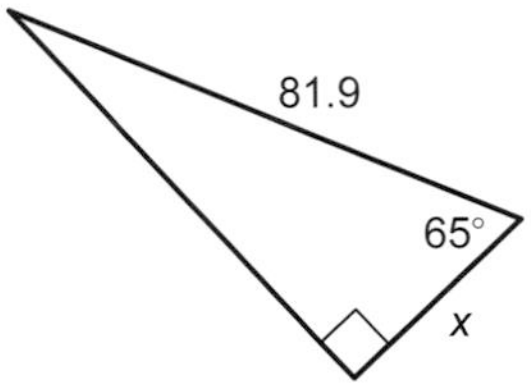

Solve. Round to the nearest tenth unless otherwise directed.

23. Stepping Stones Draven is flying a kite. He has let out all 25 m of string. The angle of elevation is 28°. If Draven is holding the end of the string 1 m above the ground, then how many meters above the ground is the kite?

Draw a sketch of the situation.

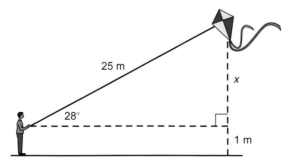

25 m

28°

x

1 m

In relation to the 28° angle, the unknown length is the ▆▆▆▆ side. The known length is the hypotenuse. Use the sine ratio.

$$\sin 28° = \frac{x}{\boxed{}}$$

$$\boxed{} \cdot \sin 28° = x$$

$$\boxed{} \approx x$$

The value of x is about ▆. Because Draven is holding the end of the string 1 m above the ground, the kite is ▆ m above the ground.

24. A wheelchair ramp rises from the ground at a 4.5° angle of elevation. The end of the ramp is 3 ft above the ground. How long is the ramp?

25. From his position 21 m above sea level, a lighthouse keeper spots a whale at a 15° angle of depression. To the nearest meter, how far is the whale from the lighthouse?

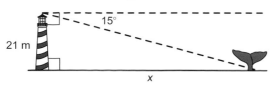

26. A ladder is leaning against a building, forming a 70° angle with the ground. The base of the ladder is 8.2 ft from the base of the building. What is the length of the ladder?

27. An escalator that joins the first and second floors of a building rises at an angle of 27°. A person travels 23 m when riding the escalator. What is the vertical distance between the first and second floors?

28. Jonathan sets a camera on a tripod to film birds in a nest. The camera is 1.8 m off the ground and 16.4 m away from the tree. The angle of elevation from the camera to the bird's nest is 29°. How far above the ground is the bird's nest?

29. Lorena determines that the angle of elevation from the end of a tree's shadow to the sun is 34°. The length of the tree's shadow is 49.5 ft. How tall is the tree?

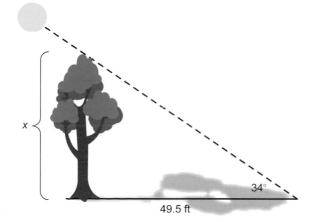

30. An 18 ft ladder is leaning against a building, forming a 60° angle with the ground. How far up the building does the ladder reach?

31. From an upper ski lift station located at an elevation of 5510 ft, a ski lift employee can spot the lower ski lift station at a 23° angle of depression. Skiers travel 3081 ft when they take the lift. What is the elevation of the lower ski lift station, rounded to the nearest foot?

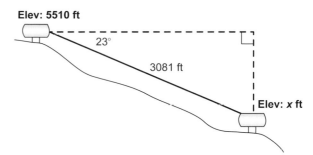

32. To plant a 4 m tree, a landscaper uses a rope to help hold it vertical. The rope extends from halfway up the tree to a stake in the ground. How far is the stake from the tree if the rope forms a 38° angle with the ground?

33. **Challenge** Catalina lives in a building that is 72 ft from the building her friend lives in. From her window, Catalina can see the top of her friend's building if she looks up at a 34° angle of elevation, and she can see the bottom of her friend's building if she looks down at a 61° angle of depression. Find the height of the building that Catalina's friend lives in.

Periodic Functions

Many real-world phenomena occur in cycles.

Some graphs are **periodic**. Periodic graphs are formed by **cycles**, or regular intervals of repeating patterns.

⬛ Analyzing a Periodic Function

DEFINITIONS

In a periodic function, the **period** is the length of one cycle. The **amplitude** is half the difference between the maximum and minimum output values.

> ▶ **TIP**
>
> A cycle is the *shortest* complete repeating pattern in a graph.

EXAMPLE 1
Identify the period and amplitude of the function.

A

B

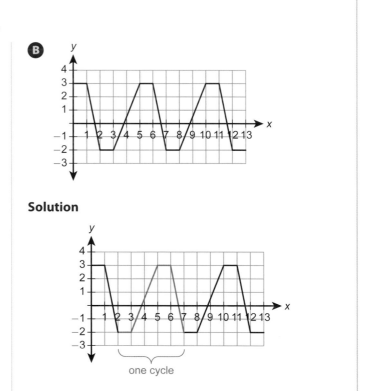

Solution

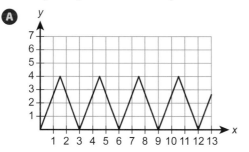

one cycle

The highlighted cycle extends from $x = 0$ to $x = 3$. The period is $3 - 0$, or 3. The maximum y-value is 4 and the minimum y-value is 0. The amplitude is $\frac{1}{2}(4 - 0) = 2$. ▪

Solution

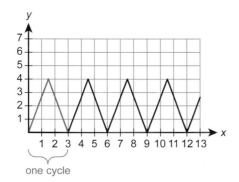

one cycle

The highlighted cycle extends from $x = 2$ to $x = 7$. The period is $7 - 2$, or 5. The maximum y-value is 3 and the minimum y-value is -2. The amplitude is

$\frac{1}{2}(3 - (-2)) = \frac{1}{2}(5) = 2.5$. ▪

Determining the Period of a Data Set

EXAMPLE 2
Determine whether the data set is approximately periodic.
If so, estimate the period and the amplitude.

The table shows the times and heights of the tides for Barren Island,
in the Chesapeake Bay, during a given time span.

Time (h)	5.76	11.76	18.01	24.56	30.56	36.68	42.68	49.25
Height (ft)	1.4	0.4	1.6	0.3	1.5	0.4	1.6	0.3

Tide High and Low, Inc. 2013

Solution Look for patterns. The tides alternate between high tides
at about 1.5 ft and low tides at about 0.35 ft. The times are all
approximately 6.25 h apart.

The data set is periodic. The period is about 6.25 h + 6.25 h = 12.5 h.

The amplitude is about $\frac{1}{2}(1.5 - 0.3)$ ft $= \frac{1}{2}(1.2)$ ft $= 0.6$ ft. ■

Graphing a Trigonometric Function

A trigonometric function, or trig function, has a trigonometric ratio in its
function rule. Trigonometric functions are periodic functions.

You can graph a trigonometric function on a graphing calculator or by using
an online tool such as Google, Desmos, or GeoGebra.

Analyzing a Trigonometric Function

EXAMPLE 3
Identify the period and amplitude of the sine function.

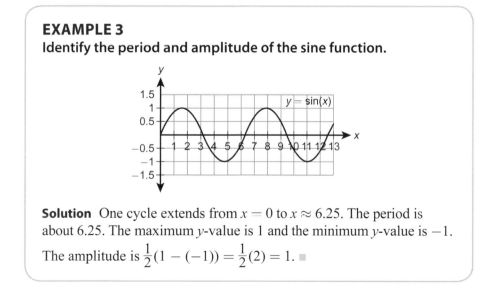

▶ TIP
Some graphing tools will show
the x-values in terms of π.

Solution One cycle extends from $x = 0$ to $x \approx 6.25$. The period is
about 6.25. The maximum y-value is 1 and the minimum y-value is -1.

The amplitude is $\frac{1}{2}(1 - (-1)) = \frac{1}{2}(2) = 1$. ■

The exact period of the sine function in Example 3 is 2π. The value of π is
approximately 3.14, so the value of 2π is approximately 6.28.

Application: Simple Harmonic Motion

The motion created by an object shifting back and forth by regular amounts is an example of **simple harmonic motion**. Simple harmonic motion can be modeled by sine and cosine functions, called **sinusoids**.

Imagine a weight on the end of a spring as the spring is compressed upward and then released. The weight would spring down below its initial, or resting, position, and then up above it indefinitely if friction were absent.

The graph shows the height y, in centimeters, of the weight, at a given number of seconds, x.

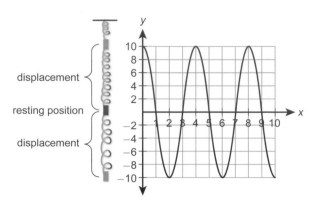

Compare the graph to the table.

Time (s)	0	1	2	3	4	5	6	7	8
Displacement (cm)	10	0	−10	0	10	0	−10	0	10

The weight's displacement at any moment is its distance from its resting position. Its maximum displacement is the graph's amplitude: 10 cm. From its resting position, the time it takes the weight to bounce one direction, then the other, and then return to its resting position is the period: 4 s.

The **frequency** of a periodic graph is the reciprocal of its period and gives the number of cycles in one unit of time. For the spring, the frequency of $\frac{1}{4}$ indicates that the weight completes one-fourth of a cycle in 1 s.

Application: Circular Motion

Suppose a fly lands on the end of the second hand of a clock at 7:45. The graph of its vertical movement for the next 2 min would form a periodic function because it would move up and down in regular intervals.

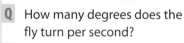

▶ **Q & A**

Q How many degrees does the fly turn per second?

A 6°/s

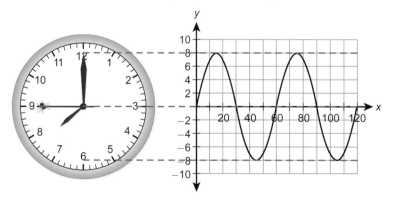

Compare the graph to the table.

Time (s)	0	15	30	45	60	75	90	105	120
Height (in.)	0	8	0	−8	0	8	0	−8	0

The length of the second hand is the graph's amplitude: 8 in. The time it takes for the fly to travel around the clock and return to its original position is the period: 60 s.

Problem Set

Identify the period and amplitude of the function.

1. **Stepping Stones** One cycle extends from $x = 0$ to $x = \blacksquare$.
   The period is $\blacksquare$.

   The maximum y-value is $\blacksquare$ and the minimum y-value is 0.

   The amplitude is $\frac{1}{2}(\blacksquare - 0) = \frac{1}{2}(\blacksquare) = \blacksquare$.

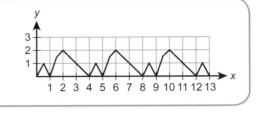

2.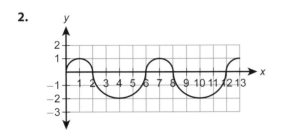

4.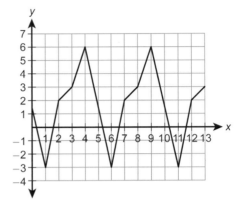

3.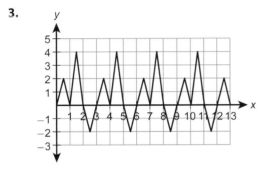

Determine whether the data set is approximately periodic.
If so, estimate the period and the amplitude.

5. The tables show the approximate hours of darkness each month in
   Anchorage, AK, where Month 1 represents January 2013.

Month	1	2	3	4	5	6	7	8	9	10	11	12
Hours	17.6	14.9	12.2	9.2	6.5	4.7	5.6	8.2	11.1	14.0	16.8	18.5

Month	13	14	15	16	17	18	19	20	21	22	23	24
Hours	17.6	14.9	12.2	9.3	6.5	4.7	5.6	8.2	11.1	13.9	16.7	18.5

USNO 2012

6. The tables show the lowest monthly temperatures in Detroit, MI,
   for 20 years.

Year	1993	1994	1995	1996	1997	1998	1999	2000	2001	2002
Temperature °F	9	−20	1	1	−6	11	−10	−2	4	12

Year	2003	2004	2005	2006	2007	2008	2009	2010	2011	2012
Temperature °F	−2	−7	−2	20	7	5	−15	3	2	4

Weather Warehouse 2013

7. The tables show the textbook sales, in thousands of dollars, at a bookstore each month for 2 years.

Month	Jan.	Feb.	Mar.	Apr.	May	June	July	Aug.	Sept.	Oct.	Nov.	Dec.
Sales	22.1	19.5	4.4	2.1	1.3	1.0	21.8	20.4	4.3	1.9	1.2	1.1

Month	Jan.	Feb.	Mar.	Apr.	May	June	July	Aug.	Sept.	Oct.	Nov.	Dec.
Sales	21.9	19.7	4.2	2.0	1.5	1.2	22.0	21.6	4.5	1.6	1.1	1.1

8. The tables show the value of a stock, in dollars, each week for 20 weeks.

Week	1	2	3	4	5	6	7	8	9	10
Value	28.56	29.91	30.04	30.69	31.58	31.07	30.91	31.43	36.31	36.78

Week	11	12	13	14	15	16	17	18	19	20
Value	36.22	32.96	31.44	29.87	19.01	18.82	18.84	18.47	19.53	21.06

For each graph of a trigonometric function:
A. Determine the function's period.
B. Determine the function's amplitude.

9.

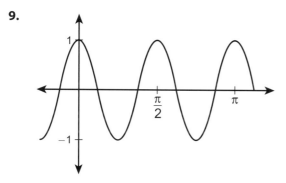

11.

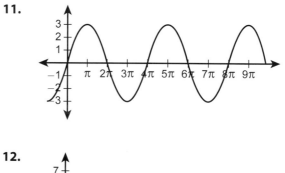

12.

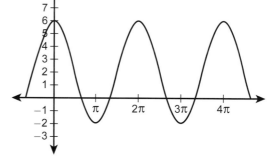

10.

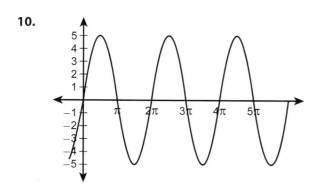

The graph shows the vertical displacement *y*, in inches, that a weight bouncing from a spring would achieve if there were no friction, for a given number of seconds, *x*.

13. What is the weight's maximum displacement?

14. From its resting position, how long does it take the weight to bounce one direction, then the other, and then return to its resting position?

15. From its lowest possible position, how long does it take for the weight to bounce up to its resting position?

16. What is the graph's frequency?

17. What does the frequency of the graph indicate in this situation?

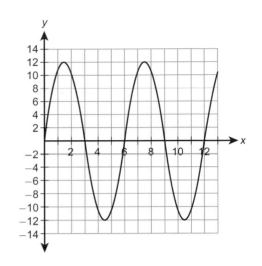

The graph shows the distance *y*, in centimeters, a pendulum moves to the right (positive displacement) and to the left (negative displacement), for a given number of seconds, *x*.

18. What is the pendulum's maximum displacement?

19. From its resting position, how long does it take the pendulum to swing one direction, then the other, and then return to its resting position?

20. Describe how the pendulum is moving during the time period from $x = 0.8$ to $x = 1.6$.

21. What percent of a full cycle is completed within 1 s?

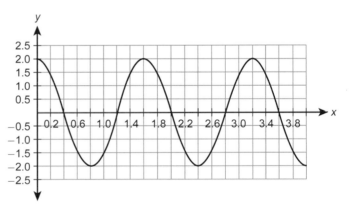

The graph shows a rider's height *x*, in feet, above or below the center of a Ferris wheel, for a given number of seconds, *x*.

22. What is the diameter of the Ferris wheel?

23. How long does it take for the wheel to make one complete revolution?

24. How many minutes does it take for the wheel to make 8 revolutions?

25. How many degrees does the Ferris wheel turn per second?

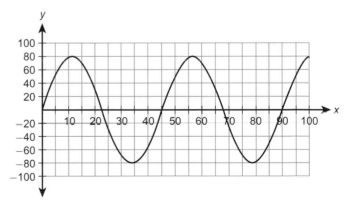

Math and Music

There are many patterns in music, including some that look like geometric transformations and others that are like geometric sequences.

Musical Notation

The most common musical notes, in terms of note duration, are whole notes, half notes, quarter notes, and eighth notes.

whole note   half note   quarter note   eighth note

Each measure in a line of music gets a certain number of beats. Measures are separated by bar lines.

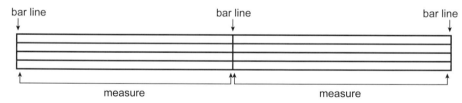

> **THINK ABOUT IT**
>
> Whole notes are like the number 1, half notes are like the fraction $\frac{1}{2}$, quarter notes are like the fraction $\frac{1}{4}$, and eighth notes are like the fraction $\frac{1}{8}$.

Musical Transformations

When you look closely at a line of music, you will often see patterns. Many of these patterns are geometric transformations. In the song "Three Blind Mice," for example, the first two measures show a translation of the notes in the first measure to the notes in the second measure. It is a translation because the notes in the first measure are shifted to the right to obtain the notes in the second measure.

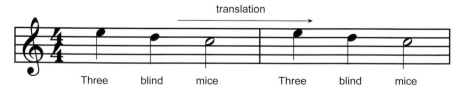

The following piece of music shows a glide reflection. Notice how the notes in the first measure are translated and then reflected to obtain the notes in the second measure.

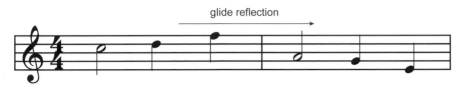

glide reflection

▶ **REMEMBER**

A glide reflection consists of a translation and a reflection.

EXAMPLE 1
What kind of geometric transformation is shown?

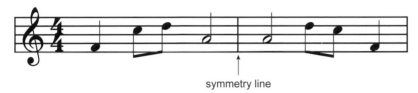

symmetry line

Solution The notes in the first measure are a mirror image of the notes in the second measure. So this musical notation is an example of a reflection. ■

➤ Frequencies of Musical Notes

When we hear sound, we are really sensing vibrations. What makes every musical note unique is how quickly the vibration happens. Faster vibrations correspond to higher notes, while slower vibrations are for lower notes.

Frequencies are measured in units called hertz, which is abbreviated Hz. Hertz basically means cycles per second, so a frequency of 60 Hz means 60 cycles/s.

The table shows what the frequencies are for notes in a two-octave range. Notice the pattern. C4 has a frequency that is about double that of C3. Also, D4 has a frequency that is about double that of D3. In fact, every time you go up an octave, you double the frequency.

Frequencies of Notes in Two Octaves	
Note	**Frequency (Hz)**
B4	493.88
A4	440.00
G4	392.00
F4	349.23
E4	329.63
D4	293.66
C4	261.63
B3	246.94
A3	220.00
G3	196.00
F3	174.61
E3	164.81
D3	146.83
C3	130.81

EXAMPLE 2
The D above D4 is D5. What is the frequency of D5?

Solution The frequency of D4 is 293.66 Hz, so D5 has a frequency that is twice that number.

$$f = 2 \cdot 293.66 \text{ Hz} = 587.32 \text{ Hz}$$

The frequency of D5 is 587.32 Hz. ■

As you go from a note to the corresponding note an octave above, you can see the ratio 2 : 1, which is the ratio of the higher frequency to the lower frequency. Another well-known relationship is the perfect fifth. For a perfect fifth, the ratio of the upper note to the note that is a perfect fifth below it is 3 : 2. So G is a perfect fifth above C. The ratio of the frequencies of G3 and C3 is $\frac{196}{130.81} \approx 1.5 = \frac{3}{2}$.

EXAMPLE 3
Determine the frequency of the note that is a perfect fifth below D4.

Solution The frequency of D4 is 293.66 Hz, so the fifth below it needs to form a ratio of 3 : 2 with that frequency. Let f be the frequency of the note a perfect fifth below D4.

$$\frac{293.66}{f} = \frac{3}{2}$$
$$2 \cdot 293.66 = f \cdot 3$$
$$195.77 \approx f$$

The frequency of the perfect fifth below D4 is about 195.77 Hz. Note that, in the table, the frequency for G3 is rounded to 196.00. ∎

Some of these ratio relationships have been known for millennia. Pythagoras thought these patterns were so perfect that he imagined that celestial bodies (the sun, moon, and visible planets) emitted music. He and his followers believed that this music of the spheres affected our lives on earth. The Pythagoreans saw math everywhere, and its applications, structure, and beauty changed how they saw the world.

Problem Set

· ·

Name the geometric transformation shown in the line of music.

1. **Stepping Stones** The notes in the first measure are ▓▓▓▓ to the right and then down to obtain the notes in the second measure. This is a ▓▓▓▓ .

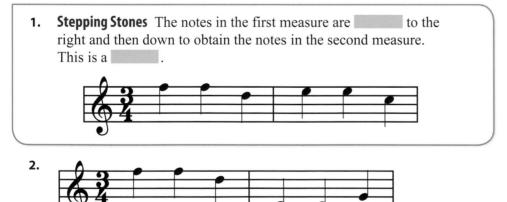

2.

3.

4.

5.

6.

Copy the line of music. Write in the notes in the second measure to show the given transformation. In some cases, more than one answer may be possible.

7. reflection

8. translation

9. glide reflection

Use the frequencies table on page 209 to determine the frequencies of the following three notes in relation to the given note:
A. one octave above
B. two octaves above
C. a perfect fifth below

10. B4

11. G3

12. E4

13. A4

CHAPTER 8   Review

Choose the answer.

1. At Hour 0, a population of bacteria is 12. Which is the best prediction for the population at Hour 8 if the population is expected to grow at a rate of 200% per hour?

   A. 3072

   B. 32,768

   C. 78,732

   D. 4,251,528

2. In 2013, a study found that a population of toads in an area was about 6200, and that it was decreasing at a rate of 7% each year. Which is the best prediction for the year in which the toad population will reach 2000?

   A. 2035

   B. 2028

   C. 2025

   D. 2019

3. What is the amplitude of the function?

   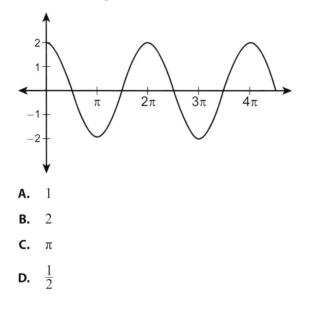

   A. 1

   B. 2

   C. π

   D. $\frac{1}{2}$

4. What is the value of cos D?

   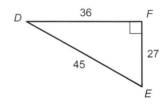

   A. 0.6

   B. 0.75

   C. 0.8

   D. 1.25

5. What is the value of x rounded to the nearest hundredth?

   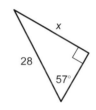

   A. 15.25

   B. 18.18

   C. 21.47

   D. 23.48

6. What is the period of the function?

   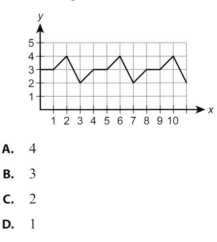

   A. 4

   B. 3

   C. 2

   D. 1

Solve.

7. According to the World Bank, the population of the Philippines in 2012 was 96.71 million, and it was growing at an annual rate of 1.7%. Predict the population of the Philippines in 2030.

8. Cesium-137 has a half-life of about 30 years. How many grams of a 210 g sample will remain after 75 years?

9. Name the geometric transformation shown in this line of music.

10. The frequency for the note E4 (the E above middle C) is 329.63 Hz.

    A. What is the frequency of E3 (one octave lower than E4)?

    B. What is the frequency of the note that is a perfect fifth below E4?

11. A ramp rises above the ground at a 4° angle of elevation. The end of the ramp is 1.5 m above the ground. What is the length of the ramp?

12. From his tree house, Josh can see a turtle at a 25° angle of depression. How far is the turtle from the base of the tree that Josh is in, if Josh is 14 ft above the ground?

13. The tables show the numbers of miles Trish ran each day during training.

Day	1	2	3	4	5	6
Miles	4.5	6.2	3.3	0	4.4	6.0

Day	7	8	9	10	11	12
Miles	3.2	0	4.4	6.1	3.4	0

Determine if the data set is approximately periodic. If so, estimate the period and the amplitude.

14. Consider the function $y = 2\sin(1.5x)$.

    A. Graph the first two cycles of the function, starting at $x = 0$.

    B. Identify the function's period and amplitude.

A wet sock is stuck to the inner wall of a washing machine's drum as it rotates at a steady speed. The graph shows the sock's displacement y, in inches, from the center of the drum, for a given number of seconds, x.

15. What is the diameter of the washing machine's drum?

16. How long does it take the sock to make one complete revolution?

17. How many revolutions does the sock make in 1 min?

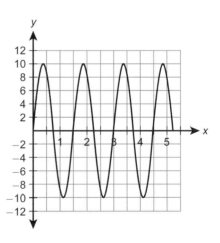

Problem	Topic Lookup
1, 2, 7, 8	Growth and Decay
3, 6, 13–17	Periodic Functions

Problem	Topic Lookup
4, 5, 11, 12	Trigonometric Ratios
9, 10	Math and Music

Extra Problems for Chapter 1
Working with Data

Measures of Center

For each data set, find the mean, median, and mode.

1. 14, 2, 7, 10, 2, 5, 2

2. 1, 8, 12, 13, 15, 3, 0, 9

3. 3, 7, 7, 11, 7, 7

4. 10, 10, 20, 15, 100, 25

Find the mean. Round to the nearest tenth if needed.

5.
Value	2	3	4	5
Frequency	9	3	2	11

6.
Value	4	6	7	9	12
Frequency	3	1	5	8	3

Solve.

7. The average of Nadine's six tests is 77. The scores on five of the tests are 88, 65, 75, 83, and 90. What is her score on the remaining test?

8. Alvin predicts he'll drive an average of 50 mi per day during his five-day vacation. On the first four days he drives a total of 221 mi. If his prediction is correct, how far does he drive on the fifth day?

Statistical Graphs

Use the graph to solve.

9. The line graph shows the number of maps sold at a town's visitor center one day.

   A. How many maps were sold on Monday, Tuesday, and Wednesday combined?

   B. Order the days of the week by number of maps sold, from most to fewest.

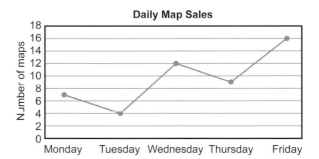

10. The bar graph shows the lengths of the longest rivers in the United States.

   A. Tell which rivers have the same length, and approximate that length.

   B. About how long is the Missouri River?

   C. About how much longer is the Mississippi River than the Yukon River?

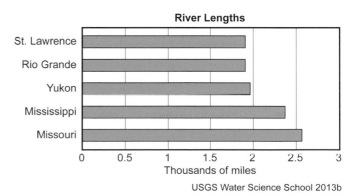

USGS Water Science School 2013b

11. The circle graph shows the percent of the 200 votes each candidate received in a club's election for a new president.

Election Results

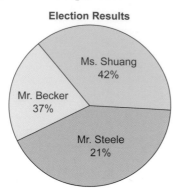

A. Which candidate won, and how many votes did he or she receive?

B. How many votes separated the winner and the candidate who came in second?

12. The histogram shows the results of a library survey that asked patrons how many books they usually borrow per visit.

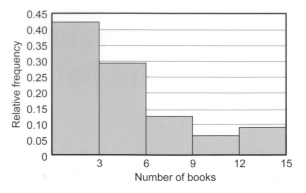

A. About what percent of those surveyed said they usually borrow fewer than 6 books per visit?

B. Given that 200 patrons were surveyed, about how many said they usually borrow at least 12 books?

Measures of Spread

For each data set, find the following:
A. five-number summary
B. range
C. IQR

13. 3, 7, 10, 15, 18, 19, 25

14. 12, 12, 14, 20, 21, 25, 40, 43

15. 43, 35, 47, 39, 50, 52, 21, 27, 43

16. −8, −6, −6, −2, 3, 6, 10

Find the standard deviation of the data set. Round to the nearest tenth if needed.

17. 21, 23, 25, 27

18. 13, 14, 15, 15, 18

19. 3, 5, 5, 5, 8, 10

20. 10, 12, 18, 200

21. 6, 10, 3, 1, 11, 4, 14, 7

22. −12, −4, 0, 3, 3

Solve.

23. The box plot shows the prices of gift baskets in a catalog.

A. Estimate the range of the prices of the baskets.

B. Estimate the range of the middle 50% of the prices.

C. Discuss the spread of the prices.

24. Without calculating, explain which data set would have the **greater** standard deviation.

Set A: 26, 29, 35, 37, 96
Set B: 85, 87, 93, 95, 96

25. Without calculating, explain which data set would have the **lesser** standard deviation.

Set A: 0, 4, 8, 12, 16, 20
Set B: 4, 6, 8, 10, 12, 14

Extra Problems for Chapter 2 Connections Between Data

Scatter Plots

The scatter plot shows the person's years of experience in metal detector use and the number of coins that person found.

1. How many coins did the person with 3 years of experience find?

2. How many people had 8 years of experience?

3. How many people found at least 6 coins?

4. How many years of experience did the person who found the most coins have?

5. What percent of the people had fewer than 10 years of experience?

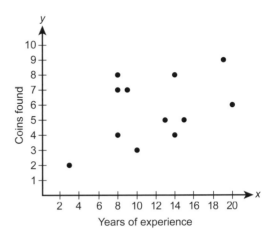

Make a scatter plot for the data. Identify any clusters or outliers.

6.

Lines	3	1	8	4	9	3	8	8	9	6
Fish	2	4	6	4	8	6	7	3	7	2

7.

Cars	3	2	6	4	5	8	4	5	7	8
Trucks	7	6	5	7	6	4	5	1	6	7

Correlation

Determine the direction and strength of the association between *x* and *y*.

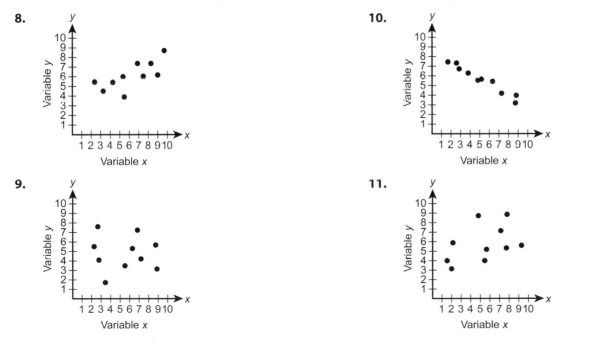

Use technology to determine the value of the correlation coefficient *r*.

12.

	Ph.D.	Professional	M.A. or M.S.	B.A. or B.S.	Associate	HS diploma	Less than HS diploma
Median weekly earnings 2012 ($)	1624	1735	1300	1066	785	652	471
Unemployment rate 2012 (%)	2.5	2.1	3.5	4.5	6.2	8.3	12.4

DOL BLS 2013

13.

	Apple	Apricot	Cherry	Grapefruit	Lemon	Mango	Peach	Plum
Vit A (IU)	54	1926	64	927	22	1082	326	345
Vit C (mg)	4.6	10.0	7	34.4	53.0	36.4	6.6	9.5

USDA ARS NDL 2012

Linear Regression

Write an equation of the linear model shown.

14.

x	y
2	6
5	7
5	9
7	10
10	10
12	10
13	12.5
15	11

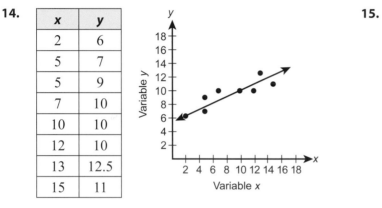

15.

x	y
6	36
12	36
16	24
22	23
25	17.5
32	13
39	13
42	8

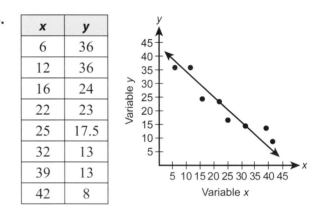

The table shows the costs of vacations to a given destination.

Number of days	3	7	5	3	2	4	4	6
Cost ($)	486	1340	982	513	450	639	570	1102

16. Find the linear regression equation using the number of days for the input variable and the cost for the output variable.

17. Predict the total cost of a 10-day vacation.

18. What percent of the variation in cost can be explained by the variation in the number of days?

More Regression

For each employee at a company, the table shows the years with the company and vacation days allowed.

Years	1	5	1	3	10	8	1	20
Vacation days	7	14	10	12	21	17	5	20

19. Find the quadratic regression equation using the years for the input variable and the vacation days for the output variable.

20. Estimate the allowable number of vacation days for an employee who has been with the company for 6 years.

Extra Problems for Chapter 3 Uncertainty

Permutations and Combinations

Find the value of the expression.

1. $_7P_4$

2. $_6P_1$

3. $_4P_2$

4. $_9C_3$

5. $_8C_8$

6. $_{11}C_9$

Use a permutation expression to solve.

7. At a car race, 24 drivers are competing to finish first through third. In how many ways can this be done?

8. A tennis tournament consists of 16 players. In how many ways can the winner and runner-up in the tournament be determined?

9. A drill instructor told 9 cadets to line up. In how many ways can the cadets line up?

10. Keisha's car collection consists of 6 antique cars. If she wants to display 4 of her cars at the auto show, in how many ways can she display the cars if they must be parked side by side?

Use a combination expression to solve.

11. Having finished their group project, the 9 members must pick 2 people to present their results to the rest of the class. In how many ways can this be done?

12. Kobe must pick 4 of 12 rocks from his collection to photograph for his science project. In how many ways can he make his selection?

13. Dr. Patel must choose 3 out of the 7 other doctors who work at the clinic to attend the seminar. In how many ways can she make her choice?

14. Caleb must select 10 teammates from a group of 24 competitors to complete his football team. In how many ways can he make his choice?

Probability

The graph shows the composition, by breed of dog, of the 50 dogs entered in the local dog show.

15. If a dog is chosen at random, what is the probability that the dog is a shepherd?

16. If a dog is chosen at random, what is the probability that the dog is a hound?

17. If a dog is chosen at random, what is the probability that it is either a sheepdog or a terrier?

18. If a dog is chosen at random, what is the probability that it is either a collie or a hound?

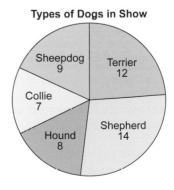

Types of Dogs in Show

Sheepdog 9

Terrier 12

Collie 7

Hound 8

Shepherd 14

Find the probability.

19. Suppose Gloria knows that the probability of her completing the marathon in less than 5 hours is $\frac{5}{7}$. What is the probability that she does not complete the race in less than 5 hours?

20. Caleb believes that he will make $\frac{3}{4}$ of the 3-pointers he shoots in a basketball game. What is the probability that he does not make a 3-pointer?

Expected Value

Greta collects North American butterflies. The probability distribution table describes her collection. Find the probability of the event.

Butterfly name	Swallowtail	White	Metalmark	Skipper	Gossamer-wing
Butterfly distribution	0.14	0.36	0.2	0.25	0.05

21. a butterfly chosen at random is a white

22. a butterfly chosen at random is a skipper

23. a butterfly chosen at random is a metalmark or a swallowtail

24. a butterfly chosen at random is a skipper or a gossamer-wing

Determine the expected value.

25. Monique has just taken up the sport of archery. She earns 10 points if she hits the bull's-eye, 2 points if she hits the target elsewhere, and −1 point if she misses the target entirely. The probability of her hitting the bull's-eye is $\frac{1}{6}$, the probability of her hitting the target elsewhere is $\frac{1}{2}$, and the probability of her missing the target is $\frac{1}{3}$.

26. Pedro is entering a 16-team spades tournament. The probability of his team playing exactly 1 game is $\frac{1}{8}$, exactly 2 games is $\frac{3}{8}$, exactly 3 games is $\frac{3}{8}$, and exactly 4 games is $\frac{1}{8}$.

Explain why the table is not a probability distribution.

27.

Result	1	11	111	1111
P	0.1	0.4	0.7	0.2

28.

Result	4	8	12	16
P	−0.2	−0.1	−0.5	−0.2

Extra Problems for Chapter 4
Math Models

Variation

Write the direct variation equation and evaluate the function for the given value.

1. If $f(x)$ varies directly with x and $f(x) = 40$ when $x = 8$, find the value of $f(x)$ when $x = 2$.

2. If $f(a)$ varies directly with a and $f(a) = 9$ when $a = 4$, find the value of $f(a)$ when $a = 6$.

3. If $g(t)$ varies directly with t and $g(t) = 60$ when $t = 80$, find the value of t when $g(t) = 75$.

4. If $h(b)$ varies directly with b and $h(b) = -18$ when $b = 6$, find the value of b when $h(b) = 15$.

Write the inverse variation equation and evaluate the function for the given value.

5. If $f(x)$ varies inversely with x and $f(x) = 20$ when $x = 3$, find the value of $f(x)$ when $x = 15$.

6. If $f(w)$ varies inversely with w and $f(w) = 5$ when $w = 4$, find the value of $f(w)$ when $w = 8$.

7. If $h(x)$ varies inversely with x and $h(x) = 10$ when $x = 3$, find the value of x when $h(x) = 1$.

8. If $g(n)$ varies inversely with n and $g(n) = 6$ when $n = 2$, find the value of n when $g(n) = 1.5$.

Write the variation equation and solve.

9. A bridge toll for a vehicle varies directly with the number of axles on the vehicle. If a 3-axle vehicle pays a toll of $8.25, what is the toll for a 5-axle vehicle?

10. The pressure of a gas varies inversely with its volume. The pressure of a gas is 25 psi when its volume is 60 in³. What is the volume when the pressure is 20 psi?

Sequences

Use an iterative formula to find the indicated term of the arithmetic sequence.

11. 57th term of the sequence 7, 15, 23, 31, . . .

12. 99th term of the sequence 4, 8, 12, 16, . . .

13. 23rd term of the sequence 12, 10, 8, 6, . . .

14. 51st term of the sequence –5, 5, 15, 25, . . .

Use an iterative formula to find the indicated term of the geometric sequence.

15. 12th term of the sequence 9, 18, 36, 72, . . .

16. 10th term of the sequence 2, 8, 32, 128, . . .

17. 9th term of the sequence 960, 480, 240, . . .

18. 14th term of the sequence 3, –9, 27, . . .

Solve.

19. The performers in a half-time show are arranged so there are 5 people in the first row, and each row has 6 more people than the previous row. How many performers are in the 25th row?

20. For her 2-week summer job, Julie suggests that she be paid $8 on Day 1, $12 on Day 2, $18 on Day 3, $27 on Day 4, and so on. If her suggestion is used, how much will she be paid on her last (10th) day of work?

Matrices

Matrix V shows the number of violation tickets written during different time periods one week on the different lines in a subway system.

$$
\begin{array}{c}
\text{Morning} \\
\text{Afternoon} \\
\text{Evening}
\end{array}
\begin{array}{cccc}
\text{Yellow} & \text{Red} & \text{Blue} & \text{Green} \\
\left[\begin{array}{cccc}
24 & 19 & 7 & 11 \\
5 & 8 & 6 & 2 \\
30 & 35 & 18 & 21
\end{array}\right] = V
\end{array}
$$

21. What are the dimensions of the matrix?

22. What is the element with address v_{12}?

23. What is the address of the element with value 2?

24. How many violation tickets were written in the afternoon?

25. How many more violation tickets were written on the red line than the blue line?

Find the product, sum, or difference, if possible.

$$
A = \begin{bmatrix} 9 & 5 \\ 2 & 3 \end{bmatrix}
\quad
B = \begin{bmatrix} 4 & 11 \\ 0 & 7 \\ 8 & 6 \end{bmatrix}
\quad
C = \begin{bmatrix} 10 & -5 \\ 3 & 12 \\ 3 & 0 \end{bmatrix}
$$

26. $6A$

27. $A + B$

28. $B + C$

29. $B - C$

Geometric Models

Answer the question about the pattern.

30. What transformations map the strip pattern XZXZXZXZXZXZXZX onto itself?

31. Tell what transformations and symmetries you see in the pattern.

32. What transformations map the strip pattern onto itself?

33. Give the name of the tiling.

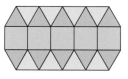

Solve.

34. A 30 in. by 40 in. photo is reduced so that its width (the shorter side) is 24 in. Find the scale factor used and the length (the longer side) of the reduced photo.

35. The scale factor of a model pickup truck to the actual pickup truck is 1 to 50.

   A. Find the length of the actual truck if the length of the model is 4.6 in.

   B. Find the area of a hubcap on the model if the area of the hubcap on the actual truck is 225 in².

   C. Find the volume of the cargo area in the actual truck if the volume of the cargo area in the model is 1.2 in³.

Extra Problems for Chapter 5
Income

Making Money

Find the weekly gross pay. Assume overtime pay for time exceeding 40 h.

1. hourly rate: $9.90, hours worked: 34

2. hourly rate: $14.36, hours worked: 40

3. hourly rate: $12.75, hours worked: 45

4. hourly rate: $13.40, hours worked: 51

Find the gross pay per pay period.

5. annual salary: $26,805, pay period: weekly

6. annual salary: $49,000, pay period: monthly

7. annual salary: $53,278, pay period: biweekly

8. annual salary: $32,450, pay period: semimonthly

Solve.

9. Ericka earns a gross biweekly salary of $1014.40. What is her gross annual salary?

10. Hayden earns a gross weekly salary of $654. Kaleb earns a gross semimonthly salary of $1460. Who has the greater annual income?

11. A customer leaves a 15% tip on a $34.20 bill. What is the amount of the tip?

12. Kenton earns a gross weekly salary of $410 plus 6.5% commission on his sales. Find his gross weekly pay for a week in which his sales totaled $4028.

Taxes and Deductions

Solve.

13. Nelson earned $379.25 in net pay for working 40 h. He paid $56.64 in federal and state taxes, and $36.11 in FICA tax. What was Nelson's hourly wage?

14. Randy's gross pay is $1396. How much of his gross pay will be deducted for the Medicare tax?

15. Carmela's gross pay is $784.25. Her deductions total $191.17. What percent of her gross pay is take-home pay?

16. Sal earns a gross monthly salary of $2400. Find his annual Social Security deduction.

17. Part of Mr. Ray's W-2 form is shown.

1 Wages, tips, other compensation	2 Federal income tax withheld
61,987.50	8,802.26
3 Social security wages	4 Social security tax withheld
61,987.50	3,843.23
5 Medicare wages and tips	6 Medicare tax withheld
61,987.50	898.82

A. What was Mr. Ray's total compensation?

B. What percent of Mr. Ray's total compensation was withheld for federal taxes?

C. How much did Mr. Ray pay in FICA tax?

18. Mrs. Sanchez's taxable income is $37,056. She is married and filing separately, and she has already paid $5098 in federal taxes. Use the 2012 Tax Table on pages A-18 and A-19 to determine if Mrs. Sanchez overpaid or underpaid, and find the amount she will receive or pay.

Banking

Use Venita Brown's check to answer the questions.

19. Who is the payer?

20. Who is the payee?

21. What is the check number?

22. What is the payer's checking account number?

23. What is the routing number of the bank from which the check is drawn?

```
Venita Brown                                              913
999 SW King Ave                  Date May 1, 2013
Seattle, WA 98115

PAY TO THE
ORDER OF    Stacy Mullins                          $  809.53
                                53
        Eight hundred nine and  /100 _____ DOLLARS

   ❋ Financial Institution

   For  Rent and Utilities            Venita Brown

   ⑆ 987654321 ⑆ 0463887326 ⑈   913
```

Use Nathan's check register to answer the questions.

24. What was Nathan's balance after his deposit on February 15?

25. What was the check number on the check that Nathan used to make his car payment?

26. How much did Nathan withdraw from the ATM on February 11?

27. What was Nathan's balance before he wrote check 1019?

D = Deposit	**AP** = Automatic Payment		**ATM** = Cash Withdrawal		**DC** = Debit Card	**SC** = Service Charge	

Date	Code or Check #	Transaction Description	Payment, Fee, Withdrawal (−)	✓	Deposit, Credit (+)	Balance	
						549	16
2/6	1017	Car payment	234 08			315	08
2/11	ATM	Theme Park	60 00			255	08
2/15	D	Payday!			490 85	745	93
2/21	1018	Internet bill	36 00			709	93
2/28	D	Payday!			490 85	1200	78
3/2	1019	Rent	550 00			650	78

Use Nathan's bank statement to answer the questions.

Account Number 330075831993			Statement period: 2/4/2013 to 3/5/2013		
Beginning Balance		**Total Deposits**	**Total Withdrawals**		**Ending Balance**
$549.16		$981.70	$332.08		$1198.78

Date	Ref #	Description	Debits (−)	Credits (+)	Balance
2/9	1017	Check	234.08		315.08
2/11		ATM–Gonzo's Get-Away Theme Park	60.00		255.08
2/11		Out of Network ATM Fee	2.00		253.08
2/15		Deposit		490.85	743.93
2/26	1018	Check	36.00		707.93
2/28		Deposit		490.85	1198.78

28. What range of dates does this bank statement cover?

29. What is the ending balance on the statement?

30. What is the difference between the total deposit amount and total withdrawal amount?

31. Compare the bank statement to the check register above.

   A. Which check did not clear the bank during the statement period?

   B. Show how Nathan would reconcile his checking account.

   C. Which transaction did Nathan forget to record?

Extra Problems for Chapter 6 Budgeting

Budget Basics

Determine the monthly amount.

1. Velena pays $210 a year for insurance. How much should she budget monthly for it?

2. Mr. Yang has an annual car insurance bill of $848 and an annual property tax bill of $2309. How much should he budget monthly for his annual expenses?

Determine the percent of income.

3. Sal budgets $1050 each month for fixed expenses. What percent of his income is that if he nets $748.18 each week?

4. Robyn budgets $380 each month for living expenses. What percent of her income is that if her annual net income is $17,396?

Determine whether the monthly budget is balanced, shows a surplus, or shows a deficit. If there is a surplus or a deficit, give the amount.

5. Everett budgeted $998 for fixed expenses, $415 for living expenses, and $45 for annual expenses. His annual net income is $20,136.

6. Tianna budgeted $2450 for fixed expenses, $1175 for living expenses, and $665 for annual expenses. Her biweekly net income is $1962.

The equation $y = 426x + 5356$ approximates a school's annual tuition, y in dollars, given the number of years since 2000, x.

7. Predict the school's annual tuition in 2023.

8. Predict the first year that the school's annual tuition will be at least $20,000.

Understanding Credit

Find the new credit card balance.

9. Jay's unpaid credit card balance is $3390.88. His APR is 18.6%. What is his new balance if he made one new transaction for $128?

10. Heather's statement shows a previous balance of $1413.92, a payment of $40, and new transactions totaling $381.51. What is her new balance if her APR is 16.2%?

Solve the loan problem.

11. Mr. Quesada took out a loan for $12,000. To pay it back, he will make 24 monthly payments of $629. How much will he pay in interest?

12. Rey's total payment for his student loan was $24,506. What was his monthly payment if he paid it off after making 120 monthly payments?

13. Diane will borrow $3000 at 13.5% APR. She will pay it back over 36 months. What will her monthly payment be? (Use the personal loan payment rate table on page A-17.)

14. Shae will borrow $2400 at 11.5% APR. She will pay it back over 2 years. What will her monthly payment be? (Use the personal loan payment rate table on page A-17.)

Housing

Determine the maximum amount the person can afford. Round to the nearest dollar.

15. Claire's gross annual salary is $19,776. What is the maximum amount of rent she can afford to pay?

16. Justin's gross weekly income is $976.80. What is the maximum mortgage amount he can afford to borrow?

Find the move-in amount.

17. Mr. Vargas is signing a lease for an apartment that rents for $1050/month. How much will he pay to move in if he must pay the first and last months' rent and a security deposit equal to 60% of his monthly rent?

18. Luke and Griffin signed a lease for an apartment that rents for $810/month. Luke will pay 60% of the rent. They will share everything else equally. How much will Luke pay to move in if they pay the first and last months' rent and a $500 security deposit?

Li Mei is buying a home for $235,000. She is making a 10% down payment and financing the rest with a 25-year loan at 6% interest.

19. How much will she borrow?

20. What will her monthly mortgage payment be? (Use the mortgage payment rate table on page A-17.)

21. What will her total payment for the home be?

22. How much interest will she pay?

23. Li Mei's home is predicted to appreciate in value by 5.5% each year. Predict the value of her home in 25 years.

Owning a Car

Dixon decided to buy a car for $14,340. He will finance $9000 of it with a 3-year loan at 3.9% APR.

24. What will his monthly auto payment be? (Use the car loan payment rate table on page A-17.)

25. How much interest will he pay?

26. What will his total payment for the car be?

27. Dixon's car is expected to depreciate an average of 13% each year during the first 6 years. Predict the value of his car in 6 years.

Solve.

28. Nina drove 518 mi on 14.7 gal of gas. Find her gas mileage, rounded to the nearest mpg.

29. Krishna is planning a 1330-mi driving trip. His car gets an average of 27 mpg, and the cost of gas is about $3.72/gal. Estimate the driving cost of the trip.

Find the total annual premium. Use the tables on page 155.

30. A 20-year-old female driver buys 50/100/25 liability insurance, and collision and comprehensive insurance, each with $250 deductibles.

31. A 28-year-old male buys 100/300/100 liability insurance, collision insurance with a $250 deductible, and comprehensive insurance with a $500 deductible.

Extra Problems for Chapter 7
Saving Money

Interest

Solve the simple interest problem.

1. Connor deposited $500 into a savings account that pays a simple annual interest rate of 1.95%.

    A. How much interest will he earn after 6 months?

    B. If he makes no other deposits or withdrawals, what will the total amount be in his account after 6 months?

2. Rimah deposited money into a savings account that pays a simple annual interest rate of 2.3%. How much did she deposit if she earned $87.40 after 4 years?

Solve the compound interest problem.

3. Paul deposited $4400 into a savings account in which interest is compounded monthly at a rate of 4.2%.

    A. Assuming he makes no other deposits or withdrawals, how much will be in his account after 10 years?

    B. How much interest will he earn after 10 years?

4. Misty deposited money into an account in which interest is compounded quarterly at a rate of 3%. How much did she deposit if the total amount in her account after 4 years was $788.89, and she made no other deposits or withdrawals?

The graph shows the total amounts in two accounts with the same principal and annual interest rate. Use the graph to solve.

5. What is the principal?

6. How much simple interest is earned after 15 years?

7. How much compound interest is earned after 20 years?

8. What is the difference in the amounts of interest earned after 40 years?

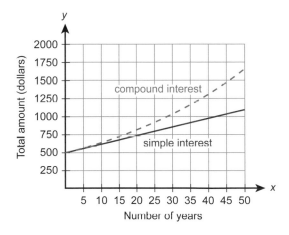

Insurance

For each person, find the following amounts:
A. how much he or she pays annually for health insurance
B. how much is deducted from his or her paycheck for health insurance

9. The total annual premium for health insurance for Demarco is $6780. His employer pays 65% of the premium and deducts the remainder from his paycheck. Demarco is paid weekly.

10. The total annual premium for health insurance for Julia is $9040. Her employer pays 80% of the premium and deducts the remainder from her paycheck. Julia is paid biweekly.

Find the person's share of the medical bill.

11. The health insurance company pays 80% of the cost of allergy shots for Yolanda, after she pays a $100 deductible. How much will Yolanda pay for her shots if they cost $1324?

12. Brian must pay a co-pay of $15 to visit a specialist. Then his insurance company pays 85% of the cost of the visit. How much did Brian pay to see the specialist if the cost of the visit was $405?

For each person, find the following amounts:
A. his or her annual life insurance premium (Use the Fly-by-Night Life Insurance Company table on page 173.)
B. how much is deducted from his or her paycheck for life insurance

13. Justin, a 22-year-old male, bought a $225,000, 20-year life insurance policy through his employer. Justin is paid monthly.

14. Lorena, a 41-year-old female, bought a $160,000, 10-year life insurance policy through her employer. Lorena is paid semimonthly.

Investments

Use the Rule of 72 to solve.

15. The value of an investment doubled in 15 years. What was the annual rate of return?

16. The value of an investment is expected to grow by 6.8% per year. How long will it take for the value to double?

Solve the stock or bond problem.

17. Mr. Blevins bought 1100 shares of a company's stock for $22/share. He pays a broker a commission of $15 to buy and sell stock. After one year, Mr. Blevins sold all his shares, when they were worth $24.90/share.

    A. What was his net gain?

    B. What was his rate of return?

18. Renatta bought a bond with a face value of $5000 and a coupon rate of 7%. The bond will mature in 5 years.

    A. What is the total amount of interest she will receive?

    B. How much interest will she receive semiannually?

Solve the retirement problem.

19. Dean's gross semimonthly pay is $1306. To maintain his current lifestyle, how much should he save up by the time he retires?

20. Violet's gross annual income is $57,903. She is paid biweekly and has 7% deducted from her paychecks for her 401(k). Her employer matches her deduction, up to 5%.

    A. How much is deducted from her paycheck for her 401(k)?

    B. How much is deposited into her retirement plan each payday?

Extra Problems for Chapter 8
More Math Models

Growth and Decay

For each problem:
A. Write a formula to model the situation.
B. Use the formula to make the desired prediction.

1. There were 60 people in a town's first annual parade. That number has been growing by about 5% each year. Predict the number of people in the town's 25th annual parade.

2. A population of 12,000 chimpanzees is expected to decline at a rate of 4% per year. Predict the chimpanzee population in 15 years.

Make the desired prediction.

3. Shirley bought an antique table for $810. It is expected to appreciate by 6% each year. Predict when the value of Shirley's table will be worth $2000.

4. In 2010, a city's population was 439,023 and declining at a rate of 0.9%. Predict when the city's population will first be below 400,000.

Solve.

5. Cobalt-60 has a half-life of about 5 years. How many grams of a 250 g sample will remain after 22 years?

6. Iodine-131 has a half-life of about 8 days. How much time has passed if 75 g of an initial 600 g sample remain?

Trigonometric Ratios

Solve.

7. Round to four decimal places.

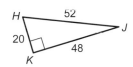

   A. What is $\sin J$?

   B. What is $\tan H$?

8. Find the value of x. Round to the nearest hundredth.

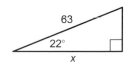

9. A 30 ft ladder leans against the side of a building, making a 55° angle with the ground. To the nearest tenth of a foot, how far up the side of the building does the ladder reach?

10. From her position 28 m above sea level, a lighthouse keeper spots a boat at a 20° angle of depression. To the nearest tenth of a meter, how far is the boat from the lighthouse?

Periodic Functions

Solve.

11. Determine the period and amplitude of the function.

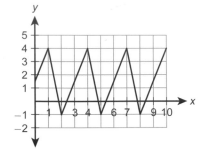

12. The tables show the height of a rider, in feet, during the first 60 s of a ride.

Seconds	5	10	15	20	25	30
Feet	5	0	10	0	6	0

Seconds	35	40	45	50	55	60
Feet	8.5	0	6	0	9	−1

Estimate the period and amplitude of the data.

13. Consider the function.

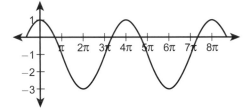

A. Identify the function's period.

B. Identify the function's amplitude.

14. The graph shows the distance y, in inches, a pendulum moves to the right (positive) and to the left (negative), for a given number of seconds, x.

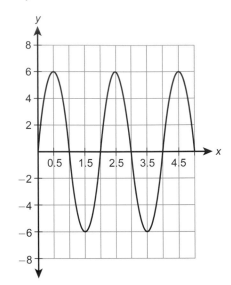

A. How far from its resting position does the pendulum move to either side?

B. From its resting position, how long does it take the pendulum to swing one direction, then the other, and then return to its resting position?

C. Describe how the pendulum is moving during the time period from $x = 3$ to $x = 3.5$.

D. What is the graph's frequency, and what does it indicate in this situation?

Math and Music

Identify the geometric transformation shown in the line of music.

15.

16.

Use the frequencies table on page 209 to determine the frequencies of the following three pitches in relation to the given note:
A. one octave above
B. two octaves above
C. a perfect fifth below

17. D4

18. F3

Financial Reference Tables

Monthly Personal Loan Payment per $100 Borrowed

	Term (months)		
Rate	24	36	60
11.5%	4.684	3.298	2.199
12.5%	4.731	3.345	2.251
13.5%	4.778	3.394	2.301

Monthly Mortgage Payment per $1000 Borrowed

	Term (years)			
Rate	15	20	25	30
3.00%	6.906	5.546	4.742	4.216
3.25%	7.027	5.672	4.873	4.352
3.50%	7.149	5.800	5.006	4.490
3.75%	7.272	5.929	5.141	4.631
4.00%	7.397	6.060	5.278	4.774
4.25%	7.523	6.192	5.417	4.919
4.50%	7.650	6.326	5.558	5.067
4.75%	7.778	6.462	5.701	5.216
5.00%	7.908	6.600	5.846	5.368
5.25%	8.039	6.738	5.992	5.522
5.50%	8.171	6.879	6.141	5.678
5.75%	8.304	7.021	6.291	5.836
6.00%	8.439	7.164	6.443	5.996
6.25%	8.574	7.309	6.597	6.157
6.50%	8.711	7.456	6.752	6.321
6.75%	8.849	7.604	6.909	6.486
7.00%	8.988	7.753	7.068	6.653
7.25%	9.129	7.904	7.228	6.822
7.50%	9.270	8.056	7.390	6.992
7.75%	9.413	8.209	7.553	7.164
8.00%	9.557	8.364	7.718	7.338

Monthly Car Loan Payment per $1000 Borrowed

	Term (months)			
APR	24	36	48	60
2.5%	42.760	28.861	21.914	17.747
2.6%	42.805	28.905	21.958	17.791
2.7%	42.849	28.949	22.002	17.836
2.8%	42.893	28.993	22.046	17.880
2.9%	42.937	29.037	22.090	17.924
3.0%	42.981	29.081	22.134	17.969
3.1%	43.025	29.125	22.179	18.013
3.2%	43.070	29.169	22.223	18.058
3.3%	43.114	29.214	22.267	18.102
3.4%	43.158	29.258	22.312	18.147
3.5%	43.203	29.302	22.356	18.192
3.6%	43.247	29.346	22.401	18.237
3.7%	43.292	29.391	22.445	18.281
3.8%	43.336	29.435	22.490	18.326
3.9%	43.380	29.480	22.534	18.371
4.0%	43.425	29.524	22.579	18.417
4.1%	43.469	29.568	22.624	18.462
4.2%	43.514	29.613	22.669	18.507
4.3%	43.559	29.658	22.714	18.552
4.4%	43.603	29.702	22.758	18.598
4.5%	43.648	29.747	22.803	18.643
4.6%	43.692	29.792	22.849	18.689
4.7%	43.737	29.836	22.894	18.734
4.8%	43.782	29.881	22.939	18.780
4.9%	43.827	29.926	22.984	18.825
5.0%	43.871	29.971	23.029	18.871
5.1%	43.916	30.016	23.075	18.917
5.2%	43.961	30.061	23.120	18.963
5.3%	44.006	30.106	23.165	19.009
5.4%	44.051	30.151	23.211	19.055
5.5%	44.096	30.196	23.256	19.101

2012 Tax Table

If line 43 (taxable income) is— / And you are—

At least	But less than	Single	Married filing jointly *	Married filing separately	Head of a household
30,000					
30,000	30,050	4,069	3,634	4,069	3,884
30,050	30,100	4,076	3,641	4,076	3,891
30,100	30,150	4,084	3,649	4,084	3,899
30,150	30,200	4,091	3,656	4,091	3,906
30,200	30,250	4,099	3,664	4,099	3,914
30,250	30,300	4,106	3,671	4,106	3,921
30,300	30,350	4,114	3,679	4,114	3,929
30,350	30,400	4,121	3,686	4,121	3,936
30,400	30,450	4,129	3,694	4,129	3,944
30,450	30,500	4,136	3,701	4,136	3,951
30,500	30,550	4,144	3,709	4,144	3,959
30,550	30,600	4,151	3,716	4,151	3,966
30,600	30,650	4,159	3,724	4,159	3,974
30,650	30,700	4,166	3,731	4,166	3,981
30,700	30,750	4,174	3,739	4,174	3,989
30,750	30,800	4,181	3,746	4,181	3,996
30,800	30,850	4,189	3,754	4,189	4,004
30,850	30,900	4,196	3,761	4,196	4,011
30,900	30,950	4,204	3,769	4,204	4,019
30,950	31,000	4,211	3,776	4,211	4,026
31,000					
31,000	31,050	4,219	3,784	4,219	4,034
31,050	31,100	4,226	3,791	4,226	4,041
31,100	31,150	4,234	3,799	4,234	4,049
31,150	31,200	4,241	3,806	4,241	4,056
31,200	31,250	4,249	3,814	4,249	4,064
31,250	31,300	4,256	3,821	4,256	4,071
31,300	31,350	4,264	3,829	4,264	4,079
31,350	31,400	4,271	3,836	4,271	4,086
31,400	31,450	4,279	3,844	4,279	4,094
31,450	31,500	4,286	3,851	4,286	4,101
31,500	31,550	4,294	3,859	4,294	4,109
31,550	31,600	4,301	3,866	4,301	4,116
31,600	31,650	4,309	3,874	4,309	4,124
31,650	31,700	4,316	3,881	4,316	4,131
31,700	31,750	4,324	3,889	4,324	4,139
31,750	31,800	4,331	3,896	4,331	4,146
31,800	31,850	4,339	3,904	4,339	4,154
31,850	31,900	4,346	3,911	4,346	4,161
31,900	31,950	4,354	3,919	4,354	4,169
31,950	32,000	4,361	3,926	4,361	4,176

At least	But less than	Single	Married filing jointly *	Married filing separately	Head of a household
32,000					
32,000	32,050	4,369	3,934	4,369	4,184
32,050	32,100	4,376	3,941	4,376	4,191
32,100	32,150	4,384	3,949	4,384	4,199
32,150	32,200	4,391	3,956	4,391	4,206
32,200	32,250	4,399	3,964	4,399	4,214
32,250	32,300	4,406	3,971	4,406	4,221
32,300	32,350	4,414	3,979	4,414	4,229
32,350	32,400	4,421	3,986	4,421	4,236
32,400	32,450	4,429	3,994	4,429	4,244
32,450	32,500	4,436	4,001	4,436	4,251
32,500	32,550	4,444	4,009	4,444	4,259
32,550	32,600	4,451	4,016	4,451	4,266
32,600	32,650	4,459	4,024	4,459	4,274
32,650	32,700	4,466	4,031	4,466	4,281
32,700	32,750	4,474	4,039	4,474	4,289
32,750	32,800	4,481	4,046	4,481	4,296
32,800	32,850	4,489	4,054	4,489	4,304
32,850	32,900	4,496	4,061	4,496	4,311
32,900	32,950	4,504	4,069	4,504	4,319
32,950	33,000	4,511	4,076	4,511	4,326
33,000					
33,000	33,050	4,519	4,084	4,519	4,334
33,050	33,100	4,526	4,091	4,526	4,341
33,100	33,150	4,534	4,099	4,534	4,349
33,150	33,200	4,541	4,106	4,541	4,356
33,200	33,250	4,549	4,114	4,549	4,364
33,250	33,300	4,556	4,121	4,556	4,371
33,300	33,350	4,564	4,129	4,564	4,379
33,350	33,400	4,571	4,136	4,571	4,386
33,400	33,450	4,579	4,144	4,579	4,394
33,450	33,500	4,586	4,151	4,586	4,401
33,500	33,550	4,594	4,159	4,594	4,409
33,550	33,600	4,601	4,166	4,601	4,416
33,600	33,650	4,609	4,174	4,609	4,424
33,650	33,700	4,616	4,181	4,616	4,431
33,700	33,750	4,624	4,189	4,624	4,439
33,750	33,800	4,631	4,196	4,631	4,446
33,800	33,850	4,639	4,204	4,639	4,454
33,850	33,900	4,646	4,211	4,646	4,461
33,900	33,950	4,654	4,219	4,654	4,469
33,950	34,000	4,661	4,226	4,661	4,476

At least	But less than	Single	Married filing jointly *	Married filing separately	Head of a household
34,000					
34,000	34,050	4,669	4,234	4,669	4,484
34,050	34,100	4,676	4,241	4,676	4,491
34,100	34,150	4,684	4,249	4,684	4,499
34,150	34,200	4,691	4,256	4,691	4,506
34,200	34,250	4,699	4,264	4,699	4,514
34,250	34,300	4,706	4,271	4,706	4,521
34,300	34,350	4,714	4,279	4,714	4,529
34,350	34,400	4,721	4,286	4,721	4,536
34,400	34,450	4,729	4,294	4,729	4,544
34,450	34,500	4,736	4,301	4,736	4,551
34,500	34,550	4,744	4,309	4,744	4,559
34,550	34,600	4,751	4,316	4,751	4,566
34,600	34,650	4,759	4,324	4,759	4,574
34,650	34,700	4,766	4,331	4,766	4,581
34,700	34,750	4,774	4,339	4,774	4,589
34,750	34,800	4,781	4,346	4,781	4,596
34,800	34,850	4,789	4,354	4,789	4,604
34,850	34,900	4,796	4,361	4,796	4,611
34,900	34,950	4,804	4,369	4,804	4,619
34,950	35,000	4,811	4,376	4,811	4,626
35,000					
35,000	35,050	4,819	4,384	4,819	4,634
35,050	35,100	4,826	4,391	4,826	4,641
35,100	35,150	4,834	4,399	4,834	4,649
35,150	35,200	4,841	4,406	4,841	4,656
35,200	35,250	4,849	4,414	4,849	4,664
35,250	35,300	4,856	4,421	4,856	4,671
35,300	35,350	4,864	4,429	4,864	4,679
35,350	35,400	4,874	4,436	4,874	4,686
35,400	35,450	4,886	4,444	4,886	4,694
35,450	35,500	4,899	4,451	4,899	4,701
35,500	35,550	4,911	4,459	4,911	4,709
35,550	35,600	4,924	4,466	4,924	4,716
35,600	35,650	4,936	4,474	4,936	4,724
35,650	35,700	4,949	4,481	4,949	4,731
35,700	35,750	4,961	4,489	4,961	4,739
35,750	35,800	4,974	4,496	4,974	4,746
35,800	35,850	4,986	4,504	4,986	4,754
35,850	35,900	4,999	4,511	4,999	4,761
35,900	35,950	5,011	4,519	5,011	4,769
35,950	36,000	5,024	4,526	5,024	4,776

If line 43 (taxable income) is—		And you are—			
At least	But less than	Single	Married filing jointly *	Married filing sepa-rately	Head of a house-hold
		Your tax is—			

36,000

At least	But less than	Single	Married filing jointly *	Married filing separately	Head of a household
36,000	36,050	5,036	4,534	5,036	4,784
36,050	36,100	5,049	4,541	5,049	4,791
36,100	36,150	5,061	4,549	5,061	4,799
36,150	36,200	5,074	4,556	5,074	4,806
36,200	36,250	5,086	4,564	5,086	4,814
36,250	36,300	5,099	4,571	5,099	4,821
36,300	36,350	5,111	4,579	5,111	4,829
36,350	36,400	5,124	4,586	5,124	4,836
36,400	36,450	5,136	4,594	5,136	4,844
36,450	36,500	5,149	4,601	5,149	4,851
36,500	36,550	5,161	4,609	5,161	4,859
36,550	36,600	5,174	4,616	5,174	4,866
36,600	36,650	5,186	4,624	5,186	4,874
36,650	36,700	5,199	4,631	5,199	4,881
36,700	36,750	5,211	4,639	5,211	4,889
36,750	36,800	5,224	4,646	5,224	4,896
36,800	36,850	5,236	4,654	5,236	4,904
36,850	36,900	5,249	4,661	5,249	4,911
36,900	36,950	5,261	4,669	5,261	4,919
36,950	37,000	5,274	4,676	5,274	4,926

37,000

At least	But less than	Single	Married filing jointly *	Married filing separately	Head of a household
37,000	37,050	5,286	4,684	5,286	4,934
37,050	37,100	5,299	4,691	5,299	4,941
37,100	37,150	5,311	4,699	5,311	4,949
37,150	37,200	5,324	4,706	5,324	4,956
37,200	37,250	5,336	4,714	5,336	4,964
37,250	37,300	5,349	4,721	5,349	4,971
37,300	37,350	5,361	4,729	5,361	4,979
37,350	37,400	5,374	4,736	5,374	4,986
37,400	37,450	5,386	4,744	5,386	4,994
37,450	37,500	5,399	4,751	5,399	5,001
37,500	37,550	5,411	4,759	5,411	5,009
37,550	37,600	5,424	4,766	5,424	5,016
37,600	37,650	5,436	4,774	5,436	5,024
37,650	37,700	5,449	4,781	5,449	5,031
37,700	37,750	5,461	4,789	5,461	5,039
37,750	37,800	5,474	4,796	5,474	5,046
37,800	37,850	5,486	4,804	5,486	5,054
37,850	37,900	5,499	4,811	5,499	5,061
37,900	37,950	5,511	4,819	5,511	5,069
37,950	38,000	5,524	4,826	5,524	5,076

If line 43 (taxable income) is—		And you are—			
At least	But less than	Single	Married filing jointly *	Married filing sepa-rately	Head of a house-hold
		Your tax is—			

38,000

At least	But less than	Single	Married filing jointly *	Married filing separately	Head of a household
38,000	38,050	5,536	4,834	5,536	5,084
38,050	38,100	5,549	4,841	5,549	5,091
38,100	38,150	5,561	4,849	5,561	5,099
38,150	38,200	5,574	4,856	5,574	5,106
38,200	38,250	5,586	4,864	5,586	5,114
38,250	38,300	5,599	4,871	5,599	5,121
38,300	38,350	5,611	4,879	5,611	5,129
38,350	38,400	5,624	4,886	5,624	5,136
38,400	38,450	5,636	4,894	5,636	5,144
38,450	38,500	5,649	4,901	5,649	5,151
38,500	38,550	5,661	4,909	5,661	5,159
38,550	38,600	5,674	4,916	5,674	5,166
38,600	38,650	5,686	4,924	5,686	5,174
38,650	38,700	5,699	4,931	5,699	5,181
38,700	38,750	5,711	4,939	5,711	5,189
38,750	38,800	5,724	4,946	5,724	5,196
38,800	38,850	5,736	4,954	5,736	5,204
38,850	38,900	5,749	4,961	5,749	5,211
38,900	38,950	5,761	4,969	5,761	5,219
38,950	39,000	5,774	4,976	5,774	5,226

39,000

At least	But less than	Single	Married filing jointly *	Married filing separately	Head of a household
39,000	39,050	5,786	4,984	5,786	5,234
39,050	39,100	5,799	4,991	5,799	5,241
39,100	39,150	5,811	4,999	5,811	5,249
39,150	39,200	5,824	5,006	5,824	5,256
39,200	39,250	5,836	5,014	5,836	5,264
39,250	39,300	5,849	5,021	5,849	5,271
39,300	39,350	5,861	5,029	5,861	5,279
39,350	39,400	5,874	5,036	5,874	5,286
39,400	39,450	5,886	5,044	5,886	5,294
39,450	39,500	5,899	5,051	5,899	5,301
39,500	39,550	5,911	5,059	5,911	5,309
39,550	39,600	5,924	5,066	5,924	5,316
39,600	39,650	5,936	5,074	5,936	5,324
39,650	39,700	5,949	5,081	5,949	5,331
39,700	39,750	5,961	5,089	5,961	5,339
39,750	39,800	5,974	5,096	5,974	5,346
39,800	39,850	5,986	5,104	5,986	5,354
39,850	39,900	5,999	5,111	5,999	5,361
39,900	39,950	6,011	5,119	6,011	5,369
39,950	40,000	6,024	5,126	6,024	5,376

If line 43 (taxable income) is—		And you are—			
At least	But less than	Single	Married filing jointly *	Married filing sepa-rately	Head of a house-hold
		Your tax is—			

40,000

At least	But less than	Single	Married filing jointly *	Married filing separately	Head of a household
40,000	40,050	6,036	5,134	6,036	5,384
40,050	40,100	6,049	5,141	6,049	5,391
40,100	40,150	6,061	5,149	6,061	5,399
40,150	40,200	6,074	5,156	6,074	5,406
40,200	40,250	6,086	5,164	6,086	5,414
40,250	40,300	6,099	5,171	6,099	5,421
40,300	40,350	6,111	5,179	6,111	5,429
40,350	40,400	6,124	5,186	6,124	5,436
40,400	40,450	6,136	5,194	6,136	5,444
40,450	40,500	6,149	5,201	6,149	5,451
40,500	40,550	6,161	5,209	6,161	5,459
40,550	40,600	6,174	5,216	6,174	5,466
40,600	40,650	6,186	5,224	6,186	5,474
40,650	40,700	6,199	5,231	6,199	5,481
40,700	40,750	6,211	5,239	6,211	5,489
40,750	40,800	6,224	5,246	6,224	5,496
40,800	40,850	6,236	5,254	6,236	5,504
40,850	40,900	6,249	5,261	6,249	5,511
40,900	40,950	6,261	5,269	6,261	5,519
40,950	41,000	6,274	5,276	6,274	5,526

41,000

At least	But less than	Single	Married filing jointly *	Married filing separately	Head of a household
41,000	41,050	6,286	5,284	6,286	5,534
41,050	41,100	6,299	5,291	6,299	5,541
41,100	41,150	6,311	5,299	6,311	5,549
41,150	41,200	6,324	5,306	6,324	5,556
41,200	41,250	6,336	5,314	6,336	5,564
41,250	41,300	6,349	5,321	6,349	5,571
41,300	41,350	6,361	5,329	6,361	5,579
41,350	41,400	6,374	5,336	6,374	5,586
41,400	41,450	6,386	5,344	6,386	5,594
41,450	41,500	6,399	5,351	6,399	5,601
41,500	41,550	6,411	5,359	6,411	5,609
41,550	41,600	6,424	5,366	6,424	5,616
41,600	41,650	6,436	5,374	6,436	5,624
41,650	41,700	6,449	5,381	6,449	5,631
41,700	41,750	6,461	5,389	6,461	5,639
41,750	41,800	6,474	5,396	6,474	5,646
41,800	41,850	6,486	5,404	6,486	5,654
41,850	41,900	6,499	5,411	6,499	5,661
41,900	41,950	6,511	5,419	6,511	5,669
41,950	42,000	6,524	5,426	6,524	5,676

* This column must also be used by a qualifying widow(er).

IRS 2012

Pronunciation Guide

The table below provides sample words to explain the sounds associated with specific letters and letter combinations used in the respellings in this book. For example, *a* represents the short "a" sound in *cat*, while *ay* represents the long "a" sound in *day*.

Letter combinations are used to approximate certain more complex sounds. For example, in the respelling of *trapezoid*—TRA-puh-zoyd—the letters *uh* represent the vowel sound you hear in *shut* and *other*.

Vowels

a	short a: **a**pple, c**a**t
ay	long a: c**a**ne, d**ay**
e, eh	short e: h**e**n, b**e**d
ee	long e: f**ee**d, t**ea**m
i, ih	short i: l**i**p, act**i**ve
iy	long i: tr**y**, m**i**ght
ah	short o: h**o**t, f**a**ther
oh	long o: h**o**me, thr**ow**
uh	short u: sh**u**t, **o**ther
yoo	long u: **u**nion, c**u**te

Letter Combinations

ch	**ch**in, an**c**ient
sh	**sh**ow, mi**ss**ion
zh	vi**s**ion, a**z**ure
th	**th**in, heal**th**
th	**th**en, hea**th**er
ur	b**ir**d, f**ur**ther, w**or**d
us	b**us**, cr**us**t
or	c**our**t, f**or**mal
ehr	**err**or, c**are**
oo	c**oo**l, tr**ue**, r**u**le
ow	n**ow**, **ou**t
ou	l**oo**k, p**u**ll, w**ou**ld
oy	c**oi**n, t**oy**
aw	s**aw**, m**au**l, f**a**ll
ng	so**ng**, fi**ng**er
air	**A**ristotle, b**a**rrister
ahr	c**a**rt, m**a**rtyr

Consonants

b	**b**utter, **b**aby
d	**d**og, cra**d**le
f	**f**un, **ph**one
g	**g**rade, an**g**le
h	**h**at, a**h**ead
j	**j**u**dg**e, gor**g**e
k	**k**ite, **c**ar, bla**ck**
l	**l**ily, mi**l**e
m	**m**om, ca**m**el
n	**n**ext, ca**n**did
p	**p**rice, co**pp**er
r	**r**ubber, f**r**ee
s	**s**mall, **c**ircle, ha**ss**le
t	**t**on, po**tt**ery
v	**v**ase, **v**i**v**id
w	**w**all, a**w**ay
y	**y**ellow, ka**y**ak
z	**z**ebra, ha**z**e

Glossary

address the location of an element in a matrix, by matrix name, row number, and column number

adjusted gross income (AGI) gross income minus adjustments

amortization the process of paying off the principal of an interest-bearing loan by making equal payments

amplitude half the difference between the maximum and minimum output values in a periodic function

angle of rotation the smallest angle by which a figure with rotation symmetry can be rotated to look exactly like the original figure

annual expenses expenses that occur once a year and can be included in a monthly budget

appreciate to increase in value over time

APR on a credit card account, the annual percentage rate of the finance charge on the unpaid balance

arithmetic sequence a type of sequence where the difference between consecutive terms is a constant

association the relationship between two variables

average the sum of the data values divided by the number of data values; the mean of a data set

balanced budget a budget in which the income equals the expenses

bank statement a monthly summary of a bank account, which is sent by the bank to the customer who holds the account

bar graph a graph that uses bars to display and compare categorical data

base pay regular pay, excluding any tips or commission

beneficiary the person named in a life insurance policy to receive the monetary benefit upon the death of the insured person

bias a process where certain outcomes are favored; questioning that leads the respondent to a particular answer

biased sample a sample that is not representative of its population

bin width the range of data values for each bar in a histogram

bivariate data data that show the relationship between two variables; paired data

bond an investment in which a government or a corporation issues a certificate of debt to an investor who lends money to it for a given time period

bounced check a check returned to a payee for insufficient funds in the account of the payer

box part of a box plot that shows the second and third quartiles of a data set

box plot a display of the five-number summary of a data set

budget a plan for spending

budget sheet a table showing expenses in categories over a regular period of time

categorical data observed data that belong to separate groups, called categories

categories descriptions that can be observed but not measured

checking account a banking account from which funds can be withdrawn by writing a check or using a debit card

circle graph a graph that uses sectors of a circle to display and compare categorical data

class interval an interval of data values used in a frequency table or a histogram

cluster a grouping of data points

coefficient of determination the square of the correlation coefficient, written as r^2; the percent of change in the response variable that is due to changes in the explanatory variable

collision insurance insurance that pays for damages to an insurance holder's vehicle if that person causes the accident

combination the number of different ways to select a number of objects from a group (without regard to order)

commission money earned by a worker for making a sale and usually calculated as a percent of a sale amount

common difference the difference between a term and the previous term of an arithmetic sequence or series

common ratio the quotient of a term and the previous term of a geometric sequence or series

compound event an event that consists of two or more simple events

compound interest interest paid on both the principal (the original amount of money) and the interest an account has already earned

comprehensive insurance insurance that pays for car damage caused by such factors as the weather or other incidents that are not accidental

constant of variation the constant rate in the direct variation equation $y = kx$; the variable k represents the constant of variation and indicates the steepness of the graph

co-payment a fee that a health insurance company requires the customer to pay to a doctor or pharmacy at the time of the medical appointment or purchase; the amount of co-payment can vary or there can be no co-payment

correlation coefficient a number used to describe the direction and strength of the association between two variables, written as r

cosine for an acute angle in a right triangle, the ratio of the length of the adjacent side to the length of the hypotenuse; the abbreviation for cosine is *cos*

coupon rate the annual interest rate paid by a bond issuer to a bondholder

credit access to borrowed money; deferred payment for goods and services, almost always with interest

credit card a card used to make purchases that are billed later

cycle a single, regular interval of a repeating pattern

data a collection of related facts; a collection of categorical or quantitative information

debit card a card used for purchases that takes funds from a checking account

deduction in terms of wages and salaries, an amount that is regularly taken out of a payment to a worker, such as a tax or a health insurance contribution

deficit a quantity smaller than what is needed, such as when income is less than expenses in a budget

depreciate to decrease in value over time

dilation a transformation that changes the size, but not the shape, of a figure

dimensions the numbers of rows and columns in a matrix

direct variation a function defined by an equation of the form $y = kx$, where k is a nonzero constant; when you use this equation, you can say that y varies directly as x

distribution the shape of the display of a quantitative data set

double bar graph a bar graph showing how two groups or subgroups of data compare to each other

element of a matrix each number or expression in a matrix

element of a set a member of a set

enlargement a dilation that increases the size of a figure; the scale factor is greater than 1 in an enlargement

event a set of one or more outcomes; an event is a subset of the sample space

expected value the predicted value of a random variable; computed as the sum of the products of the individual probabilities and their respective probabilities

experiment any process or action that yields outcomes

factorial for a positive integer n, the product of all positive integers less than or equal to n; written as $n!$

finance charge the product of the unpaid balance and the periodic rate

five-number summary the minimum, first quartile, median, third quartile, and maximum of a data set

fixed expenses in a monthly budget, expenses that are necessary and do not change from month to month

401(k) a type of retirement account; workers contribute by having deductions taken from their paycheck

403(b) a type of retirement account for employees of tax-exempt organizations, such as public schools

frequency of a periodic graph the number of cycles for one unit of time; computed as the reciprocal of the period of the graph

frequency table a table that describes the number of times a value or interval of values occurs in a data set

function a relation that assigns each member of the input values (domain) to exactly one member of the output values (range)

Fundamental Counting Principle for Addition If event A can be completed in m ways and event B can be completed in n ways and there is no way of completing both events at the same time, then the number of ways of completing event A or event B is $m + n$. If there are k ways to complete both events at once, then the number of ways of completing event A or event B is $m + n - k$.

Fundamental Counting Principle for Multiplication If event A has m possible outcomes and event B has n possible outcomes, then event A followed by event B has $m \cdot n$ possible outcomes.

gas mileage the number of miles that a vehicle can drive on a gallon of gas; calculated by dividing the number of miles driven by the number of gallons used

geometric sequence a sequence for which the ratio between consecutive terms is a constant

glide reflection a transformation that combines a translation with a reflection; the direction of the translation is parallel to the line of reflection

gross income the sum of job earnings, interest, and dividends

gross pay the amount calculated by multiplying the number of hours worked times the hourly wage; the amount before deductions are taken out

half-life the length of time that is required for half of something to decay or otherwise be eliminated

health insurance a system in which a customer pays a company to cover the customer's health-related costs such as doctor's office visits, hospital stays, and prescription drugs; usually, health insurance is obtained by annual contract between the customer and the company

histogram a graph that uses adjacent rectangles to display frequencies of quantitative data values

image in a transformation, the figure that is the result of the transformation

independent events two events related in such a way that one event's occurrence has no effect on the probability of the other event

Individual Retirement Account (IRA) a type of retirement account that a person sets up with a bank or other investment firm

interquartile range (IQR) the range of the middle half of a data set; $IQR = Q_3 - Q_1$

inverse variation a function defined by an equation of the form $xy = k$, where k is a nonzero constant

isometry a transformation that preserves the size and shape of an object's original image

iterative formula a formula by which the value of a term in a sequence can be found using a formula, or rule

leaf the rightmost digit of a data value

lease a contract between a tenant and a landlord that states conditions of the rental agreement, such as when the rent is due and the rent amount

liability insurance insurance that pays for injuries to others, and damages to their property, in an accident caused by the insurance holder

life insurance a type of insurance in which a beneficiary is named to receive a certain sum of money upon the death of the insured person

line of best fit the least squares regression line

line of symmetry the line over which you can flip a given figure, leaving the figure unchanged, or the line that divides a given figure into two congruent (mirror-image) halves

line plot a graph that displays the frequencies of quantitative data using a number line

linear regression line the line that minimizes the squares of the distances from the points in a scatter plot to the line

living expenses in a monthly budget, expenses that can rise or fall from month to month

matrix a table of numbers or expressions arranged in rows and columns

maximum the greatest value in a data set

mean the sum of the data values divided by the number of data values

measures of center a central, representative, or typical value for a data set; examples include the mean, median, or mode

measures of spread a value that indicates how much a data set varies from a central value; examples include the range, standard deviation, or variance

median the middle value when the data are ordered; if there is an even number of data points, it is the average of the two middle values

minimum the least value in a data set

mode the most common value(s) in a data set

model the equation of a line or curve that fits bivariate data

moderate association the degree of association when the points of two data sets graphed on a scatter plot are clearly either positively or negatively associated, but they do not almost lie on a line

mortgage a loan from a bank or another financial firm to a buyer to pay for real estate, such as a home

multiple bar graph a bar graph where two or more bars are used to display each of two or more categories of data

mutual fund a collection of financial securities that an investment firm manages for investors

negative association in a comparison of two data sets, as the data from one set increase, then the corresponding data from the second set decrease

net pay the amount of payment to a worker after all deductions have been subtracted from gross pay; take-home pay

new balance on a credit card statement, the total amount owed by the credit card holder

no association the lack of any association when the points of two data sets are graphed on a scatter plot; the points appear randomly scattered

outcome the result in a probability experiment

overdraft a negative balance in a checking account

overlapping events events having one or more outcomes in common

pay period the regular portion of time for which a salaried employee receives pay, such as weekly

perfect association the degree of association when the points of two data sets graphed on a scatter plot lie on a line

period the length of one cycle in a periodic function

periodic function a function that has cycles, or regular intervals of repeating patterns

periodic rate on a credit card account, the monthly interest rate

permutation the number of different ways that a group of objects can be arranged

personal loan a loan of money from a financial institution to a person for a large purchase

point-slope form (of a linear equation) an equation of a line $y - y_1 = m(x - x_1)$ that passes through the point (x_1, y_1) and has slope m

population an entire set of members or objects that you want to know something about

positive association in a comparison of two data sets, as the data from one set increase, then the corresponding data from the second set also increase

pre-image the original figure in a transformation

premium the cost paid to an insurance company for coverage

principal a sum of money that earns interest or is due as a debt

probability distribution a distribution of probabilities of all possible outcomes of an event

probability distribution histogram a histogram where the heights of the bars represent probabilities of all possible outcomes of an event

probability distribution table a frequency table where each frequency is replaced by the probability of the outcome

probability of an event the number of favorable outcomes divided by the total number of outcomes; written $P(A)$

proportion an equation stating that two ratios are equal

Q_1 the median of the lower half of the data in an ordered data set; first quartile

Q_2 the median of all the data in an ordered data set; second quartile

Q_3 the median of the upper half of the data in an ordered data set; third quartile

quartiles the three values that separate an ordered data set into four equal parts

range the difference between the maximum and minimum values of a data set

rate of return the rate, expressed as a percent, at which an investment changes in value

rate table a table that shows interest amounts for loans by interest rate and length of time for paying back the loan; rate tables can also show monthly payments

recursive formula a formula by which the value of a term in a sequence can be found by using previous values in the same sequence

reduction a dilation that reduces the size of a figure; the scale factor is less than 1 in a reduction

reflection the flipping of a figure across a line or line segment, creating a mirror image of the figure

reflection symmetry the characteristic that a figure has if it has at least one axis of symmetry; when the figure is reflected, it can be folded along an axis of symmetry and both halves will match up

register a list created and kept current by a bank customer to keep a record of all money going into and out of a bank account

regression line a line drawn or calculated to fit the linear trend of bivariate data

regular polygon a polygon that is both equilateral and equiangular

relative frequency table a table that describes the percent of occurrence of the values, categories, or intervals in a data set

rent a regular payment, usually monthly, by a tenant to an owner for the use of an apartment or a house; one rule of thumb is that a tenant should not pay more than 28% of gross monthly income for rent

rotation a transformation that moves a figure about a point in a circular fashion

rotation symmetry the characteristic that a figure has if it can be rotated around its center less than one full turn and retain the appearance of the original figure

Rule of 72 a rule for estimating the number of years it takes for an investment to double in value; 72 divided by the expected annual rate of return

salary a set amount of money that an employee will earn in a period of time, such as yearly

sample a subset of a population; a representative subset of a population used when populations are too large to study

sample space the set of all possible outcomes of an experiment

savings account a type of bank account that earns interest

scalar a quantity without dimensions, as opposed to a matrix or a vector

scale factor the ratio of the corresponding lengths in similar figures

scatter plot a graph that displays a set of bivariate data as points on a coordinate grid

security deposit in a rental agreement, an amount of money paid by the renter and held by the owner to cover damages that may occur to the property being rented; when the renter moves out, the owner will return the security deposit to the renter, less any money kept to pay for damages, if any

sequence a list of numbers that form a pattern

set a collection of objects

share a piece of ownership of a corporation

simple harmonic motion the shifting of an object or a quantity in a regular, repeating pattern

simple interest interest earned at a fixed percent of the initial deposit

sine for an acute angle in a right triangle, the ratio of the length of the opposite side to the length of the hypotenuse; the abbreviation for sine is *sin*

sinusoid a graphed curve, or wave, of a sine or cosine function

stacked bar graph a bar graph where each bar contains two or more categories of data

standard deviation a measure of spread of a data set; the standard deviation $s = \sqrt{\dfrac{\sum(x - \bar{x})^2}{n - 1}}$, where x is a data value, $\bar{x}$ is the mean of the data set, and n is the number of data values in the set; the square root of the variance

statistic a measurement that describes an attribute of a data set

statistics the science that involves the collection, analysis, and interpretation of data

stem all digits to the left of the rightmost digit of a data value

stem-and-leaf plot a table used to show the shape of the distribution of a data set

stock a certificate showing a share of ownership in a corporation

strip pattern a repeated horizontal pattern that continues indefinitely

strong association the degree of association when the points of two data sets graphed on a scatter plot almost lie on a line

surplus a quantity larger than what is needed, such as when income is greater than expenses in a budget

symmetrical a description of a data set whose values below the median are approximately a mirror image of those above the median

tangent for an acute angle in a right triangle, the ratio of the length of the opposite side to the length of the adjacent side; the abbreviation for tangent is *tan*

tax an amount of money paid under a specified system by people or businesses to a government to fund public services

tax refund an amount that a government gives back to a taxpayer who has paid more taxes than were due

taxable income gross income minus exemptions and deductions; the amount of income that can be taxed

term a number in an arithmetic sequence or a geometric sequence

term life insurance a life insurance policy that provides coverage for a given time period

theoretical probability probability based on expected outcomes; *see* probability of an event

transformation a movement or change of a figure, such as a translation, reflection, rotation, or dilation

translation the sliding of a figure in a straight path without rotation or reflection

trendline a line drawn or calculated to fit the linear trend of bivariate data

two-way table a table that displays and compares two sets of categorical data

unpaid balance on a credit card statement, the previous balance minus payments and credits made during the statement period

variable any quantity for which information is available or needed

variance a measure of variability of a data set relative to its mean; the square of the standard deviation

volunteer sampling a sampling where members choose whether or not to be part of the sample

wages a fixed payment, usually earned hourly and typically paid on a daily or weekly basis

weak association the degree of association when the points of two data sets are graphed on a scatter plot and it is just noticeable whether they are positively or negatively associated

weighted average a weighted mean for which some elements of a data set carry more importance (weight) than others

whiskers part of a box plot that shows the first and fourth quartiles

W-2 form a federal tax form that is completed by an employer and summarizes the earnings and deductions of an employee for the year

x-axis the horizontal number line in the coordinate plane

y-axis the vertical number line in the coordinate plane

y-intercept the y-coordinate of a point where a graph intersects the y-axis

Symbols

$\approx$	approximately equal to		z	z-score
$\leq$	less than or equal to		Σ	the sum of
$\geq$	greater than or equal to		$n!$	factorial of a nonnegative integer n
$\bar{x}$	mean of a sample (or data set)		$_nP_r$	permutation of n objects taken r at a time
μ	mean of a population (or data set)		$_nC_r$	combination of n objects taken r at a time
s	standard deviation of a sample (or data set)		$P(A)$	probability of event A
σ	standard deviation of a population (or data set)		A'	complement of event A, or not A
Q_1	first quartile		$E(X)$	expected value of X
Q_2	second quartile (median)		r	correlation coefficient
Q_3	third quartile		r^2 or R^2	coefficient of determination
IQR	interquartile range		$|x|$	absolute value of x
f	frequency		$\sqrt{}$	radical sign; the principal square root
P	probability		π	pi
X	random variable		$[\ ]$	brackets of a matrix

Formulary

Statistics

Mean

For a data set with n elements, the mean is

$$\bar{x} = \frac{x_1 + x_2 + \ldots + x_n}{n}.$$

Median

Arrange the values in order from least to greatest.
For an odd number of values, the median is the middle value.
For an even number of values, the median is the average of the middle two values.

Mode

The mode is the value that occurs most often in a set of data. If no one value occurs most often, then there is no mode for the set.

Standard Deviation

To find the standard deviation s of a data set with n values, where x is a data value and $\bar{x}$ is the mean, use the formula:

$$s = \sqrt{\frac{\sum(x - \bar{x})^2}{n - 1}}.$$

Counting and Probability

Factorial

$$n! = n \cdot (n - 1) \cdot (n - 2) \cdot \ldots \cdot 1 \ (n \text{ factors})$$

$$0! = 1$$

Expected Value

The expected value of X if each outcome of a random variable X is $x_1, x_2, \ldots, x_n$ and has probability $p_1, p_2, \ldots, p_n$ respectively is:

$$E(X) = x_1 \cdot p_1 + x_2 \cdot p_2 + \ldots x_n \cdot p_n.$$

Permutations

The number of permutations of n objects taken r at a time is

$$_nP_r = P(n, r) = \frac{n!}{(n-r)!}.$$

The number of permutations n objects of which p are alike and q are alike is

$$\frac{_nP_n}{p!q!},$$

where $p \leq n$ and $q \leq n$.

The number of permutations of n objects arranged in a circle is

$$(n-1)!.$$

Combinations

The number of combinations of n objects taken r at a time, with $r \leq n$, is

$$_nC_r = C(n, r) = \binom{n}{r} = \frac{n!}{r!(n-r)!}.$$

Basic Probability of an Event

$$P(A) = \frac{\text{number of favorable outcomes}}{\text{total number of possible outcomes}}$$

Probability of Independent Events

$$P(A \text{ and } B) = P(A) \cdot P(B)$$

Probability of Mutually Exclusive Events

$$P(A \text{ or } B) = P(A) + P(B)$$

Probability of Complementary Events

$$P(A') = 1 - P(A)$$

Experimental Probability of Event A

$$P(A) = \frac{\text{number of times event } A \text{ has occurred}}{\text{total number of trials of the experiment}}$$

Sequences and Series

Sequences: Arithmetic

Common difference of an arithmetic sequence $\quad d = a_n - a_{n-1}$

Iterative rule for an arithmetic sequence $\quad a_n = a_1 + (n-1)d$

Recursive rule for an arithmetic sequence $\quad a_n = a_{n-1} + d$

Sequences: Geometric

Common ratio of a geometric sequence $\quad r = \dfrac{a_n}{a_{n-1}}$

Iterative rule for a geometric sequence $\quad a_n = a_1 \cdot r^{n-1}$

Recursive rule for a geometric sequence $\quad a_n = r \cdot a_{n-1}$

General Formula for the Sum of a Series: Sigma Notation

The sum of the first n terms of a sequence can be written as

$$S_n = \sum_{i=1}^{n} a_i = a_1 + a_2 + a_3 + \ldots + a_n,$$

where i is the index, 1 is the lower limit, and n is the upper limit.

Arithmetic Series

The nth partial sum of an arithmetic series a with common difference d is

$$S_n = \frac{n}{2}(a_1 + a_2) \text{ or } S_n = \frac{n}{2}(2a_1 + (n-1)d).$$

Geometric Series

The nth partial sum of a geometric series a with common ratio r is

$$S_n = \frac{a_1(1 - r^n)}{1 - r}, \text{ or } S_n = \frac{a_1 - a_n r}{1 - r}, \text{ where } r \neq 1.$$

Matrices

Adding Matrices

$A + B = C$ if and only if $a_{ij} + b_{ij} = c_{ij}$ for all values of i and j in matrices A, B, and C.

$$A = \begin{bmatrix} a_{11} & a_{12} \\ a_{21} & a_{22} \end{bmatrix} \qquad B = \begin{bmatrix} b_{11} & b_{12} \\ b_{21} & b_{22} \end{bmatrix} \qquad C = A + B = \begin{bmatrix} a_{11} + b_{11} & a_{12} + b_{12} \\ a_{21} + b_{21} & a_{22} + b_{22} \end{bmatrix}$$

Subtracting Matrices

$A - B = D$ if and only if $a_{ij} - b_{ij} = d_{ij}$ for all values of i and j in matrices A, B, and D.

$$A = \begin{bmatrix} a_{11} & a_{12} \\ a_{21} & a_{22} \end{bmatrix} \qquad B = \begin{bmatrix} b_{11} & b_{12} \\ b_{21} & b_{22} \end{bmatrix} \qquad D = A - B = \begin{bmatrix} a_{11} - b_{11} & a_{12} - b_{12} \\ a_{21} - b_{21} & a_{22} - b_{22} \end{bmatrix}$$

Multiplying Matrices by a Scalar

$rA = C$ if and only if $r \cdot a_{ij} = c_{ij}$ for all values of i and j in matrices A and C.

$$A = \begin{bmatrix} a_{11} & a_{12} \\ a_{21} & a_{22} \end{bmatrix} \qquad C = rA = \begin{bmatrix} r \cdot a_{11} & r \cdot a_{12} \\ r \cdot a_{21} & r \cdot a_{22} \end{bmatrix}$$

Finance

Simple Interest

The amount of simple interest I earned, where P is the principal (amount borrowed, deposited, or invested), r is the annual interest rate, and t is the time in years, is given by

$$I = Prt.$$

Compound Interest

The total amount A of an investment with initial principal P, earning compound interest at an annual interest rate r and compounded n times per year for t years, is

$$A = P\left(1 + \frac{r}{n}\right)^{nt}.$$

Rule of 72

By the Rule of 72, the approximate number of years it takes for an investment to double in value is 72 divided by the expected annual rate of return, written as a percent.

$$\text{number of years to double} \approx \frac{72}{\text{rate of return (\%)}}$$

Pay

$$\text{gross pay (without OT)} = \text{hours worked} \cdot \text{hourly rate}$$

$$\text{overtime pay rate} = 1.5 \cdot \text{hourly rate}$$

$$\text{overtime pay} = \text{overtime pay rate} \cdot \text{overtime hours}$$

$$\text{gross pay (with OT)} = \text{regular pay} + \text{overtime pay}$$

Federal Insurance Contributions

$$\text{Social Security tax} = 6.2\% \cdot \text{gross pay}$$

$$\text{Medicare tax} = 1.45\% \cdot \text{gross pay}$$

$$\text{FICA tax} = \text{Social Security tax} + \text{Medicare tax}$$

Credit Cards

$$\text{unpaid balance} = \text{previous balance} - \text{payments and credits}$$

$$\text{periodic rate} = \frac{\text{APR}}{12}$$

$$\text{finance charge} = \text{unpaid balance} \cdot \text{periodic rate}$$

$$\text{new balance} = \text{unpaid balance} + \text{new transactions} + \text{finance charge}$$

Housing and Transportation

Maximum monthly rent   monthly rent $\leq 0.28 \cdot$ gross monthly income

Maximum mortgage   mortgage $\leq 2 \cdot$ gross annual income

Value of a home with appreciation $P = V(1 + r)^Y$, where V is the original value of the home, r is the rate of appreciation, and Y is the number of years in the future

Value of a car with depreciation $P = V(1 - r)^Y$, where V is the original value of the car, r is the rate of depreciation, and Y is the number of years in the future

Miles per gallon $\text{mpg} = \dfrac{\text{number of miles driven}}{\text{number of gallons used}}$

Exponential Growth and Decay

Exponential Growth

If a quantity is growing exponentially from the initial amount b, where r is the fixed percent expressed as a decimal and t is the time period, then the total amount y after t time periods is

$$y = b(1 + r)^t.$$

Exponential Decay

If a quantity is decaying exponentially from initial amount b, for time t and with decay rate r, then the amount y remaining after t time periods is

$$y = b(1 - r)^t.$$

Half-Life

The amount y of a radioactive substance after t time periods, where b is the initial amount and h is the half-life, is

$$y = b(0.5)^{\frac{t}{h}}.$$

Trigonometry

Ratios

$\sin A = \dfrac{\text{opposite}}{\text{hypotenuse}}$

$\cos A = \dfrac{\text{adjacent}}{\text{hypotenuse}}$

$\tan A = \dfrac{\text{opposite}}{\text{adjacent}}$

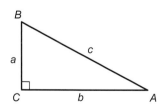

Hint: Remember SOHCAHTOA.

Periodic Functions

Amplitude

$$\text{amplitude} = \frac{1}{2}(\text{maximum value} - \text{minimum value})$$

Geometry

Circle

Circumference $C = \pi d = 2\pi r$

Area $A = \pi r^2$

Prism: Cube

Volume $V = s^3$

Surface area $S = 6s^2$

Prism: Rectangular

Volume $V = lwh$

Surface area $S = 2lw + 2lh + 2hw$

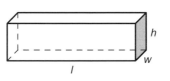

Rectangle

Area $A = lw$

Perimeter $P = 2l + 2w$

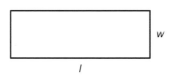

Square

Area $A = s^2$

Perimeter $P = 4s$

Triangle: General

Area $A = \frac{1}{2}bh$

Perimeter $P = a + b + c$

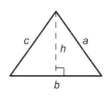

Triangle: Right

Pythagorean theorem $a^2 + b^2 = c^2$

Coordinate Geometry

Line

Slope $m = \dfrac{\text{rise}}{\text{run}} = \dfrac{\text{vertical change}}{\text{horizontal change}} = \dfrac{y_2 - y_1}{x_2 - x_1}$

Equation Forms

Standard $Ax + By = C$

Slope-intercept $y = mx + b$

Point-slope $y - y_1 = m(x - x_1)$

General Applications

Distance

For uniform motion, where d is distance, r is rate, and t is time,

$$d = rt.$$

Temperature Conversion

$F = \dfrac{9}{5}C + 32$, where F is degrees Fahrenheit and C is degrees Celsius

Selected Answers

CHAPTER 1 Working with Data

Pages 4–7

1. 0.5 **3.** 0.75 **5.** 0.875 **7.** 0.8 **9.** 0.06 **11.** 15%
13. 40.2% **15.** 160% **17.** 0.4% **19.** 500% **21.** 7.6
23. 10.5 **25.** 8.4 **27.** −13.5

Pages 8–11

1. 6.5 **3.** 5.5 **5.** 107.5 **7.** 115 **9.** 14.3 lb **11.** 2.3 years,
or 27.6 months **13.** 7 **15.** −3°F **17. A.** 48; **B.** 30
19. A. 9; **B.** 6 and 12 **21. A.** 162; **B.** no mode
23. A. −0.5; **B.** −1 **25.** 10.5 **27.** median: 2 years;
mode: 3 years **29. A.** $15/h; **B.** $13/h; **C.** median

Pages 12–17

1. $1500 **3.** $1250 **5.** 6 mi **7.** Clara **9.** 6 years
11. cheetah **13.** $2.10 **15.** May **17.** 5.9°F **19.** 2
21. 8 **23.** 99°F **25.** 4 **27.** 12 **29.** 8 **31.** 5 **33.** 76%
35. 8 **37.** D

Pages 18–21

1. A. min: 2, median: 7, Q_3: 10; **B.** range: 10; **C.** IQR: 6.5
3. A. min: 7, Q_1: 13, median: 18, Q_3: 30.5, max: 38;
B. range: 31; **C.** IQR: 17.5 **5. A.** min: 75, Q_1: 91.5,
median: 150, Q_3: 195, max: 203; **B.** range: 128;
C. IQR: 103.5 **7. A.** 6; **B.** 50% of the singers are within a
6-year range of ages; **C.** The ages are more spread out in
the ages below 31; The difference in the median age and
minimum age is much greater than the difference in the
maximum age and the median age. **9. A.** 21 in.; **B.** 18 in.;
C. Because the box is longer than the whiskers, the heights
within the box are more spread out.

11. Step 1 $\bar{x} = 10$

   Step 2 Complete the table.

   Step 3 $\dfrac{138}{5-1} \approx 34.5$

   Step 4 $\sqrt{34.5} \approx 5.9$

x	$(x - \bar{x})^2$
5	25
7	9
8	4
10	0
20	100
	Sum: 138

13. 2.9 **15.** 4.9 **17.** The mean would be greater and the
standard deviation would be smaller. **19.** Data Set C

Pages 22–23

1. B **3.** A **5.** B **7.** C **9.** 475 g **11. A.** 41.5; **B.** 6
13. A. range: 18; **B.** median: 40; **C.** The data in the lower
half are much more spread out, because the range of the data
is 12. The data in the upper half are less spread out since the
range of the data is 6. **15. A.** Blake; **B.** Rory and Elise;
C. Rory

CHAPTER 2 Connections Between Data

Pages 26–29

1. $(-5, 1)$ **3.** $(-3, -4)$ **5.** $(6, -1)$ **7.** $-\dfrac{3}{4}$ **9.** 1
11. $y - 3 = -1(x - 2)$ **13.** $y = \dfrac{1}{2}(x - 4)$
15. $y + 4 = -2(x + 1)$

Pages 30–33

1. 55, 0

3.

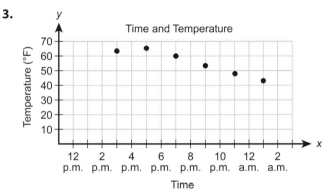

5. The six points with numbers of pull-ups between 8 and
10, and number of push-ups between 12 and 14 form a
cluster; The points with coordinates (2, 19) and (17, 17) are
outliers. **7.** The five points with number of blackbirds seen
between 4 and 7, and number of robins seen between 5 and
10, form a cluster; The five points with number of blackbirds
seen between 9 and 12, and number of robins seen between
10 and 14, form a cluster; The three points with number of
blackbirds seen between 13 and 15, and number of robins
seen between 16 and 190, form a cluster; There are no clear
outliers. **9.** 19.21 s **11.** 2004 **13.** Thursday **15.** 40 min

Pages 34–39

1. positive direction; moderate positive association
3. positive direction; moderate positive association
5. positive direction; strong positive association
7. rise from left to right; strong positive association
9. no association

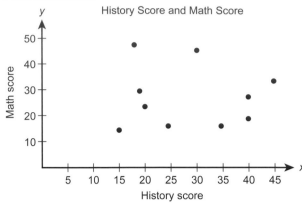

11. Plot C   **13.** Plot A   **15.** $r \approx 0.64$ **17.** $r \approx -0.86$
19. strong positive correlation   **21. A.** In each data set, there is a moderate correlation;   **B.** In Data Set A there is a moderately positive correlation and in Data Set B there is a moderately negative correlation.   **23.** Sample answer: the number of hours of sunlight during the day in the given city

Pages 40–45

1. electricity used; electric bill   **3.** number of runners; number of injuries   **5.** $y = -\dfrac{3}{4}x + \dfrac{367}{4}$ **7.** $y = 0.6x + 7$

9. 6.3 cm   **11.** 117.8 cm   **13.** 136.7 cm   **15.** For every increase of 1 month, the average weight increases by 1.2 lb.
17. 20.9 lb   **19.** $y = -1.36x + 24.591$
21. $y = 2.643x - 5202.357$ **23.** $14,686.52
25. On average the cost of tuition at a 4-year institution increases $937.98 each year.   **27.** 0.661; 66.1% of the variation in the scores the teacher gave on an essay is explained by the model that is based on the length of the essay.
29. $1.18   **31.** $8.98   **33.** 90.7% of the variability in the federal minimum wage is explained by the model that is based on the number of years after 2000.

Pages 46–51

1. quadratic model   **3.** linear model   **5.** 177 ft   **7.** 462 ft
9. $y = -0.078x^2 + 8.407x - 92.892$ **11.** 4191 mi
13. $y = -0.107x^2 + 9.008x - 28.851$ **15.** 18.4
17. 41.5   **19.** $y = 4179.748 \cdot 0.7412^x$ **21.** $71.45
23. $y = 0.8921 \cdot 1.068^x$ **25.** $3.55   **27.** quadratic model

Pages 52–53

1. C   **3.** B   **5.** D
7.

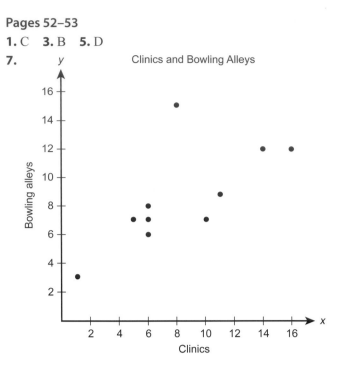

9. (1, 3), (8, 15)   **11.** Sample answer: The more opportunities people have to be active, the more often they will be injured.   **13.** The slope, 5.772 (thousands), indicates the number of additional automobiles registered in Delaware each decade.   **15.** 553,114   **17.** 33   **19.** approximately $176 trillion

CHAPTER 3   Uncertainty

Pages 56–59

1. 17   **3.** 18   **5.** 20   **7.** 8   **9.** 30   **11.** $\dfrac{3}{10}$ **13.** $\dfrac{111}{200}$
15. $\dfrac{1}{10}$ **17.** 120   **19.** 362,880

Pages 60–63

1. 42   **3.** 11   **5.** 1   **7.** 120   **9.** 40,320   **11.** 120
13. 362,880   **15.** 15   **17.** 7   **19.** 20   **21.** 1   **23.** 20
25. 15   **27.** 21   **29.** combination   **31.** permutation

Pages 64–67

1. 47%   **3.** 33%   **5.** $\dfrac{4}{7}$ **7.** $\dfrac{9}{10}$ **9.** $\dfrac{3}{20}$ **11.** $\dfrac{3}{10}$ **13.** $\dfrac{1}{4}$
15. The law of large numbers is not being used.
17. The law of large numbers is being used.

1.

Atlanta Falcons' scoring	Rushing touchdowns	Receiving touchdowns	Returns	Field goals	Extra points	2-Point conversions
P	0.1	0.26	0.02	0.27	0.36	0

3.

Game	1	2	3	4	5
P	0.24	0.2	0.36	0.08	0.12

5. The table violates the second property of probability distributions because the sum of all probabilities is 1.5, which is not equal to 1.   **7.** The table violates the second property of probability distributions because the sum of all probabilities is 0.9, which is not equal to 1.   **9.** 7%   **11.** 15%   **13.** 8%   **15.** 1.08   **17.** 2.63   **19.** 1.4

1. D   **3.** C   **5.** B   **7.** D   **9.** 11%   **11.** 1,192,052,400   **13.** combination
15. The table violates the second property of probability distributions because the sum of all probabilities is 0.85, which is not equal to 1.   **17.** 56%

CHAPTER 4   Math Models

1. –54   **3.** 31   **5.** –25   **7.** 15   **9.** 2   **11.** 36
13. A. A line passing through a vertex and the center creates mirror images; The triangle has reflection symmetry; There are three lines of symmetry;   **B.** The figure looks like the original after one-third of a turn around its center, so it has rotation symmetry; The angle of rotation is $\frac{360°}{3} = 120°$.

15. A. The hexagon has reflection symmetry. There are six lines of symmetry;   **B.** The figure looks like the original after one-sixth of a turn around its center, so it has rotation symmetry; The angle of rotation is $\frac{360°}{6} = 60°$.

17. A. A vertical line drawn through the center creates mirror images; A horizontal line drawn through the center creates mirror images; The figure has reflection symmetry; There are two lines of symmetry;   **B.** The figure looks like the original after a half turn around its center, so it has rotation symmetry; The angle of rotation is $\frac{360°}{2} = 180°$.

1. 24   **3.** 9   **5.** $18   **7. A.** 8 ft;   **B.** 7 s;   **C.** The constant of variation is 2 and it represents the wolf spider's top speed in ft/s.   **9.** 10   **11.** $\frac{1}{2}$ **13.** 24 min   **15. A.** 2;   **B.** 8;

C. The constant of variation is 8 and it represents the number of slices per pizza.

1. 9, 14, 19, and 24   **3.** –21, –14, –7, and 0   **5.** 143
7. 982   **9.** 44   **11.** $69,400   **13.** $a_n = a_{n-1} + 25$
15. 5, 20, 80, and 320   **17.** –2, –6, –18, and –54
19. 131,072   **21.** 524,288   **23.** 33,554,432   **25.** 2.37 cm
27. $a_n = 10 \cdot a_{n-1}$ **29.** neither   **31.** arithmetic

1. 2   **3.** 3   **5.** d_{13} **7.** 3 × 3   **9.** $\begin{bmatrix} 11 & 8 \\ 15 & 6 \end{bmatrix}$ **11.** 60
13. 39%   **15.** 254   **17.** 21   **19.** gray T-shirts   **21.** 7
23. $\begin{bmatrix} 24 & 54 \\ 78 & 30 \end{bmatrix}$ **25.** $\begin{bmatrix} 200 & 30 \\ 20 & 60 \\ 150 & 140 \\ 110 & 90 \end{bmatrix}$ **27.** $\begin{bmatrix} 19 & 17 \\ 44 & 36 \end{bmatrix}$

29. $\begin{bmatrix} 11 & 2 \\ 5 & 15 \\ 8 & 19 \end{bmatrix}$ **31.** $\begin{bmatrix} 5 & 0 \\ 5 & -3 \\ -2 & -3 \end{bmatrix}$

33. $\begin{bmatrix} 1054.9 & 954.8 & 748 \\ 1106.6 & 1034 & 898.7 \\ 752.4 & 577.5 & 509.3 \end{bmatrix}$

1. The pattern maps onto itself in the following ways: a horizontal translation, a reflection across a horizontal line, a 180° rotation, and a reflection across a vertical line.   **3.** The pattern maps onto itself in the following ways: a horizontal translation, a glide refection, a 180° rotation, and a reflection across a vertical line.   **5.** The pattern includes vertical and horizontal translations of the same figure. Also, each figure has horizontal symmetry.   **7.** Because 144° does not divide evenly into 360°, a decagon does not tile a plane.   **9.** 4^4
11. $\frac{2}{3}$ **13.** $\frac{3}{1}$ **15.** 40 cm   **17.** 27 mm   **19.** 0.48 ft²
21. 6750 m³

1. B   **3.** D   **5.** C   **7.** C   **9.** 36   **11.** 18   **13.** 10, 26, 42, and 58   **15.** 10, 30, 90, and 270   **17.** 145   **19.** 4096
21. $\begin{bmatrix} 16 & 30 \\ 12 & 6 \end{bmatrix}$ **23.** $\begin{bmatrix} 17 & 29 \\ 27 & 5 \end{bmatrix}$ **25.** $\frac{1}{3}$ **27.** 14.5 ft²

CHAPTER 5 Income

Pages 108–111
1. $1.64 **3.** $0.43 **5.** $60 **7.** 20% **9.** 2222%
11. 700% **13.** 18 **15.** $21.29 **17.** 35

Pages 112–115
1. $348.75 **3.** $475.28 **5.** $1432.75 **7.** $571
9. $2970.42 **11.** $26,520 **13.** Antonio **15.** 50 h
17. $6.27 **19.** $11.50 **21.** $3.74 **23.** $78.80
25. $301.70 **27.** $987.50

Pages 116–121
1. $580.19 **3.** $10.75 **5. A.** $28.52; **B.** $6.67
7. A. $132.07; **B.** $30.89 **9.** 75% **11.** 78%
13. $410.28 **15.** $607.10 **17.** $31,478.32
19. $2408.10 **21.** $25,471.15 **23.** $4099 **25.** $209

Pages 122–127
1. Karl Logan **3.** $49.70 **5.** a concert ticket
7. 3141592654 **9.** Thirty-five and $\frac{00}{100}$ **11.** One thousand
one hundred forty-five and $\frac{96}{100}$ **13.** 3 **15.** $40
17. 2718281828 **19.** $870 **21.** $625 **23.** $950
25. $56.34 **27.** $68.34 **29.** barber; $14.50 **31.** $9.95
33. 7/1; $148.00 **35.** $40.43 **37.** The ending balance,
shown at the top of the bank statement is $1067.02. Check
number 559 did not clear the bank yet. Subtract that amount
from the ending balance: $1067.02 − $285 = $782.02; Check
number 560 did not clear the bank yet. Subtract that amount
from $782.02: $782.02 − $49 = $733.02; The deposit on
7/15 has not been processed so add this to $733.02:
$733.02 + $210.38 = $943.40; Joy's register is up to date.

Pages 128–129
1. C **3.** A **5.** C **7.** C **9.** $30,940 **11.** $451.01
13. $324 **15.** 663; 818 **17.** 80% **19.** $650.20
21. 3/16, 3/23; $520.81, $550.56

CHAPTER 6 Budgeting

Pages 132–135
1. 953 **3.** $31.06 **5.** $5490 **7.** $6.03 **9.** $933.03
11. $44,304 **13.** $30,667 **15.** $42,240

Pages 136–139
1. living expense **3.** annual expense **5.** $78.17 **7.** $29.58
9. 36% **11.** 5.9% **13.** fixed: 65%; annual: 5%; living: 29%
15. $540 **17.** surplus of $39 **19.** surplus of $96
21. $208,026 **23.** $56,000

Pages 140–145
1. Oct. 6, 2013–Nov. 2, 2013 **3.** 4 **5.** 15.99% **7.** 39%
9. $11.64 **11.** $1272.80 **13.** $624.40 **15.** $415.31
17. $84.50 **19.** $81.19 **21.** $250.88 **23.** $1189.08

Pages 146–151
1. $924 **3.** $679 **5.** $473 **7.** $1745 **9.** $2760
11. A. $116,160; **B.** $129,760 **13. A.** $95,680;
B. $110,380 **15. A.** $122,240; **B.** $888.93;
C. $190,567.40; **D.** $31,767.40 **17. A.** $151,200;
B. $955.74; **C.** $381,866.40; **D.** $192,866.40
19. $431,213 **21.** $166,225

Pages 152–157
1. A. $295.28; **B.** $1173.44; **C.** $17,168.44
3. A. $316.63; **B.** $1503.24; **C.** $17,898.24 **5.** $12.01
7. $10,424 **9.** $4786 **11. A.** 32 mpg; **B.** $29 **13.** 28 mpg
15. $50 **17.** $1142.60 **19.** $1723.60 **21.** $829

Pages 158–159
1. B **3.** C **5.** C **7.** D **9.** $152,269 **11.** $23.30
13. A. $170.32; **B.** $4087.68; **C.** $487.68 **15.** $146,216
17. A. $225.36; **B.** $1521.60; **C.** $17,751.60

Chapter 7 Saving Money

Pages 162–165
1. 220 **3.** 88 **5.** 69 **7.** 11 **9.** 5 **11.** 12 **13.** 269.042 **15.** 0.000596875
17. 4,716,348,257.04 **19.** 14.08 **21.** 2250 **23.** 5.25

Pages 166–171
1. $93.60 **3.** $157.17 **5.** $318.86 **7.** $425 **9.** $200
11.

3	$18,564.43	$137.69 $\left(\$18{,}564.43 \cdot 0.089 \cdot \frac{1}{12}\right)$	$220.21 ($357.90 − $137.69)	$18,344.22 ($18,564.43 − $220.21)

13. $1611.87 **15.** $2472.82 **17.** $159.37 **19.** $4125 **21.** $940 **23.** $80
25. $320 **27.** Account A **29.** 35 years

Pages 172–175

1. A. $780; **B.** $30 **3. A.** $1276.80; **B.** $53.20
5. $698.35 **7.** $55.90 **9.** Carter; $1.40 **11.** $142.80
13. A. $730; **B.** $30.42 **15. A.** $1168; **B.** $97.33
17. A. $687.60; **B.** $28.65 **19.** $435.50

Pages 176–181

1. 10.3 years **3.** 4.8% **5. A.** $12,292; **B.** $2704; **C.** 22%
7. A. $5521.47; **B.** −$67.71; **C.** −1% **9. A.** $1878;
B. $2180; **C.** 116% **11. A.** $1200; **B.** $30
13. A. $27,000; **B.** $450 **15. A.** $44.66; **B.** $66.99
17. A. $128.04; **B.** $256.08 **19. A.** $194.86; **B.** $334.05
21. $110.53 **23.** $2,059,200 **25.** $677,400

Pages 182–183

1. C **3.** A **5.** B **7.** A **9.** $476.10 **11.** $1757.73
13. A. $1440.60; **B.** $27.70 **15.** $42.75 **17.** $25,008
19. $325.30

CHAPTER 8   More Math Models

Pages 186–189

1. 1.25 **3.** 0.07 **5.** 30 **7.** $\frac{1}{10}$ **9.** $\frac{3}{4}$ **11.** $\frac{7}{8}$

13. reflection

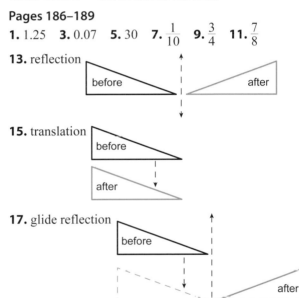

15. translation

17. glide reflection

Pages 190–195

1. A. $y = 1,360,301(1.012^t)$; **B.** 1,768,505 **3. A.** $y = 15(1.2^t)$;
B. 93 **5. A.** $y = 1700(1.12^t)$; **B.** $16,399 **7.** late in the
year 2011 **9.** 61 years **11. A.** $y = 10,000(0.85^t)$; **B.** 4437
13. A. $y = 1810(0.96^t)$; **B.** 1109 **15. A.** $y = 779(0.78^t)$;
B. $225 **17.** during the 11th year **19.** during the 25th year
21. 25 mg **23.** 4.95 g **25.** 23 billion years

Pages 196–201

1. 0.8 **3.** 1.3333 **5.** 0.8 **7.** cosine **9.** tangent
11. cosine **13.** cosine **15.** cosine **17.** 12.14 **19.** 31.53
21. 32.12 **23.** 12.74 m **25.** 78 m **27.** 10.4 m **29.** 33.4 ft
31. 4306 ft **33.** 178.5 ft

Pages 202–207

1. period: 4; amplitude: 1 **3.** period: 3; amplitude: 3
5. period: 12 months; amplitude: 6.9 **7.** period: 6 months;
amplitude: 10.55 **9. A.** period: $\frac{\pi}{2}$; **B.** amplitude: 1

11. A. period: 4π; **B.** amplitude: 3 **13.** 12 in. **15.** 1.5 s

17. $\frac{1}{6}$ of its cycle in 1 s **19.** 1.6 s **21.** 62.5% **23.** 45 s

25. 8° per second

Pages 208–211

1. translation **3.** reflection **5.** reflection
7.

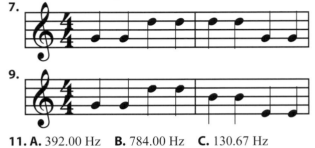

9.

11. A. 392.00 Hz **B.** 784.00 Hz **C.** 130.67 Hz
13. A. 880.00 Hz **B.** 1760.00 Hz **C.** 293.33 Hz

Pages 212–213

1. C **3.** B **5.** D **7.** 131.23 million **9.** reflection
11. 21.5 m **13.** period: 4 days; amplitude: 3.1 **15.** 20 in.
17. 40 revolutions in 1 minute

Pages A-1–A-2

1. mean: 6, median: 5, mode: 2 **3.** mean: 7, median: 7,
mode: 7 **5.** 3.6 **7.** 61 **9. A.** 23; **B.** Tuesday, Monday,
Thursday, Wednesday, Friday **11. A.** Mrs. Shuang, 84;
B. 10 **13. A.** min: 3, Q_1: 7, median: 15, Q_3: 19, max: 25;
B. range: 22; **C.** IQR: 12 **15. A.** min: 21, Q_1: 31, median: 43,
Q_3: 45, max: 52; **B.** range: 31; **C.** IQR: 14 **17.** 2.6
19. 2.5 **21.** 4.4 **23. A.** range: 75; **B.** middle 50%
range: 18; **C.** The spread of prices within the IQR is very
small; The spread of prices above the IQR is very large by
comparison. **25.** Set B

Pages A-3–A-4

1. 2   **3.** 6   **5.** $41\frac{2}{3}$%   **7.** no clusters; (5, 1) is an outlier.

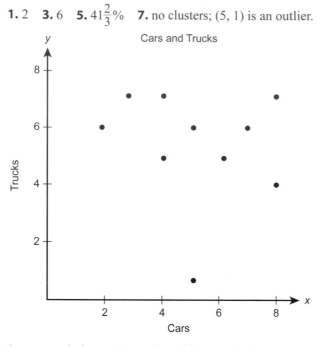

Cars and Trucks

9. no association   **11.** weak positive association
13. approximately 0.0233   **15.** $y = -1x + 45$
17. approximately $1876.78
19. $y = -0.0726x^2 + 2.19x + 5.284$

Pages A-5–A-6

1. 840   **3.** 12   **5.** 1   **7.** 12,144   **9.** 362,880   **11.** 36

13. 35   **15.** 28%   **17.** 42%   **19.** $\frac{2}{7}$ **21.** 36%   **23.** 34%

25. 2.33   **27.** The table violates the second property of probability distributions because the sum of all probabilities is 1.4, which is not equal to 1.

Pages A-7–A-8

1. 10   **3.** 100   **5.** 4   **7.** 30   **9.** $13.75   **11.** 455   **13.** −32
15. 18,432   **17.** 3.75   **19.** 149   **21.** 3×4 **23.** v_{24}
25. 31   **27.** Because their dimensions are different, the matrices cannot be added.

29. $\begin{bmatrix} -6 & 16 \\ -3 & -5 \\ 5 & 6 \end{bmatrix}$

31. This pattern includes vertical and horizontal translations of the same figure. When you look at two rows at a time, you see glide reflections. Also, each figure has vertical symmetry, horizontal symmetry, and 90° rotational symmetry.
33. 3^3, 4^2 **35. A.** 230 in.;   **B.** 0.09 in²;   **C.** 150,000 in³

Pages A-9–A-10

1. $336.60   **3.** $605.65   **5.** $515.48   **7.** $2049.15
9. $26,374.40   **11.** $5.13   **13.** $11.80   **15.** 76%
17. A. $61,987.50;   **B.** 14%;   **C.** $4742.04   **19.** Venita Brown   **21.** 913   **23.** 987654321   **25.** 1017   **27.** $1200.78
29. $1198.78   **31. A.** rent;   **B.** Nathan would add his rent check of $550 to his ending balance in his checkbook to get $650.78 + $550 = $1200.78. He would then subtract the $2 he forgot to record from this amount to get $1198.78;
C. $2 Out of Network ATM Fee

Pages A-11–A-12

1. $17.50   **3.** 32%   **5.** surplus of $220   **7.** $15,154
9. $3571.44   **11.** $3096   **13.** $98.96   **15.** $461.44
17. $2730   **19.** $211,500   **21.** $423,307   **23.** $896,147
25. $551.52   **27.** $6218   **29.** $183   **31.** $1697.25

Pages A-13–A-14

1. A. $4.88;   **B.** $504.88   **3. A.** $6691.72;   **B.** $2291.72
5. $500   **7.** $300   **9. A.** $2373;   **B.** $45.63   **11.** $344.80
13. A. $855;   **B.** $71.25   **15.** 4.8%   **17. A.** $3160;
B. 13%   **19.** $313,440

Pages A-15–A-16

1. A. $y = 60(1.05^t)$;   **B.** 193   **3.** during the 15th year
5. 11.84 g   **7. A.** 0.3846;   **B.** 2.4   **9.** 24.6 ft   **11.** period: 3; amplitude: $\frac{5}{2}$ **13. A.** period: 4π;   **B.** amplitude: 2

15. translation   **17. A.** 587.32 Hz;   **B.** 1174.64 Hz;
C. 195.77 Hz

Illustrations Credits

Key: t = top; b = bottom; c = center; l = left; r = right

All illustrations © K12 Inc. unless otherwise noted

Front and back cover: Interior of pyramid at the Louvre Museum, Paris. © Lindom/Dreamstime.com.

Chapter 1: 3, 4 (bl) © Mel Evans/Associated Press. **9** (br) © Charles Rex Arbogast/Associated Press. **13** (tr) © Stocktrek/Corbis. **18** (cr) © Windwardskies/Dreamstime.com.

Chapter 2: 25, 26 (bl) © Blend Images/ERproductions Ltd./Getty Images. **30** (br) © Action Plus Sports Images/Alamy. **36** (cr) © Roza/Dreamstime.com. **40** (cr) © David R. Frazier Photolibrary, Inc./Alamy. **48** (c) © iStockphoto/Thinkstock.

Chapter 3: 55, 56 (bl) © Blend Images/Alamy. **60** (br) © Clive Rose/Getty Images. **65** (tr) © BigStockPhoto. **70** (bc) © iStockphoto/Thinkstock.

Chapter 4: 77, 78 (b) © Neutronman/Dreamstime.com. **89** (tr) © iStockphoto/Thinkstock. **93** (tr) © Brankatekic/Dreamstime. com. **99** (t) © Kornilov15/Dreamstime.com. (c) © iStockphoto/ Thinkstock. **102** (tl) © Kornilov15/Dreamstime.com. (tr) © Kornilov15/Dreamstime.com. (cl) © Zoonar/Thinkstock. (cr) © Jadehawk/Dreamstime.com. (br) © Brad Calkins/Dreamstime.com. **104** (cr) © Kornilov15/Dreamstime.com.

Chapter 5: 107, 108 (bl) © Sergii Moskaliuk/123RF Limited. **117** (br) © Ron Chapple Studios/Thinkstock. **118** (t) © K12 Inc./ Internal Revenue Service/IRS.gov. **119** (cr) Internal Revenue Service/IRS.gov. **121** (cr) © K12 Inc./Internal Revenue Service/ IRS.gov. **123** (br) © Image Source Plus/Alamy.

Chapter 6: 131, 132 (bl) © Ed Pritchard/Getty Images. **136** (br) © Jamie and Judy Wild/Danita Delimont/Alamy. **147** (tr) © iStockphoto/Thinkstock. **148** (tr) © iStockphoto/Thinkstock. **153** (br) © Barbara Gentile/Getty Images.

Chapter 7: 161, 162 (bl) © Americanspirit/Dreamstime.com. **168** (tr) © Dreamshot/Dreamstime.com. **172** (cr) © Florian Franke/ Corbis. **177** (tr) © Walter Geiersperger/age fotostock.

Chapter 8: 185, 186 (bl) © Mark McClare/Dreamstime. com. **191** (tr) © José Enrique Molina/age fotostock. **209** (cr) © iStockphoto/Thinkstock.

Appendix: A-8 (cl) © Design Pics/Thinkstock. (cr) © Kornilov15/ Dreamstime.com. **A-18, 19** (c) Internal Revenue Service/IRS.gov.

Data Sources

Chapter 1   Working with Data

NOAA (National Oceanic and Atmospheric Administration) NCDC (National Climatic Data Center). 2012a. "Quality Controlled Local Climatological Data." Accessed May 9, 2013. http://cdo.ncdc.noaa.gov/qclcd/QCLCD.

————. 2012b. "U.S. Tornado Climatology." Accessed March 1, 2013. http://www.ncdc.noaa.gov/oa/climate/severeweather/tornadoes.html.

NOAA (National Oceanic and Atmospheric Administration) NHC (National Hurricane Center). 2012. "2011 Atlantic Hurricane Season." Accessed March 8, 2013. http://www.nhc.noaa.gov/2011atlan.shtml.

————. 2013. "2012 Atlantic Hurricane Season." Accessed March 8, 2013. http://www.nhc.noaa.gov/2012atlan.shtml.

San Diego Zoo. 2013. "Animal Bytes: Mammals." Accessed March 1, 2013. http://www.sandiegozoo.org/animalbytes/a-mammal.html.

Smithsonian Institution, Global Volcanism Program. 2002a. "Volcanoes of Canada and the Western USA." Accessed March 8, 2013. http://www.volcano.si.edu/world/region.cfm?rnum=1210.

————. 2002b. "Volcanoes of Mexico and Central America." Accessed March 8, 2013. http://www.volcano.si.edu/world/region.cfm?rnum=14.

————. 2002c. "Volcanoes of South America." Accessed March 8, 2013. http://www.volcano.si.edu/world/region.cfm?rnum=15.

usgovernmentspending.com. 2013. "U.S. Federal Budget FY13 Estimated Spending Breakdown." Accessed May 29, 2013. http://www.usfederalbudget.us/federal_budget_detail_fy13.

USGS (U.S. Geological Survey) National Earthquake Information Center. 2009. "Earthquake Information for the 1990s." Accessed March 8, 2013. http://earthquake.usgs.gov/earthquakes/eqarchives/year/info_1990s.php.

————. 2012. "Earthquake Facts and Statistics." Accessed March 8, 2013. http://earthquake.usgs.gov/earthquakes/eqarchives/year/eqstats.php.

Weather Underground, Inc. 2013a. "Hurricane Archive: North Atlantic." Accessed March 8, 2013. http://www.wunderground.com/hurricane/hurrarchive.asp?region=at.

————. 2013b. "Hurricane Archive: Western Pacific." Accessed March 8, 2013. http://www.wunderground.com/hurricane/hurrarchive.asp?region=wp&MR=1.

Chapter 2   Connections Between Data

American Heart Association. 2013. "Target Heart Rates." Accessed June 5, 2013. http://www.heart.org/HEARTORG/GettingHealthy/PhysicalActivity/Target-Heart-Rates_UCM_434341_Article.jsp.

CIA (Central Intelligence Agency). 2013. "The World Factbook." Accessed April 17, 2013. https://www.cia.gov/library/publications/the-world-factbook/fields/2102.html.

DOL (U.S. Department of Labor). 2012. "Wage and Hour Division (WHD)." Accessed April 19, 2013. http://www.dol.gov/whd/state/stateMinWageHis.htm.

DOT (U.S. Department of Transportation) FHWA (Federal Highway Administration) Office of Highway Policy Information. 2012a. "Highway Statistics Series: Buses." Accessed April 22, 2013. http://www.google.com/publicdata/explore?ds=gb66jodhlsaab_#!ctype=l&trail=false&bcs=d&nselm=h&met_y=Buses&scale_y=lin&ind_y=false&rdim=state&ifdim=state&tdim=true&hl=en_US&dl=en_US&ind=false.

————. 2012b. "Highway Statistics Series: Automobiles per licensed driver." Accessed April 22, 2013. http://www.google.com/publicdata/explore?ds=gb66jodhlsaab_#!ctype=l&trail=false&bcs=d&nselm=h&met_y=Autos_driver&scale_y=lin&ind_y=false&rdim=state&ifdim=state&tdim=true&hl=en_US&dl=en_US&ind=false.

————. 2012c. "Highway Statistics Series: Trucks." Accessed April 23, 2013. http://www.google.com/publicdata/explore?ds=gb66jodhlsaab_#!ctype=l&trail=false&bcs=d&nselm=h&met_y=Trucks&scale_y=lin&ind_y=false&rdim=state&ifdim=state&tdim=true&hl=en_US&dl=en_US&ind=false.

————. 2012d. "Highway Statistics Series: Travel per person." Accessed April 23, 2013. http://www.google.com/publicdata/explore?ds=gb66jodhlsaab_#!ctype=l&trail=false&bcs=d&nselm=h&met_y=VMT_person&scale_y=lin&ind_y=false&rdim=state&ifdim=state&tdim=true&hl=en_US&dl=en_US&ind=false.

————. 2012e. "Highway Statistics Series: Nominal cost of gas." Accessed April 23, 2013. http://www.google.com/publicdata/explore?ds=gb66jodhlsaab_#!ctype=l&trail=false&bcs=d&nselm=h&met_y=Gas_Nom&scale_y=lin&ind_y=false&rdim=state&ifdim=state&tdim=true&hl=en_US&dl=en_US&ind=false.

————. 2012f. "Highway Statistics Series: Automobiles." Accessed April 25, 2013. http://www.google.com/publicdata/explore?ds=gb66jodhlsaab_#!ctype=l&trail=false&bcs=d&nselm=h&met_y=Auto&scale_y=lin&ind_y=false&rdim=state&idim=state:DE&ifdim=state&hl=en_US&dl=en_US&ind=false.

eTForecasts. 2013. "Worldwide PC Market." Accessed April 23, 2013. http://www.etforecasts.com/products/ES_pcww1203.htm.

International Olympic Committee. 2012. "Olympic Medalists." Accessed April 15, 2013. http://www.olympic.org/athletes.

MeasuringWorth.com. 2013. "What Was the U.S. GDP Then?" Accessed April 25, 2013. http://www.measuringworth.com/datasets/usgdp/result.php.

MSTE (Office for Mathematics, Science, and Technology Education), University of Illinois. 2013. "U.S. Temperatures." Accessed April 17, 2013. http://mste.illinois.edu/malcz/DATA/WEATHER/Temperatures.html.

Road Safety Authority. 2007. "Stopping distances for cars." Accessed April 24, 2013. http://www.rulesoftheroad.ie/rules-for-driving/speed-limits/speed-limits_stopping-distances-cars.html.

ShrpSports 2013. "NBA Conference Standings After Apr in 2012–13 Season, Eastern Conference." Accessed March 11, 2014. http://www.shrpsports.com/nba/stand.php.

U.S. Department of Education NCES (National Center for Education Statistics). 2012. "Fast Facts: Tuition costs of colleges and universities." Accessed May 8, 2013. http://nces.ed.gov/fastfacts/display.asp?id=76.

USDA (U.S. Department of Agriculture) ARS (Agricultural Research Service). 2002. "Nutritive Value of Foods." Accessed April 17, 2013. http://www.ars.usda.gov/SP2UserFiles/Place/12354500/Data/hg72/hg72_2002.pdf.

USGS (U.S. Geological Survey) Water Science School. 2013a. "How much of your state is wet?" Accessed April 17, 2013. http://ga.water.usgs.gov/edu/wetstates.html.

World Bank. 2013. "Mobile cellular subscriptions (per 100 people)." Accessed April 23, 2013. http://data.worldbank.org/indicator/IT.CEL.SETS.P2.

www.fueleconomy.gov (U.S. Department of Energy, Energy Efficiency & Renewable Energy and U.S. Environmental Protection Agency, Office of Transportation & Air Quality). 2013. "Fueleconomy Top Ten." Accessed April 16, 2013. http://www.fueleconomy.gov/feg/topten.jsp.

Chapter 3   Uncertainty

ESPN.com. 2013a. "Chicago Bears 2012 Statistics." Accessed May 10, 2013. http://espn.go.com/nfl/team/stats/_/name/chi/chicago-bears.

———. 2013b. "Atlanta Falcons 2012 Statistics." Accessed May 10, 2013. http://espn.go.com/nfl/team/stats/_/name/atl/atlanta-falcons.

U.S. Census Bureau. 2011. "Statistical Abstract of the United States: 2011." Accessed May 10, 2013. http://www.census.gov/compendia/statab/2011/tables/11s1329.pdf.

Chapter 5   Income

IRS (Internal Revenue Service). 2012. "2012 Tax Table." Accessed March 20, 2013. http://www.irs.gov/pub/irs-pdf/i1040tt.pdf.

UtahStubs.com. 2013. "Pay Stubs for Utah Employees only at UtahStubs.com." Accessed on May 15, 2013. http://www.utahstubs.com/.

Chapter 7   Saving Money

S&P Dow Jones Indices. 2013. "S&P 500." Accessed September 20, 2013. http://us.spindices.com/indices/equity/sp-500.

Chapter 8   More Math Models

Tide High and Low, Inc. 2013. "Regions with Tide Predictions." Accessed September 17, 2013. http://www.saltwatertides.com/pickpred.html.

USNO (U.S. Naval Observatory). 2012. "Duration of Daylight/Darkness Table for One Year." Accessed September 17, 2013. http://aa.usno.navy.mil/data/docs/Dur_OneYear.php.

Weather Warehouse. 2013. "Past Monthly Weather Data for Detroit, MI." Accessed September 17, 2013. http://weather-warehouse.com/WeatherHistory/PastWeatherData_DetroitMetropolitanArpt_Detroit_MI_January.html.

Extra Problems

DOL (U.S. Department of Labor) BLS (Bureau of Labor Statistics). 2013. "Education pays …" Accessed April 26, 2013. http://www.bls.gov/emp/cp_chart_001.htm.

USDA (U.S. Department of Agriculture) ARS (Agricultural Research Service) NDL (Nutrient Data Laboratory). 2012. "National Nutrient Database for Standard Reference Release 25." Accessed April 26, 2013. http://ndb.nal.usda.gov/ndb/search/list?format=&count=&max=25&sort=&fg=Fruits+and+Fruit+Juices&man=&lfacet=&qlookup=&offset=0.

USGS (U.S. Geological Survey) Water Science School. 2013b. "Lengths of the major rivers." Accessed March 8, 2013. http://ga.water.usgs.gov/edu/riversofworld.html.

Appendix

IRS (Internal Revenue Service). 2012. "2012 Tax Table." Accessed March 20, 2013. http://www.irs.gov/pub/irs-pdf/i1040tt.pdf.

Index

Page references in **bold** indicate definitions and formulas.